IN SEARCH OF
BIRDS IN THE
SCOTTISH
HIGHLANDS

Dedicated to Valerie, Trevor, Dawn and Wendy O'Shea, companions on many bird watching expeditions and valuable helpers with this book and to Robin and David de la Motte who typed much of the manuscript.

Copyright © Brian O'Shea and John Green
Illustrated by John Green
Front Cover: Osprey, back: Rosefinch
Book design: Michal Boncza
Published by Artery Publications 1990
11 Dorset Road, London W5 4HU
Typesetting by LaserPrint Ltd, 24 New Broadway, Ealing W5.

ISBN O 9513909 1 0

IN SEARCH OF BIRDS IN THE SCOTTISH HIGHLANDS

BRIAN O'SHEA
AND
JOHN GREEN

ILLUSTRATIONS BY JOHN GREEN

The familiar names of former counties, Caithness, Argyle, Sutherland etc are used throughout this book to describe different parts of the Highlands. In 1975 they were incorporated into larger administrative regions.

Osprey

Buzzard

INTRODUCTION

Those of you who have read our earlier book *In Search of Birds in Mid-Wales* will appreciate our liking for bird watching away from the madding crowd. There is a thrill of adventure in seeking elusive and interesting species in the setting of wild country and watching the birds in their natural habitats. Nowhere can this be enjoyed in greater fullness than in the Highlands of Scotland.

In Mid-Wales we wrote as resident bird watchers relating to the visitor. In Scotland we are visitors ourselves, sharing our experience with others and thereby illustrating what exciting birds may be seen even with a limited knowledge of the region. Our exploration was assisted and inspired by such classic authors as Nethersole Thompson, Seton Gordon and Fraser Darling, as well as the factual information yielded by recent bird reports, the *BTO Atlas of Breeding Birds in Britain and Ireland* and the comprehensive *Birds in Scotland* by Valerie Thom. Above all, we have drawn upon our previous tours in the Highlands to which we have returned again and again since our first visit in 1958.

The Highlands of Scotland hold many interesting species found scarcely anywhere else in Britain. They include the **Red-**and **Black-throated Diver, Slavonian Grebe, Greenshank, Dotterel, Ptarmigan, Snow Bunting, Crested Tit, Golden Eagle, Osprey,** and several species of duck. All of these were encountered on the trip among a total of 110 species.

On the other hand such common birds as the **Jay** and **Magpie** remained undiscovered north of the Highland Line. In fact there are much lower concentrations of many birds typical of the lowland counties, common birds like **Blackbirds, Thrushes, Blackcaps** and **Garden Warblers.** As more than ample compensation for this, there are many exciting species which may be seen with little difficulty. Sometimes, particularly on north-western moorlands it is possible to walk all day and see very few birds. At other times, for example, in places close to water there are enclaves rich in wild life. **Common Gulls, Oyster-catchers, Ringed Plovers, Sandpipers, Elder Duck, Mergansers, Wigeon, Black Guillemot** and many other species are often common in suitable habitat.

In the last 20 or 30 years many new species have started to colonise the Highlands for the first time. **The Wood Sandpiper, Temmincks Stint, Goldeneye** and **Wryneck** are a few. Others such as the **Shorelark, Purple Sandpiper** and **Scarlet Rosefinch** may well soon follow suit, but species such as these may breed without being discovered in such an area of low population where much of the country is difficult to reach.

Beyond the Highlands, the northern and western isles have their own wealth of birds. The greatest concentrations of **Guillemots, Razor-bills, Puffins, Fulmars** etc. are to be found on the cliffs of these islands. There are some special rarities, the **Whimbrel, Red-necked Phalarope** and **Leach's Fork-tailed Petrel,** together with those pirates, the **Great** and **Arctic Skuas.** These are discussed along with other interesting island birds in the section on the **Far North** and **Rare Breeding Birds,** but this book is mainly concerned with those birds to be found on the mainland and which are more easily accessible to the average visitor.

The Highlands of Scotland, covering nearly a fifth of Britain, have a far lower density of population than any other region of these islands, but this was not always the case. Wars between the feuding clansmen, the brutal clearances of people to make way for sheep in the 18th and 19th centuries and the conversion of huge estates for purely hunting and fishing, all played their part. In common with many other rural areas of Britain people were driven by dire economic necessity to man the mushrooming factories which sprang up during the industrial revolution. For these and other reasons, often arising out of human tragedy, a rich natural heritage has been bequeathed to us today.

How safe is this natural paradise for wildlife in the Highlands and Islands? So far it is surprising how little has been spoilt by the encroach-ment of modern commercial and industrial development. The relent-less march of quick-growing conifer plantations covers an increasing acreage of moorland, creating ecological changes with uncertain con-sequences for wildlife. Afforestation on a grand scale poses a potential threat to birds like **Merlins, Grouse** and **Golden Plover** which nest on the moors, and the **Golden Eagles** which feed either on medium-sized mammals and birds or rely on carrion from the sheep-grazed grounds in the west. Other species, like **Crossbills** and **Siskins,** it must be admitted, have benefited from the expansion of commercial forests.

In these days of rapid development all can change suddenly before the interested public becomes really aware. The fate of the Flow Country in central Sutherland and Caithness is a good example. As we write, a quarter of this unique habitat of myriads of lochs and blanket bog has disappeared under the spruce plantations while con-servationists now fight to preserve most of the rest. Although the government has withdrawn tax concessions for investors in plantations in this country, they have actually increased grants for development. The Flow Country contains amazingly large concentrations of certain

British birds, according to R.S.P.B. figures: 60% of **Greenshank,** 40% of **Dunlin** and **Scoter,** 20% of **Black-throated Divers** and **Wigeon,** 18% of **Golden Plover** and 14% of **Red—throated Divers** breed here. As you can see it is well worth protecting.

Game-keeping interests have always held a high profile in Scotland and still do so today. Although many estates are enlightened there are others where persecution of **Buzzards, Eagles** and raptors is practised on a large scale in defiance of law and public opinion. It was not long ago that we witnessed the devastation that chemicals can wreak on wildlife, with the decimation of **Peregrine Falcons** and **Sparrowhawks** in some parts of Britain, due to Dieldrins building up in their bodies from eating contaminated prey. Populations of other birds of prey were affected, though less severely. Thankfully these particular compounds have been withdrawn from use in agriculture, but changes in farming practice remain one of the biggest threats to our wildlife today.

Although there are vast numbers of lochs and lochans in Scotland, water habitats for certain species, like **Black-throated Divers** and **Slavonian Grebes** are vulnerable to disturbance or flooding caused by hydro-electric schemes and other factors. A fresh human interest in living in remote places, the growth of outdoor leisure pursuits like skiing, mountaineering, hill-walking, sailing and yes, bird-watching too, all cause pressure on the environment. The Highlands, we hope, will prove resilient enough to absorb these human needs for recreation and yet retain their wild beauty. Opportunities to retreat from the routines of organised work and daily struggles of existence must be retained for the sanity of future generations as well as our own.

It would be foolish, however, to imagine that the Highlands are indestructible. As we have said, commercial exploitation aided by modern technology creates rapid, irreversible change. If two million square miles of the Amazon rain forest can be cleared, according to expert forecasts, within 30 years and with disastrous ecological repercussions, then northern Scotland is no less vulnerable.

We would hope that all who read this book will share our joy of the Highlands and support efforts to protect these mountains together with important wildlife places in all other parts of these islands and beyond. Our book is written in a descriptive form beginning with the difficult task of trying to convey a sense of the incredible beauty of northern Scotland. Various bird watching adventures follow, while at *Ringed* the end of the book is an annotated check-list of the birds breeding *Plover* in Scotland with comments on their status and distribution. *chick*

THE AREA

The Highlands of Scotland remain one of the few real wildernesses in Europe. In many places it is possible to drive for many miles with hardly a house in sight, let alone a hotel or cafe. Once away from the road the moors and hills are uninhabited places. The country is rugged and mountainous with more than 350 peaks exceeding 3,000ft. These mountains are known as Munros and many of them hardly feel the tread of hill-walkers from one year to the next, unlike the highest peaks of the Lake District or the mountains of Snowdonia. There is hardly a town with more than a few hundred inhabitants west of the Great Glen, and even Inverness, the capital of the Highlands with 40,000 people, and Fort William with a population of 12,000, hardly rank as metropolitan centres.

Since I was a child the Highlands of Scotland have conveyed a sense of magic to me, years before I ever crossed into its realm of mountain and glen. It represents lofty crags, mist-shrouded peaks, deep mysterious lochs, space and freedom and the haunt of **Eagles** and **Ospreys** in remote wild places. It is an escape from the confines of congested roads, square-fenced fields and the dreary monotony of flat country. Its brave, challenging landscape is a place for inspiration, a place to draw breath, a place for adventure.

Although always wild, the countryside is rarely bleak except in inclement weather and, it must be said, there are many rainy days in this region, especially in the west. There is a richness of colour enhanced by the changing northern light which brings constant tonal variety to the scenes. Sometimes reflections in the waters of numerous lochs faithfully mirror the skies and surrounding hills. Purples and blues of distant peaks blend with the variety of greens, sepias and browns of lower hills and forest. In the late summer the heather moors provide a carpet of purple which turns red-brown in winter. The numerous sea lochs often penetrate deep inland culminating sometimes in thrift-covered flats or rocky shores. The western seas are clear and it may be possible to peer 40ft down to the seabed, so transparent is the water. In bright summer light the bays in the north and west are as blue as any mediterranean sea and a good deal cleaner, but of course colder than their Spanish or Grecian counterparts.

Throughout the western and northern Highlands are thousands of fresh water lochs. Many are several miles long. Amongst the biggest are Lochs Shin, Ness, Awe and Lomond, all about twenty miles or more long, whilst many more exceed five miles in length. These lochs are generally narrow-perhaps a mile or less, but some are of great depth. Loch Ness descends for more than 700ft (200 metres), while Loch Morar near Mallaig is over 1000ft (300 metres) deep.

Some of these lochs are idyllic, studded with islands and surrounded by trees. Loch Maree and Loch Lomond are good examples as are some of the lochs of Easter Ross. Others are high wild waters edged by steep barren moorland slopes or crags, places like Loch Loyne or Mullardoch. Those harnessed for hydro-electric schemes with barren shores, where the water level rises and falls, have relatively little bird life. The smaller lochs, usually at higher altitude or in clusters near the coast or on the larger islands of the north or Hebrides, are found in profusion and are often rich in trout and bird-life. **Dunlin, Red-throated Divers, Common Gulls, Mergansers** and **Teal** are just a few of the species which may be found on them.

Scotland is the land of high mountains and sparkling rivers and these are found everywhere feeding and draining the lochs and tarns. Some are crystal clear streams rippling over stones and shingle, others are violent torrents gouging fissures in the rocks as they swirl and tumble, white and foaming, down steep glens.

The mountain scenery is varied. The lofty peaks of Perthshire, Ben More, Ben Vorlich and Ben Lawers tower above deep, green, loch-filled glens, rising steeply through wooded, grass and heather slopes. These scenes are grand but gentle, having more in common with the cosiness of the Cumbrian lakes than the wild places further north. Oaks are characteristic in these southern glens along with other deciduous trees which are scarce in, say, Sutherland or Inverness where, apart from the birch, it is the pine which predominates. Some of the lochs have become notable places for leisure activities in recent years. Loch Katrine in the popular Trossachs, until recently, had paddle steamers while Loch Earn is a coveted place for those who prefer the slap and billow of sail.

Perthshire, the seat of Scottish aristocracy, is studded with proud mansions and castles built in the unique Scottish Neo-Gothic style, with romantic turrets, lying in magnificent grounds. Game-keeping is widely practised on the grouse moors where birds of prey are sometimes given short shrift. For this reason the **Golden Eagle** is far scarcer here in Perthshire than it is in the deer forests of the west.

Northwards of the salmon-rich Loch Tay lies the wilder terrain of

Glen Lyon, Loch Rannoch and beyond that the rarely explored vast-ness of Loch Ericht and the Ben Alder Range. To the east civilisation prevails in character Highland towns like Aberfeldy and Pitlochry until the wide open moors of Drumochter or Braemar are reached on the way to the Cairngorms. Despite their altitude these mountains of the 4,000ft plateau are unimpressive at a distance and look deceptively ordinary when viewed from the Spey valley.

The Spey valley has 'the feel' of human habitation and Aviemore with its modern hotels and entertainments is hardly the place for those wishing to get away from it all, but the expansive old Caledonian Forests of Abernethy, Glen More and Rothiemurchus have thousands of acres of beautiful Scots Pines, open heather glades and small quiet lochs. The area is a jewel among bird watching haunts, ranking with the Cairngorms as one of the outstanding areas in Britain to see **Crested Tits, Scottish Crossbills, Ptarmigan, Dotterel** and **Snow Buntings.**

Despite these undoubted attractions we must admit a sneaking pre-ference for the western routes northwards. Loch Lomond ranks among the most beautiful of Scottish lochs, while beyond its northernmost shores the land is a vast wilderness of moorland with towering mountains almost overwhelming in their desolation on wet and misty days. The steep green mountains of Argyle topped with formidable crags reach their most impressive proportions in the magnificent pass of Glencoe remembered for the massacre in 1692, when the Mac-

Donalds were rewarded with treacherous murder after playing host to the Campbells.

Ben Nevis, like the Cairngorms, belies its lofty status from the western aspects, but a walk to its summit on a clear day reveals unforgettable views ranging nearly 100 miles from Mull in the south to the Moray Firth.

As if these treasures were not enough, the most enticing and enchanting scenes, many would argue, lie north and west of the Great Glen especially near the west coast. Few will visit this glorious country for birds alone, since most of the typical Highland species can be seen more easily elsewhere. Until the 1960s most of the roads were single track with passing places, but times have changed. Nevertheless this region is the most sparsely populated in Britain, containing hardly a single town away from the east coast.The mountains tend to have a more individual character and their rock structure is different, being mainly of gneiss and sandstone. Small freshwater lochans and tarns lie in abundance close to numerous sea lochs which indent the coastline. The seascapes are dotted with hazy-blue islands which turn jet-black as the sun sinks below the horizon, glazing the waters a brilliant white. This western seaboard is noted for the brilliance of its sunsets. The plains, wet flows and moors of central Sutherland and Caithness are less picturesque, but harbour many exciting birds hidden in remote places.

This then is the prospect awaiting those prepared to venture to the Highlands. The opportunity is there to see fascinating birds in incomparable surroundings. You will encounter just a selection of them as you accompany us on a fortnight's holiday at the beginning of June.

Peregrine Falcon

GOING NORTH

Greylag Geese

Our journey began in the English Midlands and only three hours later we were speeding along the A74 from Carlisle, Highland-bound. Endless hours on motorways can be very wearisome and we had been tempted to break our journey to look for moorland waders on the Pennine fringes which approach close to the highway at Penrith. Resisting this we pressed on beyond Carlisle, with the Cumbrian mountains to our south-west receding further into the distance.

At Beattock Summit, the highest point of the road on the Southern Uplands we looked forward with great anticipation to reaching our immediate goal, that most enchanting of Highland waters, Loch Lomond. Soon we were on the outskirts of Glasgow, through the city centre and onto the Dumbarton Road. The gaunt, sooty sandstone streets, the traffic noise and the derrick-webbed skyline of the old shipyards were left behind us as at last we turned towards the loch. From the great sprawling city to the glorious mountains and lochs is a sudden and dramatic transformation scarely imaginable unless you have been this way before. We knew what to expect and now looked forward to two full weeks of bird-watching free of any worldly considerations or competing demands upon our time. Our most pressing worry or concern would be whether we would find an **Eagle** in Glen Etive or a **Greenshank** on Rannoch Moor.

Mountain peaks loomed promisingly on the horizon as the glint of shining water heralded our first longed-for sight of Loch Lomond. Little time was lost in passing the lower end of the loch where crowds of people milled about near the clusters of small boats moored near the village of Balloch. Wearily we drove the last few miles and were thankful to leave the car and settle our cases in a comfortable guest house, nestling deep in a wooded hillside.

At last we could relax and stroll down to the water's edge to take a closer look at Loch Lomond. The newly widened road assaulting the shoreline had severely mauled the west bank, although the 'bonnie banks' immortalised in that haunting Jacobite song still managed to preserve some dignity. Birch and Alder trees grow among sand and shingle along the flatter stretches, while elsewhere oakwoods cling to banks where bracken and other vegetation covers thin soils over rocks which rise abruptly from the loch. The inshore waters are for the most part shallow before descending suddenly into the dark depths. There are wooded islands out in the loch but near the shore the smallest islets have just enough room to provide nesting sites for single pairs of **Common Gulls,** only a few metres out from the bank.

At Luss, a neat village with wooded bays and a pier providing good views in both directions, several male **Goosanders,** striking in their pied plumage, flew to and from a small inlet to feed. Soon we discovered many others, female 'redheads' as well as male birds, fishing or resting out on the loch. Not far away **Oystercatchers** were nesting on shingle patches, while **Sandpipers,** with wings bowed, flew from steep grass banks. The misnamed **Grey Wagtails** hunted for mayflies from the rocks of a woodland burn, while a **Redstart** flitted from a crevice in a stone wall. Nearby a pair of **Dippers** carried food to their offspring in a domed wren-like nest, well hidden beneath an ivy-covered bank of a stream tumbling into the loch.

Loch Lomond has much to recommend it from a bird-watcher's point of view, although there are few of the special rarities associated with the Highlands. Nevertheless a wide selection of birds can be seen around its shores: **Woodwarblers, Redpolls, Siskins** and birds like the **Pied Flycatcher** and **Green Woodpecker,** both of which are generally scarce in the north, can be found in the woodlands here.

Across the mile-wide waters of the middle section of the loch stands Ben Lomond, its reflection sharply mirrored in the calm waters on still evenings. Ben Lomond, the most southerly of the Munros, is not especially noted for its birds although **Ptarmigan** are still to be found on its higher slopes. Next to Ben Nevis it is one of Scotland's most climbed mountains and one of the few with a path right to the top. The gradients are quite easy and the summit can be reach in two or three hours, offering wide views to the south.

The south-eastern shores of Loch Lomond are good for wintering geese and duck. Autumn brings a veritable invasion of **Wigeon, Goldeneye, Pintail, Teal** and **Scaup, Grey-Lags** and a few **Barnacle Geese.** Further east, towards Aberfoyle, the Queen Elizabeth Forest Park harbours a splendid range of raptors including **Hen Harrier, Peregrine, Long** and **Short-eared Owls** and **Merlin.**

A mere three miles to the west of Tarbet on Loch Lomond are the salty waters of Loch Long. Sometimes submarines of the nuclear fleet may be seen here, but the bird-watcher's interests will be directed towards more peaceful objects, like the **Fulmars, Cormorants, Black Guillemots** and other seabirds, in contrast to the species to be found on the fresh waters of Loch Lomond. Beyond the village of Arrochar is the pass of Glen Croe rising relentlessly for four miles until it reaches the highest point, aptly named 'Rest and be Thankful'. The most dramatic peak rising from the so-called Arrochar Alps is the Cobbler, whose wild jagged crest of mica-schist has helped to make Arrochar a popular rock-climbing centre.

Among these mountains are several pairs of **Golden Eagles** and sometimes one will delight the keen-eyed tourist who stops to admire the view from the top of the pass. Further west and north lie the lower Argyle hills where **Hen Harriers** quarter moors and conifer plantations for their prey. The signpost pointing to Campbeltown, 100 miles away near the Mull of Kintyre indicates the isolation of this long narrow peninsula where **Buzzards, Red-throated Divers, Eagles, Harriers** and many other species may be found in an atmosphere of peace and seclusion.

Whinchat

RANNOCH MOOR

Resisting the attractions of western Argyle and the Arrochar Alps, *Short-eared* the next morning we set off towards Rannoch Moor. Our route lay *Owl* along the narrow northern end of the 24 mile Loch Lomond, across wild hills with snow-capped Ben More rising nearly 4,000ft on our right.

One or two **Whinchats** perched prominently on fence posts and there were two or three **Wheatears** displaying their characteristic white rumps as they flitted among rocks near the roadside . The only other birds were a pair of **Hooded Crows** which flew into a gnarled oak tree as we passed by. This area represents the dividing line between the **Carrion Crow** to the south and the grey 'Hoodie' which replaces it further north. Although the **Hooded Crow** looks quite different, having much grey in its plumage on back and underparts, the two types are sub-species and interbreed in a wide band of country where their ranges overlap.

A deterioration in the weather meant that most birds would choose to keep well to cover: there was a threat of rain as the mist hung from the hill slopes and the high peaks were enveloped in swirling cloud. Soon we were surrounded by miles of soaking wilderness as the rain lashed the road in front of us. We turned at Crianlarich and continued on to the even more remote Tyndrum, made slightly less so by the sight of its cosy hotel by the roadside.

The road winds upwards, past Loch Tulla and on to the moor of Rannoch, at 1000ft (300 metres) above sea level, a vast triangle of wilderness enclosing an area of nearly 60 square miles. In foul weather there is hardly a place more desolate in all Scotland. It is largely a flat or gently undulating terrain carpeted with heather, cotton and tussock grass, and littered with small lochs and peat pools. Twelve miles of energy-sapping, treacherous bog and heather covered moorland east lies the single-track railway from Glasgow to Fort William. A few miles further on lies Loch Rannoch.

Despite its uncompromising and at times forbidding aspect Rannoch Moor is a pearl among bird-watching haunts. In good weather it is sometimes possible with little exertion to see some exciting species. In past years we have seen **Eagles** and **Hen-Harriers** close to the road and watched a pair of **Greenshank** calling excitedly as they gathered their newly-hatched offspring not far from Loch Ba. **Merlin** fly from peat banks and **Golden Plover** call plaintively from raised hummocks.

None of these species are in evidence when we set foot on the moor and head towards the raggle-taggle of lochs and pools. Nevertheless we are comforted by an improvement in the weather, as fleecy clouds form high in the sky and areas of clear blue appear. The Black Mount and Glen Coe can be seen rising clear on the horizon, smudged pastel-blue by the intervening atmosphere. The air is still and there is little sign of bird-life as we pick our way between the treacherous peat pools. Our aim today is to locate that dainty little wader, the **Dunlin** and if possible to find a nest, according to some experts one of the most difficult waders' nests to find. When approached on the nest it slinks off and runs some way before taking off and flying low, to settle 50 metres or so away. Because of its small size and camouflaged colour it is very hard to see before it is well away from the nest, and trying to follow it back as it weaves its way between the vegetation is almost impossible.

We approach the first loch which is peppered with small rocky islets and girded with grass and heather. We can see a group of **Red-breasted**

Dunlin **Mergansers** dozing by the water's edge, their heads tucked into their backs while one or two others dive for fish out on the water. We skirt the loch so as not to disturb their siesta and move further into the moor. A **Red Grouse** utters his gutteral quivering croak as he flies up in front of us, skimming the heather before plunging into rank vegetation a hundred metres away. There is no sign of **Dunlin** yet, but a **Meadow Pipit** flutters off her small neat nest cradling five eggs, densely covered in brown speckles.

After about an hour wandering over the moor, sometimes sitting down for a few minutes just to listen and enjoy the sense of space around us, accompanied by the croaking of more **Red Grouse,** I spy our first **Dunlin.** It is crouching quite still on some brackish mud bordering one of the small bays of the lochan. As we watch, four more skim past over our heads and alight further along the shore, just hidden beyond a peat hag. **Dunlin** often nest gregariously and it seemed likely that there might be several pairs close at hand.

The light breeze now brings us the characteristic descending reeling notes of a male **Dunlin** some way off. Movement in that direction is barred by a deep water-filled channel, but in the meantime our first **Dunlin** has moved onto a prominent grass tuft and replies to his rival beyond the ditch. Then there is a movement and the female bird is seen walking among the short grass on a delta by the shore and then flies off over the water. We make a half-hearted search but give up, soon realising we stand little chance of finding the nest.

As we trudge back towards the car we hear again the familiar reeling sound and spot a **Dunlin** cockily atop a hummock. Soon he and his partner are darting and dancing around us, approaching tantalisingly close so that we can see their jet-black belly patches, slightly curving slender bills and richly-mottled back plumage. They appear and disappear behind the tussocks, popping up unexpectedly just to confuse us. A brief search will almost certainly be unsuccessful and anything more will prevent the female from returning to her nest for an unacceptably long time. We decide to leave a handkerchief tied to a tall piece of heather, close to where we had first seen her and return again the next day.

Our overnight stay was at an old, grey granite farmhouse situated at the end of a stony track, winding several hundred metres back from the road. Although surrounded by moorland, the house was fronted by a reasonably well-tended lawn, bordered by a few ash trees and a wispy hedge, offering a modicum of shelter from blistering winter winds. Nearby was a field with patches of reed and short grass cropped by sheep and at the far end of this, a wide shallow river flowed between shingle banks and marshy ground. As we walked down the track not far from the river we were welcomed by the fluting calls of **Curlews** and melodious piping of a pair of **Redshank** landing in the field.

Such rivers in the Grampians are rarely disappointing and are often rich in bird-life. One of the characteristic birds is the **Oystercatcher** and as we followed the river's meandering there were two females tip-toeing from their nests, one from a shingle bank and the other from a narrow pebble-strewn grassy island in mid-stream. Their mates were piping from the field to distract our attention whilst, less slowly,

Wheatear   a **Ringed Plover** left the cover of a bank to flit downstream where it joined a **Sandpiper** bobbing at the shoreline. A pair of wheeling **Lapwings** in a neighbouring field made a total of six different waders in the space of a few minutes! Not a bad selection for a rather ordinary upland river, but by no means unusual in the Highlands.

Early next morning we set off in anticipation to complete our business on Rannoch Moor. We don our wellingtons, negotiating our way carefully around deep gullies and trudge through soggy patches of moss-covered bog to the site of our last pair of **Dunlin.** Soon we hold them in full focus of our binoculars and take up a high position in order to get a good view as the birds bob and jerk their way through the vegetation, first in one direction, then in the other. One bird had flown across a water-filled ditch and had disappeared from sight, quite near to our handkerchief marker. We now approach quickly but stealthily over the ground, keeping as low as we can. Near a small pool, with tussocks of reed and wispy grass, the **Dunlin** flies up several metres in front of us. It may have walked some distance but we start to search the immediate area thoroughly. This is close to the marker we left there the previous day. Suddenly, John calls out, barely hiding his excitement, "You need look no further gentlemen!" Success at last. A beautifully concealed nest with a clutch of four eggs blending with the vegetation and with arching grass pulled over it. The site was almost surrounded by water, with a pool on one side and a shallow water-filled channel on the other. We then retire quickly from the scene, allowing the little black-bellied wader to continue incubating without further interference.

There are probably 4 or 5,000 thousand pairs of **Dunlin** breeding in Britain and they are commonest in the northern and western isles and the Flow Country of Caithness and Sutherland. There are also good numbers on the wet peat moors of the northern Pennines in England.

Keeping company with the **Dunlin** had been a pleasurable experience although we were faintly disappointed at seeing none of the rarities: the **Greenshank, Merlin** or **Eagles** of previous visits. Despite its riches it is not always possible to discover the moor's hidden secrets in one day's bird-watching. Sometimes you can walk for miles and see nothing while at other times exciting surprises wait in store.

Perhaps this is the place to point out that virtually all of the rarer species of, say, less than 2-3000 pairs described in this book receive "special protection" under the 1981 Wildlife and Countryside Act and it is illegal to disturb them at their nesting sites. In the case of less scarce species the safety of the nest and its contents should be foremost in your mind if you come across one. Avoid sudden flushing of birds from nests – they may desert if startled, cover your tracks and replace any disturbed vegetation and keep a sharp eye open for predators like gulls or crows which readily steal eggs and chicks if given the chance.

As we arrive back at the car we notice a **Meadow Pipit** perched on an old twist of wire and carrying an enormous caterpillar in its beak. It is clear that it has young so we decide to spend a few more minutes watching it back. She soon ignores us and flies 20 metres or so onto the moor and drops down into the heather. It is clear where she's gone down because a patch of cotton-grass is growing conveniently nearby. We saunter over to take a peek at its nest. Imagine our amazement to see just one enormous fledgling straddling the nest and totally concealing it with its bulk. Its back was barred with purply brown and its beak, still hungrily ajar, revealed a brilliant crimson lining. The poor little **Pipits** must be working themselves skinny to feed this enormous interloper. They are a favourite victim of the **Cuckoo,** but sometimes the most unlikely victims are chosen to foster the young. On one occasion I recall finding a large hole bored in the dome of a **Wren's** nest which contained a single large **Cuckoo's** egg!

Cuckoo nestling

Golden Eagle

Peregrine Falcon

CAMP AT GLEN GARRY

The short drive to the impressive Pass of Glen Coe was uneventful. There are **Golden Eagles** in the steep green glens of Argyle and the sighting of one of these great birds is a definite possibility along the narrow road winding for ten miles down Glen Etive. With so much to see and so many haunts to explore there is no time for this diversion. We soon arrive at the head of Glen Coe with ragged, snow-capped peaks towering above us on either side as the road plunges down the pass. Its unadorned bareness gives Glen Coe a brutal majesty full of mystery and foreboding, its muscular rocks scored by corries and crevices. Dark clouds swirl around the high peaks, water gushes over slippery rocks and seeps down moss-covered boulders near the roadside. It is too cloudy today to see **Peregrine Falcons** circling the cliff-tops although I have seen them before on clear days above this dramatic glen.

Scanning the high ridges and crags with our binoculars we saw a wing emerge from a low misty cloud. We had a brief glimpse of a large dark bird with splayed finger-tipped wings before it disappeared into the mist once more. It was surely an **Eagle** in this kind of Wagnerian setting high above the pass, but could we be absolutely certain? We hesitated...the silhouette of the much smaller **Buzzard** can be similar enough to confuse or cause doubt despite the enormous size difference, particularly where there are no objects for reference. Our wish for a second sighting was not granted and we were left debating the identity of the bird with no chance of confirming our opinions.

We moved on. Our speculations were brought to an end by the resounding tones of a lone piper in colourful regalia, his ancient tunes reverberating through the glen. A number of tourists stood by admiringly and some tossed coins into his 'bunnet', placed strategically on a large stone. We stood awhile, absorbing the unique atmosphere created by the blend of Scottish bagpipe music and mountain glen, here magnified by the memories of history where, not far away the massacre of 1692 took place in the 'Glen of Weeping'.

The ferry crossing at Ballachulish for many decades drastically shortened the long haul around the deep oily-looking waters of Loch Leven. The ferry boat would struggle to maintain a straight course in the swirling current until at last its cars could disembark up the clanking ramp into that part of the Highlands known as Lochaber. For some years now there has been a bridge making the journey slightly faster but less romantic than the old ferry. To our right we could soon see the mountains of the flat-topped, mis-shapen Ben Nevis Massif, while the long, wide sea loch, Loch Linnhe ran parallel to our route on the left. Beyond that, to the west in the direction of Loch Sunart and Ardnamurchan are mountains seldom visited by the average tourist. Although the Scottish fishing industry has seen more prosperous days, there were still one or two fishing boats out on the water as we arrived at Fort William.

Fort William is a popular tourist centre and deservedly a focal point for visitors to the Highlands. We had little reason to linger however and after stocking up with provisions and enjoying a hearty restaurant meal, we were soon heading towards Spean Bridge. There were few birds to interest us in the Great Glen itself. Loch Lochy is a small version of Loch Ness which is nearly twenty miles further north, but neither of these deep, dark-waters are rich in birds. Their banks are, for the most part, straight with too little waterside vegetation to attract wildlife.

The road towards Kingussie to the north-east, passes through some grand country to Loch Laggan and beyond, although modern conifer plantations have left their mark. There are small roads creeping through lonely glens in the Monadhliaths where **Eagles** and **Peregrines**

Black-throated Diver

can be encountered if you take the time to stop and are prepared to be patient. To the west, soon after Fort William lies the 'Road to the Isles', by Loch Eil, Glenfinnan and Lochailort to Mallaig, a picturesque route available to both motorist and steam-rail enthusiasts. Further north but also west of the rift valley lies Loch Arkaig. The route to Arkaig goes along the famous 'Dark Mile' where, in 1746 'Bonnie Prince Charlie' hid in caves and trees during the Jacobite rising. Loch Arkaig itself is famous as one of the last sites of the **Osprey** in Scotland before it became extinct around 1916. A pair nested at this traditional site year after year in the top of an old tree on an island to the eastern side of the loch.

Leaving memories of **Ospreys** of bygone days in the waters and hills of Loch Arkaig we turned out of the Great Glen towards Loch Garry, just a few miles away. At Invergarry the Glen Garry Castle Hotel, a centre for fishing, grouse shooting and deer-stalking in the region, stands near the remains of the old castle where Prince Charlie sheltered after the battle of Culloden. Before us the gleaming waters of Loch Garry beckoned, its shimmering surface shining beyond the slender Birch trees and coils of fresh green ferns feathering its banks. The old single-track road, now fallen into disrepair once forced the impatient traveller to survey its beauty at leisure. Despite sunken shores caused by hydro-electric schemes and the presence of square pens of the trout fisheries at the lower end of the loch, the scene is still peaceful and attractive. Looking to the south across the loch, rolling hills and forests undulate in layers up into the distant mountains. Silvered waters recede into the distance towards the west, where silhouetted purple peaks blend hazily with the evening sky.

It was not long before we had pitched our tent in a quiet glade and *Wigeon (male)* were scanning the water for signs of some of the birds we hoped to see there. We were not disappointed. A sleek **Black-throated Diver** was fishing out on the water, but near enough for us to discern its pale grey head, velvet throat and stark black and white markings on neck and back. These divers usually nest on small islands and slip quietly off their one or two large eggs directly into the water. They are ungainly on land, only able to waddle short distances. Usually they choose grassy sites but I have seen one nesting on a bare mud islet with head held low to avoid detection. These wonderful birds of the far north - and there are no more than 100 pairs in the Highlands - are extremely vulnerable to flooding and disturbance. Breeding success is so poor that there is serious concern over the future of the **Black-throated Diver** in Scotland. The even rarer **Slavonian Grebe** is almost as vulnerable and disturbance of both species at the nest should be avoided at all costs

After watching the **Black-throated Diver** we scan the water for duck at a point higher up the loch where there are wet paches of ground, low sweeping shores and promontories covered with heather. There are a few pairs of **Wigeon** which rise steeply from the surface of the water and circle twice at speed before separating like an air display team. The males splash down on the water while the females descend towards their nests, far off in lush vegetation. One or two **Teal** browse near the water's edge while a pair of **Mergansers** swim in the shelter of a small bay. Close by a **Greenshank** probes elegantly in shallow muddy water before flying off, revealing a deep white rump and plain dark wings, which distinguish it in flight from its commoner cousin the **Redshank,** which has prominent wing bars. Its triple fluting call carries clearly over the loch.

In this general vicinity west of the Great Glen there are a few pairs of **Common Scoters** which breed only on a small number of lochs in Scotland, mostly further north. The male **Scoter** is the only duck which is completely black, relieved only by a yellow patch on its beak, while

Common Scoters

the female is dull brown with paler underparts. Most of us will be more familiar with them as winter visitors in coastal waters where they may gather in sizeable flocks.

For those with time to linger, the long 20 mile jaunt along a narrow road culminating at Loch Hourn on the west coast is well worth while. There are **Divers** on the lochs, **Dunlin** in some of the marshes and **Greenshank** can be watched flying from Loch Quoich (pronounced Kooich) to their hill nesting haunts. **Golden Eagles** may often be seen, patrolling the higher slopes to the north where they nest in remote glens. Our excursion the following day, however, was to take us in the opposite direction back to Lochaber and on to Fort Augustus in search of rare **Grebes.**

Greenshank

IN SEARCH OF GREBES AND DIVERS

Early morning sunlight warmed the chill air inside the tent canopy and stimulated a chorus of bird song outside. Yellow-green **Siskins** combed the pendulant birch twigs, while **Redpolls** trilled overhead. **Goldcrests** recited their repetitive squeaky songs from the tops of firs and the drumming of a **Great Spotted Woodpecker** reverberated from deeper in the wood. As we freshened ourselves in the clear sparkling water from the stream, a **Willow Warbler** carried juicy caterpillars to its young nestlings hidden in the undergrowth. Camping is a wonderful way to enjoy the busy birdlife of the early hours on a fine morning.

Within the hour we were motoring along Glen Mor towards Fort Augustus at the lower end of Loch Ness. In the general vicinity of this loch, famous for its monster, are some wonderful haunts. Loch Ness itself, mysterious looking, where a play of light on the dark water can look deceptively like a weird moving object, has little birdlife. Not far away, Glen Affric, reputed to be one of the most beautiful glens in Scotland, has **Scottish Crossbills** and perhaps even a few pairs of **Crested Tits.** I have seen **Eagles** over the corries of the steep mountains which rise above the wild Loch Mullardoch. It was just a few years ago that we discovered a pair of **Redwing** nesting in a pine and Rhododendron copse, approached by a track winding through a forest at the rear of a caravan site.

We knew there were **Slavonian Grebes** nesting in thin emergent reed on lochans either side of Loch Ness and our aim was to locate and observe some of these delightful little water birds if we could. We didn't expect a lot of difficulty in finding them since, like their cousins the **Great Crested Grebes,** they are conspicuous birds usually spurning cover as they display or dive for fish on the open water. You should look for them on shallow lochs with a thin cover of reeds.

At Loch Tarff there were **Sandpipers** calling excitedly to their young, **Redpolls** in the Birch crowns and a number of **Common Gulls** nesting

Common Gull

by the shore. Incredibly, one pair built a nest on the top of a broken Birch stump only two metres from the ground, just by the roadside. As we slowed down to observe it more closely, the female flew off, revealing a clutch of eggs. Further on, a **Black Grouse** skimmed over the road in front of us, and plonked down in the deep heather. At another loch side, different in character, with rough grass meadows and short pasture cropped by sheep, there were several pairs of **Redshank** and **Lapwing.** Then something happened to really excite us. We spotted a **Short-eared Owl** hovering and quartering the heather moor systematically with strong silent wing beats, then gliding with its wings held in a shallow "V". The second of the pair appeared as if from nowhere, looking more like a headless **Buzzard** than an **owl.** We watched them for some time as they hunted for voles until eventually they disappeared from view over surrounding hills. There and then we decided to come to this area later, on the return leg of our journey in the hope of seeing them actually feeding their young.

The weather conditions were appalling with a soaking, misty rain and we had so far had little incentive to leave the comfort of our car; the promise of good weather had not been fulfilled but in spite of this we had seen a number of interesting birds. Our main mission, however, remained to be accomplished: sightings of **Slavonian Grebes.**

The rain lessened to a slight drizzle as we approached the side of a small loch along a narrow road. Near the water's edge the ground was flat and marshy while asparagus-like reed stems thinly stubbled the water for a distance of about 50 metres out from the edge. This was ideal grebe country and we were not surprised, although none the less delighted, to see two birds out on the water. We focus on the birds from the car window and quickly confirm their identity. They are swimming serenely, preening and rolling on their sides to reveal the pale underside beneath their chestnut flanks. What lovely birds they are! They seem unconcerned by our presence, their golden horns each side of the head showing boldly even on this grey afternoon as they shake and turn their heads.

Spurred on by these sightings, we try our luck at another suitable loch, this time a larger one with two or three shallow bays nurturing beds of the **grebes'** favourite reeds. At first we can see nothing except a pair of **Teal** and some **Common Gulls,** but there is a track cut in deep heather running parallel with a fence skirting a Birch copse leading to the water's edge. The drizzle has at last given way to clearer skies and for the first time today we can stretch our legs as the sun begins to warm the soaked earth. We move deliberately but quietly along the track until we have a view of a wide bay on our left. As we scan the inshore waters with our binoculars, sure enough, although partly veiled by the reeds, we can just make out the chestnut, black and gold of a **Slavonian Grebe** sitting on its sodden mound of a nest. We approach no closer. There are only about 70 or 80 pairs of this species in Scotland and we have already indicated that they are struggling to maintain even this strength and any undue disturbance could cause breeding failure. Out in the middle of the lake the male bird rolls and turns, dives and surfaces, his red eye showing clearly now due to the much improved visibility.

Not far from here the R.S.P.B. has established a new reserve at Loch Ruthven, a water which usually has several pairs of breeding **Slavonian Grebes.** It was here in 1908 that the first Scottish nest of this species was found, heralding the beginning of the colonisation by these grebes of the Highlands. Hopefully the purchase of this site will provide a permanent, undisturbed and safe haven for these rare birds.

By late afternoon we were once more at Loch Garry enjoying views of our now familiar **Black-throated Diver,** which was swimming, like all divers, low in the water and diving for fish, the water pearling off its back as it re-emerged from the depths. Suddenly my friends call out. They are amazed by the sudden appearance of a long, sleek, dark-brown, furry animal with a cream chest scurrying across the path and into some undergrowth. It happened so fast that I missed it and rued my ill-luck, since it would probably be a long time before a second chance to see the elusive Pine Marten came my way . Like Wild Cats, which also inhabit these regions, they are rarely seen in broad daylight. We all have stories of just missing out on some rare bird or, in this case mammal. I consoled myself with thoughts of the many interesting species we had seen during the day which was now drawing to a close. The dark purplish waters dissected by a narrow pencil beam of moon-light lapped gently on the shore as a lone **Woodcock** croaking his courtship notes flew close to our tent, creating a relaxed atmosphere in which to turn in for a night's rest.

*Slavonian
Grebe*

IN SEARCH OF
RED-THROATED DIVERS

The next morning we awoke early to the thunderous sound of the burn careering down its rocky course close to our tent. The song birds were already wide awake with **Redpolls** and **Chaffinches** singing from the Birches. This was an occasion however, when a leisurely wash in the crystal clear pools was out of the question. Through the mosquito mesh at the entrance to our makeshift home there was a swarm of the minute but dreaded Scottish midge. Although each individual is as small as a pin-head they amass in their thousands and are almost impossible to shake off. They emerge in damp places from June until September to plague tourists or anyone else, in the most merciless and unrelenting fashion. There was no escape, and we knew from experience that we would have to pack our bags, tent and all, and get

Red-throated Diver

out as fast as we could if we were not to be eaten alive. Our packing arrangements were hasty, and to say the least, none too dignified as we threshed the air in frenzy to discourage our tormentors.

The road from Invergarry to Dornie is one of the finest mountain roads in Britain. It rises high above Loch Garry where you can look upon the whole stretch of loch set in the subtle beauty of its surrounding hills. Soon the long arching sweep of Loch Loyne, a barren water set among moors and rocks, lies far below to our left. For many miles the road drops, steeply at first, through ever wilder mountain country towards Loch Cluanie, a high, bare loch often surrounded by hanging mists with hills rising steeply to far off crags. Slowly the road descends to Glen Shiel, famous like other Scottish glens for long past battles. It is a glen full of colour, heather, bracken, grass and rocky outcrops with wild orchids sending up their purple spikes among the sedge. The famous peaks known as the 'Five Sisters of Kintail' tower above us while the Falls of Glomach, the highest in Britain, spray downwards into some remote valley beyond. These falls are reputed to be the most spectacular in Britain but are quite difficult to reach and are, not without good reason, known as the 'hidden falls'.

The next few miles to Loch Duich are uneventful except for the appearance of a medium-sized grey bird, which breaks the spell of the glen as it flies low over the trees and alights on the bare branch of a Rowan, its tail fanned and its wings slightly drooping. It utters a few clear echoing 'cuckoos' and then drops into the heather and bracken, no doubt depositing its unwelcome gift into another unsuspecting **Pipit's** or **Whinchat's** nest. In some years the meadows and glens are redolent with the familiar calls of the **Cuckoo** but this is the first adult bird we have heard or seen on our journey.

Loch Duich, approached from the pass of Glen Shiel, provides one of Scotland's most spectacular views: a glistening sea-loch with the jagged Cuillin hills of Skye on the horizon and framed by mountain scenery to left and right. This is a sea-loch, girded by the twisted ribbons of Bladder wrack, sprawling in abandon over its dark, rocky shores. Its sharp smell of salt and seaweed is a contrast to the pine resin or peat smells inland. We take a stroll along the edge of the loch where **Herons** pick their way cautiously along the shoreline, peering myopically into the tidal waters for eels. Near an old stone parapet overlooking the waters, we catch a glimpse of a shiny, furred head, poking up inquisitively. There is a rapid swish of a long tail, a slight ripple and the Otter has vanished. Staring hopefully at the spot makes no difference; he gives us no encore. Otters can often be spotted along this western coast, fishing in the shallow waters of the sea-lochs close to the shore but glimpses like this are often all that one catches.

Dornie, a lochside village a few miles further on, provides perhaps the best known postcard view of Scotland with its castle standing on a rock just off the shore, but close enough to be spanned by an old stone footbridge. Many years ago a thriving fishing industry was based here but the only fishing now is of trout and salmon caught by anglers in the river which flows past the village.

In the bay we noted a grass covered island cut off at high-tide, but connected to the mainland at ebb-tide, where two male **Eiders** were rocking gently in the waves. These birds looked very smart in their white dinner-jackets and black trouser underparts, as though ready to go to a party if their wives could be persuaded to leave their nests and join them. The island looked ideal for breeding **Eiders,** and there was also a colony of **Common Gulls** nesting there among the shingle, grass or driftwood. One pair had chosen a select position inside an old, discarded tyre. The gulls' squawking and wheeling dominated even the fluting of a few pairs of **Oystercatchers** which were nesting near the shore.

On close inspection there were several more **Eiders.** They nest sometimes in deep vegetation but often they choose more open positions than most ducks and usually lay only four or five eggs, surrounded by soft down feathers, so beloved by eiderdown makers in days gone by. They are second only to the **Mallard** as the most numerous breeding duck in Britain although few are found on coasts south of the Scottish border.

After breakfast and a wash and brush-up, mercifully in the absence of the midge squadrons, we are ready to drive on towards Torridon, intending to see again a pair of **Red-throated Divers** which we had located in that district on a holiday several years ago. Already we had seen three pairs of **Black-throated Divers** on our journey north but as yet no 'Red-throats'. Unlike the former, which make their homes on large fresh-water lochs often more than a mile in length, the slightly smaller and slender **Red-throated Diver** chooses to breed on small, often treeless lochans or tarns, and the birds usually fly to the sea to feed. The distribution of this diver tends to be more coastal therefore than its rather more strikingly marked relative.

Our journey takes us by Loch Carron and Kishorn where some of the massive North Sea oil rigs were built, but with the recession in the rig-building industry this deep-water yard is now almost deserted. The road rises steeply upwards along the snaking pass of Bealach na Ba, the 'pass of the cattle', reaching nearly 2,000ft as it winds its way

Eiders

between the peaks of Applecross. **Eagles** can be seen hereabouts whilst **Ptarmigan** inhabit the higher slopes. Herds of Red Deer are not a rare sight either, but today we are unlucky. The mists hang low over the peaks and blanket even the lower slopes towards Applecross. Last time we were here a pair of **Eagles** appeared right above our heads and circled around inquisitively before drifting off in the direction of Skye. On clear days there are fine views of Skye and Raasay, lying in turquoise-blue waters or appearing as black shapes set in brilliant white seas on still evenings.

At Applecross, having disappointingly seen little of interest due to poor visibility, we turn along the tortuous coast road which follows a wind-blown stretch of exposed foreland bravely defying the winter gales. Even today, in late spring there is a chill, blustery wind rocking the car. The view offers a scene of scattered, isolated crofters' homes recently repainted by brave new tenants seeking a life of peace and freedom in this wilderness, far removed from the comforts of urban dwelling. A few **Eider Duck** huddled together in deep-sheltered coves, a pair of **Rock Pipits** dashed down a steep gulley to the cracked rock face where they probably had a brood of young, and a **Raven** honked in defiance overhead.

Our **Red-throated Diver** location is very typical: three small lochans close together not far from the sea. We walk in the teeth of the wind, our cheeks smarting under its lash and our eyes filling with tears, making any sort of observation difficult. The way ahead lies along a narrow path skirting a low, heather covered rise until at last, with a sigh of relief, we flop down in the lee of the hill, sheltered from the gusts. Before us lie two of the tarns, their grey surface water ruffled by the unrelenting wind. At first, there is no sign of any birds at all, let alone **Red-throated Divers;** but bird-watchers know that patience is an essential virtue and we will wait hopefully for our birds to turn up. Half an hour later our endurance is rewarded when we spot two large birds lumbering into view from the sea, their rapid wing beats, heavy bodies and long necks identifying them clearly as divers. They pass over the first lochan and both land on the second one, furthest from us, just within our view. After a few minutes both divers rise heavily from the water, skim the lowest point between two small hills close by and disappear. Their flight path would take them once again towards the sea but also towards the third lochan out of our view, only a few minutes walk away.

We lose no time in dislodging our by now frozen bodies from their damp bed and clamber cautiously to the summit of another hill at the top of which there will be a clear view of 'lochan number three'. Gasping, but still undetected we reach the top of the rise and peer through tunnels of heather, scanning the water with our high-powered binoculars. To our delight, the female **Red-throated Diver** can be seen, its back awash and its neck just above the water, swimming determinedly towards the bank. A moment later she turns towards a reedy patch and hoists herself onto a low mound by the shore. She shuffles onto her nest, warily keeping her surroundings under observation. We are too far away to see anything in the nest but assume she must have one, or perhaps two large olive eggs spotted with black or dark brown. We watch as she slowly relaxes and withdraws her head onto her breast. Satisfied that there will be no more activity from the divers for a while, we retreat slowly down the slope towards our car, our pleasure dissipating the cold in our bones.

There are about 700 pairs of **Red-throated Divers** in Scotland, most of them in the far west, the Hebrides, Caithness and the Northern Isles.

Grey Heron

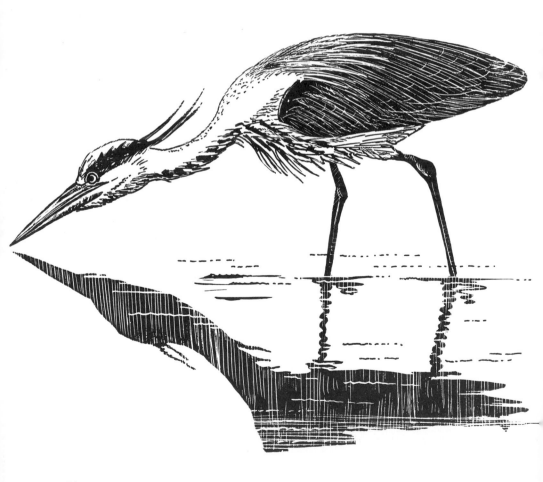

THE FAR NORTH AND
RARE BREEDING BIRDS

Loch Torridon, in Wester Ross, is one of those sea lochs which reflect deep peacock-blue in the sunlight, surrounded by its red sandstone mountains. In the bays are islands formed with steep cliffs where colonies of **Black Guillemots** nest in the recesses and **Shags** occupy the more exposed ledges. The **Guillemots'** large white wing patches contrast sharply with their otherwise all velvet black plumage. It is a smaller bird than the **Common Guillemot.**

In May and June the flats around the loch-head are carpeted with pink thrift and the neighbouring slopes of Scots Pine combine to produce a rich and colourful panorama. Sadly it was time to turn around and head for Skye on the return route. The lure of the northlands prompted some hesitation in our minds, but time compelled us to restrain our impulses to go on. Our memories were of past adventures since we had been this way several times before. Your own travels may well take you further north, so for the sake of completion we will give a brief account of bird-watching possibilities there.

North and east of Torridon is Loch Maree, reckoned by many to be the most beautiful loch in Scotland. It is studded with tree-embellished islands, and has as a backdrop the monumental Slioch and Ben Eighe, Liathach and other impressive peaks. Many years ago I met a veteran American tourist who had travelled widely in many lands and who enthused that this was the finest scenery he had ever seen. Few who have visited this area and seen it to best advantage, would argue.

For those lucky enough to be travelling along this circuitous coastal road the seascapes, lochs and mountains provide a continuous source of wonder: Loch Maree, Loch Ewe, Gruinard Bay, Loch Broom, and the McDonnel Range. In 1970 the first ever pair of **Great Northern Divers** was found breeding on a loch in Wester Ross. This mainly

North American species has been noted often enough in northern waters in summer, and breeding had been awaited for a long time.

Loch Broom is a wide sea-loch on whose eastern shore lies the small fishing port of Ullapool which owes its existence to the now scarce herring. Beyond here is the Gneiss country, a rock-strewn, stony landscape, with open sea-lochs haunted by the sound of wailing **Red-throated Divers.** Old stone crofters' cottages warmed by blazing peat fires blend with the landscape. I recall spending a week in such a cottage and being taken by the owner on a fishing trip for our supper. We walked about a mile over the moor to a small acidic lochan, where he proceeded to haul no less than ten brown trout out of it in the space of two hours, using nothing more sophisticated than a long stick, a length of strong twine and a bent pen.

Sutherland is the South Land of the Vikings and was occupied by them for nearly two hundred years. In the west it is a land of strangely shaped, sheer or hump-backed mountains rising straight out of the surrounding moorland. The Birch woods of these Wester Ross and Sutherland coasts sometimes have breeding **Redwing** and there are divers on the lochs and lochans. In Sutherland the **Black-throated Diver** is perhaps commoner than anywhere else in the Highlands. The same is true of the **Greenshank,** a bird particularly associated with the Gneiss and Flow Country, where up to 60% of the Scottish population are said to breed. The nest of this species is reckoned to be the hardest to find of all British birds. The female sits tight on her nest scrape on the moors, and tracking it back to its nest is a time consuming process only to be achieved in gradual stages, beginning at the lochsides where the birds feed.

The **Corncrake** is still to be heard 'crecking' in grassy meadows or even in quite small nettle-bed patches close to crofters' cottages. Unfortunately this species is one of the British birds to suffer most from modern farming technology, having been driven virtually to extinction in many areas by mechanised grass cutting. Significant populations of this bird are now only to be found in Ireland and the Hebrides.

Rocky outcrops and islets of sheltered bays and sea-lochs are home to large colonies of **Arctic Terns,** the most numerous of all British terns. The island of Handa, an R.S.P.B. reserve, just two miles from the shore, has huge colonies of **Auks, Shags, Fulmars** and other seabirds. **Herring Gulls** sometimes nest even on the beaches while small numbers of that powerful pirate, the **Great Skua** or 'Bonxie' as it is called, are also present. A few pairs of **Arctic Skuas,** sleeker and faster than the larger birds, are also found on Handa which represents little more than an outpost for both species which are found in their greatest numbers in Orkney and Shetland. The world distribution of the 'Bonxie' is interesting. It is mainly a bird of the southern sub-antarctic regions, but in the northern hemisphere is virtually confined to the Faeroes, one or two outposts of Norway and the northern islands of Scotland.

Handa, with its 300 ft Torridon-sandstone cliffs rising sheer out of the sea, is a seabird metropolis of the north-west coast. Scarcely less impressive for birds are the enormous cliffs of Cape Wrath at the north-western tip of Britain and Clo Mor a few miles to the east.

These places, however, do not compare with the vast wealth of seabirds of the Orkney and Shetland Isles: 160,000 **Fulmars,** 20,000 **Arctic Terns,** 170,000 **Puffins** are the mind-boggling estimated totals of these seabirds shared between the northern isles. In addition there are 1,000 pairs of **Arctic Skuas** and nearly 7000 pairs of **Great Skuas** (about three quarters of these totals for each species are on Shetland).

Apart from seabirds, the Shetlands are also noted for those two rare waders, the **Whimbrel,** a smaller relative of the **Curlew,** and the diminutive **Red-necked Phalarope** of which there are probably less than 50 pairs left, mostly on Fetlar. One of the most notable ornithological events of recent decades was the breeding of **Snowy Owls** on Fetlar, an occurrence fully documented by Bruce Tulloch.

A pair of those archetypal birds of the Arctic bred in 1967 for the first time but unfortunately the attempt at colonisation petered out after a few years due to a shortage of male birds. **Long-tailed Duck** and **Velvet Scoters** are often present in northern waters in summer although the latter has never been proved to breed and the former has not done so since about 1912.

The western islands, the Hebrides, are hardly less notable for their seabirds. On the Machair of North and South Uist there are high concentrations of **Dunlin, Ringed Plover** and other waders. The recent development of sheep farming, however, could put this unique habitat at risk. Until quite recently the largest colony of truly wild **Grey-lag Geese** in Britain was found on Loch Druidibeg, a national nature reserve on South Uist.

There remain the small islands and rocky outposts, home to large numbers of sea-birds. The huge gannetry on St. Kilda, the largest in the world, holds about 40,000 pairs of these birds which plummet into the sea after fish. In contrast, the darkly plumaged **Leach's (fork-tailed) Petrel,** about 8 inches (20cm) long, breeds in underground

Goldeneye

burrows on a few remote rocky islands in the Flannens, St. Kilda, North Rona and Sula Sgeir. Estimation of its numbers is made very difficult by its nocturnal feeding habits.

Returning to the mainland, there are several exciting new species just settling to breed in the Highlands, mainly in the northernmost county districts of Caithness, Sutherland, Inverness and Ross and Cromarty. The **Temminck's Stint,** that tiniest of waders, is holding perhaps a handful of territories in Ross and Cromarty and Inverness, while the **Wood Sandpiper** also breeds, a few pairs ranging from Sutherland down to Invernesshire. The **Turnstone** probably and the **Purple Sandpiper** definitely have also bred, while the **Green Sandpiper,** a tree–nesting bird, bred in 1917 and again in 1959. The most surprising recent record is that of an **American Spotted Sandpiper** which nested on Skye, three thousand miles off course from its normal breeding range. Of these, the **Purple Sandpiper** at least, is a good candidate to colonise the Highlands in the footsteps of the **Stint** and **Wood Sandpiper.** Most of these waders are, of course, more often seen on passage at inland waters, whilst the **Turnstone** is commonly seen and the **Purple Sandpiper** frequently seen probing amongst rocks in the intertidal zone around our shores in winter.

The **Shore Lark** was found breeding in 1977 and in one or two subsequent years and in 1968 a nest and eggs of a **Bluethroat** was found in the Spey Valley. Unfortunately the eggs were destroyed by a predator. The **Lapland Bunting** is another passerine which has bred for the first time in recent years. Breeding was first proved in 1977 when as many as 16 pairs were located. In 1979 there were 14 pairs at 3 sites but this promise of colonisation was not maintained and by 1982 there was no evidence at all of breeding in the Highlands. That close relative of the **Chaffinch,** the **Brambling,** more commonly seen in winter, has often been heard singing in northern Birch woods. The first definite attempted breeding was in Sutherland in 1920 and no known further attempt was confirmed until 1969. The first known successful nest was discovered in 1982 and two more pairs bred in the following year.

Many of these rare or occasional breeding species are, as we have said, much commoner in winter or on passage. This holds particularly true of the **Redwing** and **Fieldfare,** those two striking and familiar thrushes which are to be seen everywhere in fields and hedgerows during the colder months.

On my last visit to the Highlands I had encountered three singing male **Redwings,** but this time so far we had seen none. Regular nesting only started in the 1950s rising to a peak of over 100 pairs, then dipped steeply before rising again in the early eighties. **Redwings,** which are widely scattered in the northern Highlands, seem to like the vicinity of human habitation and open woods with Birch and Rhododendron. The **Fieldfare** is also attempting to establish itself in Britain, but in far smaller numbers and more hesitantly than the **Redwing.** No more than a few pairs settle here to breed in any one year, and records have ranged from Orkney and Shetland as far south as Derbyshire.

Redwing   The Highlands are so vast and difficult to work with few roads and energy-sapping terrain, that some of these rare species may be more frequent in summer than is supposed. Some will remain undiscovered and you could be as likely as anyone else to encounter something unusual. If you do, the R.S.P.B. or other conservation agencies would be pleased to hear from you. The most important consideration, of course, is to avoid any disturbance which might increase the risk of breeding failure.

Our holiday produced just such an unexpected encounter: we had just finished brewing some tea in a sheltered spot by a river bridge, when John heard a liquid-fluting song coming from a low tree among the sedge and brambles. "It's a **Rosefinch**", I suggested with a mixture of wild optimism and humour, as we both moved towards the tree, knowing that whatever the bird was, it was a species unfamiliar to us. As we all know optimism is often quickly dampened in the wake of closer examination but in this case our excitement was fully justified.

There, perched conspicuously near the top of the bush, only two metres from the ground, was one of the most colourful birds I have ever seen. It had a bright crimson-red head, breast and rump, with pale, pinkish-white under-parts, brown wings and tail. The exotic-looking bird continued to sing from its perch for about a minute accompanied in the background by the scratchy notes of **Sedge Warblers.** It fluttered across the river into some gardens close to a small group of houses.

A male **Scarlet Rosefinch** in breeding plumage is quite unmistakable, but the pleasure of confirming our find led us to reach for our field-guide. Satisfied that there could be no mistake, we crossed the bridge and trained our binoculars on the bird again. He was far too pre-occupied chasing female **Chaffinches** to worry much about us, which suggested that he had no female. The chances of finding one of his own species, whose breeding range normally extends no nearer to Scotland than Poland or Sweden, seemed quite remote.

Nevertheless we knew the **Scarlet Rosefinch** had bred at least once in Scotland and is a candidate for possible colonisation. What a wonderful addition to Scotland's avifauna it would be too! We were left wondering whether this lone male was the offspring of a local breeding pair from a previous year or even perhaps, one individual of a small colony trying to establish a foothold in the area.

This is the stuff of which dreams are made! Perhaps we should now return to more mundane reality and continue the course of our journey, leaving the **Rosefinch** to its secret location somewhere within a few miles of our main holiday route.

Scarlet
Rosefinch

IN SEARCH OF EAGLES

We were planning our next visit to Skye where we had seen several **Eagles** some years ago. A view of these noble-looking birds is our chief target as far as Skye is concerned but we are in no hurry. As we pass Loch Carron for the second time the sun is shining and the glint of reflected light on the water beautifully enhances the serenity of this sea-loch. Its shores are flat and shingly towards its head and are intersected by mud and sandy gullies, along which the tidal salt waters flow. At this time of year, those areas above high tide are carpeted in bright pink thrift. **Ringed Plovers** are running to and fro while **Oystercatchers** sit rather too conspicuously on their nest scrapes amongst the thrift. **Lapwings** are sunning themselves on the salt-flats and a pair of **Redshank** fly over, revealing their white wing-bars as they land in a field, fluting excitedly. At the far end of this field, cropped by sheep and with shallow pools of water, something unusual attracts our gaze. No less than a dozen **Grey-lag Geese** are calmly grazing in the marshy herbage. We are by no means sure whether these are truly wild birds or feral stock which are found in several parts of the British Isles. The only true wild geese resident in Britain are on the north-west coast and outer isles and these birds are in ideal natural habitat. We are inclined to believe we are looking at the real thing. As we ponder, there is a sudden ripple through the flock, a noisy honking and all twelve geese are airborne climbing steadily in a rough 'V' formation as they disappear out of sight.

In winter large flocks of geese are a common sight in several parts of Scotland, particularly in coastal districts. Apart from **Grey-lags, Pink-footed Geese** are to be found in good numbers with the largest concentrations in eastern counties, while the **White-fronted** and **Barnacle Geese** are found in western areas, particularly the islands. Of these Islay is the most outstanding, holding 75% of the wintering British population of **Barnacle Geese** (about 15,000).

The village of Loch Carron is a quiet place, sheltered from Atlantic storms by the Isle of Skye, so its waters are invariably calm. There are a few boarding houses and a string of white cottages facing the shore. Not far from here there were **Mergansers** and a solitary **Red-throated Diver** with body low, fishing far out in the rippling waters of the loch. In the absence of the **Grey-lag Geese** our attention turned once again to the common yet attractive selection of waders on the inshore flats, close to the estuary where the river water enters the loch. Among the **Lapwings, Oystercatchers** and **Ringed Plovers,** a rather agitated **Common Sandpiper** paced up and down on the mud-banks, appearing and then disappearing from view as it worked its way towards us along a deep gulley. My brother, Mick, speculated that it must have a nest. John greeted this derisively and I fully agreed with his scepticism, offering a small wager to back my opinion, since the surrounding terrain looked unsuitable. A car can often serve well as a hide and the **Sandpiper** approached closely as we sat huddled and attentive, our minds concentrated by the fine drizzle now giving us ample incentive to remain in the dry and comfort of the car. Inexorably the **Sandpiper** emerged from the ditch, crept up a slope and tiptoed across the tarmaced road on which we were parked. We looked around as she proceeded, now quickly and with determination into the grass at the side of the roadway. I began to feel glad we had not also promised to eat our hats as the **Sandpiper** moved stealthily among the herbage behind the car and suddenly disappeared.

It was a lovely nest with four marbled eggs and the good-humoured amusement we shared was well worth the price of standing my brother a good meal that evening. Waders' nests just a metre or two from minor roads are a charming Scottish feature which I have witnessed before on past visits to Scotland.

There are **Eagles** and **Peregrine Falcons** in glens close to here, but we hastened now towards The Kyle of Lochalsh and the short ferry crossing to Kyleakin on Skye. We planned an overnight stay at Broadford where **Corn Buntings** and **Corncrakes** used to be heard in the damp meadows, and **Greenshank** bred close by. The **Corn Bunting** has now become a very scarce bird in the Highlands and is rarely encountered away from east coast districts. At Broadford we stayed in a Gaelic-speaking household where the landlady was warm-hearted and generous, traits so often found among traditional Highland people. The location would serve us well in exploring the surrounding area, particulary the neighbourhood of Elgol, only 12 miles away across the wasp's waist of Loch Slapin where I once saw a **Golden Eagle** circling lazily directly over the road.

Skye is the largest of Scottish islands, a place of haunting beauty, for the most part treeless, but full of colour on sunny days, with rusty-red, flat-topped hills and rocks splattered with yellow, grey and green lichens, skirting clear blue bays. On wet days, which are by no means uncommon in these parts, the aspect can be dreary if not oppressive.

The island has mixed claims as far as bird watching is concerned. Seabirds are surprisingly few and there are none of the unique island species such as the **Red-necked Phalarope,** the **Skuas** or the **Whimbrel,** which are for example found on Shetland. Not unexpectedly, for an island so close to the mainland, it has correspondingly similar species. There are more than a dozen pairs of **Golden Eagles,** nesting mostly at cliff eyries. The **White-tailed** or **Sea Eagle,** once extinct in Britain, has been re-introduced recently on Rhum, where over 80 young birds have been released as fledglings from Norway in the past 10 or 12 years in an attempt to re-establish the species in Scotland. The survival rate appears to be good and breeding has taken place with 3 successful pairs present in 1989, rearing 5 young. Birds are now scattered widely over the western islands and thanks to the work of people like John Love of the Nature Conservancy Council the project shows every sign of being successful.

This area was one of the 'Erne's' last strongholds in the Highlands before it was harried out of existence by the gun and the pole-trap, the gamekeeper and crofter. The Victorian passion for shooting almost any creature that moved and of collecting stuffed specimens and eggs drove more nails into the coffin of this huge bird's destiny. A few pairs survived until early into the 20th century with the last pair on Skye in 1912.

The **Sea Eagle** has a large vulturine appearance on the wing, short in the tail but with a wing span of nearly 8 feet, exceeding that of the

Golden Eagle. It feeds on similar prey to the latter species but will often take seabirds and fish from the lochs. Many of its former ledges on Skye and elsewhere have since been occupied by the powerful **Golden Eagle** so we await further developments with intense interest.

Our car drive to Elgol failed to turn up any sightings of **Eagles** at reasonable range although we did see one at a considerable distance flying over a low moor near the sea. At close quarters there is an obvious huge difference in size between **Eagle** and **Buzzard,** but this is often blurred at long range because of the difficulty of allowing for distance. The **Eagle** has more head out in front and more tail, with a larger and more powerful beak. The adult is generally dark brown, but young immature birds can appear more mottled, like a **Buzzard.**

Giving up on **Eagles** for the time being we wander along the road above Elgol to watch some of the more mundane birds. The high banks of the roadside are covered in thick heather and our attention is drawn to finch-like twittering above our heads. We see two dumpy little finches fly over and land in the heather not far ahead of us. Through the binoculars they look dullish, rather like **Redpolls** but lacking the crimson head colour or black chins. Their yellow bills and pink rumps identify them as **Twites** and distinguish them from the rather similar **Linnets** which incidentally are not found on Skye. On approaching closer, one of the birds flies off, but the other remains, now hidden in heather. She is sitting on a small nest woven with fine roots and grass, lined with feathers and containing 5 bluish eggs. On the other side of the road a pair of **Wheatears** are feeding their young in a crevice beneath a rock. On a slope a short way down the road, a brightly painted male **Stonechat** is 'chipping' excitedly amongst the gorse, his velvet-black head, white 'collar' and rose-pink chest showing up conspicuously against the sombre background. There are some meagre spruce trees where two or three **Siskins** are playing in the upper branches. The birds are probably breeding, but the few trees hardly seem sufficient for their needs.

Although the clouds are still draping the hills we decide to risk a climb in the hope that they may clear during our ascent. The crags rise steeply from the roadside above Elgol and although they are not high, the climb is strenuous. We come out onto a high moor with scattered peat pools and stony hill tops. Confounding our hopes, the cloud is still around and visibility limited, but now we are up here we decide to look around.

Just below us, on the steep, scree-strewn slope we catch a glimpse of two dark birds and a flash of white at their throats: a pair of **Ring Ouzels** are darting after each other. As we continue, we catch their chinking, thrush-like notes emanating from the gulley below. A **Buzzard** braces itself against the air currents just above a ledge, hovering in search of rodent prey. On the open moor our movements are followed by a surprising number of northern **Golden Plover,** resplendent in their gold-freckled back plumage and rich black underbelly. There were 6 or 7 pairs on the drier patches of higher stony ground, one or two acting as sentries, standing proudly on the summits, piping their warnings of approach.

White-tailed Eagle

The cliffs around the tidy little village of Elgol look out over Loch Scavaig and the Isle of Soay: a minor road will take you to the eastern side of the peninsula and here you can visit the famous Spar Cave described in Sir Walter Scott's *Lord of the Isles*. It used to be decorated with beautiful stalactites, but tourists have destroyed them. The cave's inner chamber has a circular pool like white marble.

The bay of Loch Scavaig is studded with skerries (rocky islets) keeping larger boats out of the bay. The steep-sided island of Rhum stands dark and imposing, four miles across the water. Towards evening you can watch hundreds of birds skimming the silvery waves, their long dark wings beating strongly as they repeatedly switch direction. These are the **Manx Shearwaters** which breed at their largest colony in the British Isles, 2,500 feet high on Askival, the highest mountain on Rhum. On the rocks below, grey striated **Rock Pipits** are chasing sandflies to feed their young, waiting hungrily in their nest in a cliff crevice.

To the north-west lie the jagged peaks of the Cuillin mountains which offer some of the severest challenges to mountain climbers anywhere in the British Isles. The word Cuillin comes from the old Norse 'Kjollen' meaning keel-shaped ridge.

On good summer evenings a view out to the western horizon can offer scenes of unparalleled dramatic beauty. Here the northern light lingers almost to midnight in June and the fiery sunsets over the jagged Cuillin hills are sights which remain imprinted in your memory long after your holiday is over. So it was on this occasion. As we turned once more towards Broadford the mountains turned an uncanny violet colour framed by a soft pink sky. To the east, the dark forms of mountains, islands and rocks slowly turned black contrasting with the smooth silvery-white sea and pale sky. Our visit to Skye had been too short, but we still had much to see elsewhere and sadly, our time was not elastic.

The next afternoon saw us at Dornie once more, this time camping out in a small glen on the shores of Loch Long. Here we intended to look at some of the smaller glens in the neighbourhood, close to the

Five Sisters and in the mountains near Glen Elg, hoping eventually to see our elusive **Eagles.**

Before turning in for the night, after some searches in the local hills we decided to have a pint or two at the local pub in Dornie. On the way there we observed **Mergansers** swimming languidly out in the loch and several **Herons** stalking elegantly on the shoreline. **Pied Wagtails** performed acrobatics to catch the swarming insects and a russet-tailed **Redstart** sang its sad little song from a moss-bearded willow.

In the pub, over a beer and a warming dram, we chatted to some of the regulars who were discussing politics in the wake of the recent elections.

Strolling back along a track at the head of Loch Long, towards Killilan house, John had gone on ahead and I stood for a moment adjusting my binoculars. A young, bearded man, rucksack-laden, hailed me just as he was entering a cottage. "Are you bird-watchers?", he asked rhetorically, but in a friendly way. I replied that we were and animatedly he began to tell me what he had discovered: he'd been climbing that day in a nearby glen and on descending a steep cliff, some 300 metres high, he'd come across a **Golden Eagle's** eyrie, containing two young birds. I made a mental note of the directions the climber enthusiastically, if rather incautiously gave me. I called my colleagues back, whereupon he explained again with reference to an Ordnance Survey map. This was a piece of luck we had not expected and that night we settled into our sleeping bags full of anticipation for the next day.

It is several miles away and we drive as far as the road takes us, to the foot of the hills, and walk the rest. We follow a small burn along a narrow glen for about two miles. It is bare and empty apart from a few stunted Hawthorn bushes now dusted white with blossom, their heavy scent carrying far; erect Foxgloves stand stiffly in small groups, protruding from the scree on the slopes; to our right a steep cliff, of the kind our mountaineering friend described, walls-off the glen. We have already walked over a mile but still there is no sign of an **Eagle,** nor much else in this quiet secluded spot. As we round a bend and look up at the ridge above us, a large dark form appears from over the lip. The broad wings are splayed at their extremities as it circles silently almost above us, monitoring our movements.

At long last the 'Lord of the Glens' deigns to show himself to us. We train our binoculars on him, admiring his mastery of the air, following him as he again disappears over the ridge. We know we must now be near the eyrie so we begin scanning the cliffs around us, remembering that our acquaintance had told us that it was not far above a steep, grassy slope, only 10 or 15 metres from the foot of the cliff. Then we see it: a bulky stack of sticks, like a huge Raven's nest, on a ledge recessed into the rock face. However, as we examine it closer we see that it is an old nest, but only 30 metres or so further along the cliff, slightly higher and wedged between two vertical columns of rock was the new nest. It was a broad, deep structure composed of heather and young wood, obviously freshly built. From so far below in the glen we can see nothing over the brim of the nest. The young climber had told us that the eyrie contained two fluffy-white chicks, perhaps two or three weeks old, and we were happy enough to take his word for it. A nest with two young is quite unusual because, although **Golden Eagles** invariably lay two eggs, after hatching the weaker of the two chicks usually dies, being killed by its elder sibling. Sometimes, as appears in this case, two eaglets are reared successfully.

Not wishing to disturb the birds we do not linger, being more than satisfied at this unexpected gift. The adult birds are not to be seen, but as we leave the area one of them appears again from over the cliff-top. This time, it seems larger than before and we assume it to be the female. She circles over the eyrie to make sure the chicks are unharmed and then flies to the opposite side of the glen, lands on a large rock and watches, as if to see us off its territory.

The position of this nest reminded us that **Golden Eagles** do not choose to nest on windswept, north-facing crags in defiance of wind and rain, nor on mountain summits as romantic legend would have it. They usually nest no more than about 500 metres above sea level in sheltered, steep-sided glens, offering some protection from the elements.

Despite continuing persecution on some estates, the Scottish **Golden Eagle** population is among the highest in Europe. There are about 400 pairs, a figure only equalled in Spain, where the total area is much greater and consequently the concentration of birds much lower than in the Highlands. This is a wonderful achievement for British conservation when you consider that the **Golden Eagle** only escaped the fate of the **Sea Eagle** by the skin of its beak! Like all birds that eat carrion, it is particularly vulnerable to traps and poisons set illegally by people who begrudge this regal bird its domain.

The **Golden Eagle** feeds mainly on medium-sized mammals like Hares and Rabbits or on ground-nesting birds like **Grouse.** It may sometimes take lambs but it is much more likely to feed on the carcasses of dead sheep. People seeing the birds doing the latter have often wrongly concluded that the **Eagle** has first killed the sheep.

RETURN TO THE SHORT-EARED OWLS

Our first week in Scotland had been attended by mixed weather to say the least, but despite this we were more than satisfied with our sightings and discoveries so far. We now wished to spend more time watching those ghostly spirits of the moor, the **Short-eared Owls.** After an overnight stop we found ourselves travelling once more along the narrow winding road that led into the heart of their territory. Here there was no habitation and certainly no accommodation to be found, and as the weather was dry we decided to use our tent again.

We traversed the area seeking a suitable site and were motoring slowly along a small road bordered by fields and ditches, when we suddenly felt ourselves transfixed by piercing eyes: there right in front of us sitting on a dead side branch of an old Ash tree was a very alert **Short-eared Owl,** its body and head stretched to its full height, staring down at us, as if intimating that we were unwelcome interlopers in its territory. It watched us for a few seconds unmoving then silently swung off its perch, flapping over the field, following the irrigation ditch. We chose a soft clearing of grass and heather near a small fir wood, with a stream for washing nearby. It was close to an old grey stone bridge, typical for the Highlands, and was not far from where we had just seen the owl.

We pitch our tent and decide to split up in order to examine our moorland environment more efficiently. I stay in the vicinity and John takes the car to drive slowly around the area. It is now twilight, a time beloved of **Short-eared Owls** for hunting, and it is only a short time before we see the birds. I wander up a narrow track over a slope thickly covered in heather, then down the other side, into a shallow valley between the hills, then up a gentle gradient on to the open moor. There are clumps of rushes and high-growing patches of heather.

During my wandering I am delighted by four plump male **Black Grouse** flying across my path, their white under-tail coverts flashing in the last rays of the evening. As I watch them disappearing in the distance I become aware of a strange high-pitched coughing above me. I look up and see the silhouette of a **Short-eared Owl** obviously unhappy at my intrusion. I retreat immediately not wishing to remain an un-welcome guest. In the meantime John is also encountering owls, but this time a different pair. As he drives down the slope he sees a pair of owls in the valley, systematically quartering the wet ditches and swampy low-lying parts for small voles or mice. He stops the car to watch them.

This area, off the main thoroughfare of the Great Glen, is a real backwater. The only traffic is the odd Landrover of a local farmer every few hours or so, otherwise the only sounds are the winds rustling the vegetation, the usual peep-peep of springy pipits and the occasional grrh, grrh of **Grouse** hidden in the heather.

One of the owl pair disappears over a hill top but the other remains in the valley hunting. At regular intervals it drops down into the rush, then rises again to continue hunting. Now it has something clutched in its talons, flying over the road to the other side of the moorland slope. It flies with a clear determination circling once over a spot on the slope and then decending quickly into the heather. It remains there for a few minutes then flies up and continues to search for prey. This happens twice and it becomes very clear that the spot in the heather conceals fledging owls.

By now the light is almost gone and we return to our camp site to exchange notes. We are amazed that we have both encountered owls

Short-eared Owl chick

and that there are clearly two pairs in this small area. I, too, am convinced that my owl has young.

We enjoy a cup of coffee made with the clear mountain water and while we sip it, savour not only our drinks but also the still calm of the moors now covered in the cloak of night. As we sit there we catch the soft croaking sound of a roding **Woodcock** and see its plump snipe-like silhouette sailing over the tops of the fir trees. Despite the fact that our tent is pitched close to the road, we pass the night in serene and undisturbed sleep, hearing only one car.

The following day we return to where we have seen the birds. John has retained a visual marker in his head so that we can locate the spot where his owl landed with its prey. After a short walk towards the slope and a rapid search we find what we are looking for: in a flattened patch under the heather a pair of the most frightening and hypnotic eyes are staring up at us. They are large and of a bright yellow around a velvet-brown pupil. It is a young owl but almost fully fledged, its soft down-feathers still clinging in wisps to the new rich brown feathers which are now emerging. Its sharp beak is half agape in a threatening gesture. On the flattened vegetation around it are the small corpses of Voles, forming its reserve larder, although it hardly needed them, appearing to be very plump and well fed.

We return to our car, but linger on the road watching the adult birds bringing regular meals of small rodents to their offspring; there are obviously two because the adults perform 'drops' at two different sites. As soon as the young owls can move about they leave the nest site and wander quite a distance from it, still being fed by their parents.

The **Short-eared Owl** is a variable resident, its numbers fluctuating according to the quantity of Voles it can find on the moors and in the plantations. There are probably three pairs in this small area and we were to see another on the Perthshire moors later on in the holiday.

The **Short-eared Owl** is one of the scarcer owls in Britain but it is more frequently observed than its cousin, the **Long-eared Owl,** which often roosts tucked up close to the trunk of a tree in a wood, only emerging in full darkness when you may hear its dull triple hoot. The **Short-eared Owl** is diurnal, hunting mainly during the day, making it easier to watch. There are **Long-eared Owls** in this part of Scotland too, and in Britain as a whole there are probably about 5000 pairs of each species.

Black Grouse

BIRDS OF THE SPEY
AND CAIRNGORMS

Osprey   We stood, still only half awake, absorbing the hazy sunshine and looking eastwards from our hilltop site. Before us stretched a huge, undulating, deep-green blanket merging into a soft blue towards the horizon of distant hills. This is the Spey Valley, boasting the largest area of natural Scots Pine forest in the whole of Britain.

The Spey Valley is renowned for its variety of exciting species of birds, some of which are found in greater numbers than elsewhere in Scotland. Such species include the **Crested Tit, Scottish Crossbill, Capercaillie** and on the lofty 4,000 ft (1230m) high plateau of the Cairngorms, the **Dotterel** and **Snow Bunting.**

At first the Spey Valley gives the impression of being relatively flat and rather disappointing when coming from the dramatic and rugged peaks of the west, but this impression is only transitory. The natural pine forests of Rothiemurchus, Abernethy (now an R.S.P.B. nature reserve) and Glenmore are unique: small stands of naturally growing Scots Pines, with their light coppery trunks and thick umbrellas of dark-green needle foliage are separated by open areas of heather, bilberry and lichen and small lochs which are rounder and shallower than the deep rift ones in the west. In sunlight the scenery offers a richness of colour and feeling of gentle harmony not found elsewhere in the Highlands. One such place is the area around Loch an Eilean where, in the 19th century an **Osprey** built its nest on the old castle ruins on a small island year after year. Unfortunately in later years this nest was repeatedly robbed as elsewhere in the Highlands until the species dwindled to extinction.

The **Osprey** is among the most famous of Scottish birds and its return to Speyside in the 1950s is an exciting and gladdening saga. Like the **Sea Eagle** it survived persecution only until the first or second decade of this century, the last pairs nesting further west, near Loch Loyne and Arkaig. Its fish-eating habits made it unloved by the salmon and trout fishing fraternity. Unlike the **Sea Eagle** the **Osprey** is a passage migrant, visiting our shores in spring and autumn on its passage to and from its main breeding haunts in Scandinavia and its wintering grounds in western Africa. In the early 1950s a pair bred at a secret locality in the top of a Scots Pine in the Spey Valley. A few years later, after mixed success – it was often robbed by egg collectors under the noses of its protectors – the R.S.P.B. bought the site and created a secure fortress there so that it could breed successfully.

This now famous site of Loch Garten is visited annually by thousands of curious tourists and bird-watchers, and its success in helping to re-establish the **Osprey** as a regular breeding bird in our country is well documented.

It was not long before a second pair bred at another locality, followed by a third. Now there are more than 50 pairs of this fine bird breeding in the Highlands. In 1989 55 pairs produced a total of 75 young, the most fledged for over a 100 years.

On this trip we do not make the pilgrimage to Loch Garten but are nevertheless rewarded with a sighting of a bird. While driving through the Rothiemurchus Forest we pause by a small loch and are delighted to see an adult **Osprey** perched classically on a dead branch of a tall pine tree growing at the lochside. It sat there for quite a long time, and while we watched a steady number of cars built up around us, drawn by our binoculars trained on the loch.

To watch the birds fishing is perhaps one of the most exhilarating bird-watching experiences. The birds flap languidly over the water, their keen eyes looking out for the shadowy forms of fish close to the surface. When they espy one they fly down low and with their long, outstretched legs grasp their prey and pull it out of its element, its twisting body throwing off pearls of water in its attempt to escape the long, sharp claws gripping it tightly. Often the **Osprey** becomes half submerged in such dives and only with heavy, powerful wing-beats can it escape the cloying liquid together with its prey. In Scotland they will take trout and salmon but also pike from the lochs.

On this same loch there is a lone female **Goldeneye** swimming close to the shore. With this bird, too, there is a Scottish success story to relate. The first pair of **Goldeneye** bred in 1970 but there are now more than 70 pairs in Scotland, many of them utilising boxes specially placed for them. In fact their settlement in the Highlands owes much to this use of nest boxes.

Early next morning, in bright sunlight coaxing the rich soft colours from the vegetation, we make some forays into the remnants of the old Caledonian Forest. Between the sturdy pines are the more fragile Rowans and Birches, allowing much light to penetrate to the forest floor, encouraging a rich undergrowth to flourish.

A pair of Red Squirrels dart across our path and chase each other up a pine, springing like trapeze-artists from one slender branch to another in the treetops. Northern Scotland is the main refuge for this, less aggressive cousin of the imported Grey Squirrel, and we must say that it saddens us to know that this russet little creature is now so scarce. After the squirrels have disappeared we discover a small group of **Crested Tits** foraging in the upper twigs of some pines and are able to watch them for several minutes as they daintily spring from sprig to sprig in their search for insects. There are perhaps a thousand pairs in Scotland, nearly all confined to the Spey and Findhorn valleys with a few pairs in neighbouring ones. This restricted range is more surprising when it is remembered that **Crested Tits** are widespread on the continent of Europe. Hopefully this delightful tit will eventually break out of its Speyside home into other areas.

In a thick stand of pines near a lochside, not far from where we just watched the **Crested Tits,** there is a heavy rustling in the branches. As we examine the trees with our binoculars several reddish-pink birds emerge, together with some greenish-grey ones: pairs of **Scottish Crossbills** are busy tearing at the pine cones in search of succulent pine seeds. We can now see their perfectly adapted crossed mandibles as they prise out the seeds, showering the floor with debris. Their large, dumpy shape is a good characteristic with which to identify them in flight when you can often hear their distinctive chip-chip-chip call.

The **Scottish Crossbill** is currently recognised as a distinct species by a number of authorities on the subject , though the debate is likely to remain unsettled. It has a beak intermediate in thickness between
Crested Tit   the **Common Crossbill** (found in other parts of Britain, since it first

bred in East Anglia in 1910) and the **Parrot Crossbill** of northern Europe. The **Scottish Crossbill** uses its heavier bill to tackle cones of the Scots Pine whereas the **Common Crossbill** settles for the seeds of the Spruce cones. There are perhaps 1500 pairs of **Scottish Crossbills** and they are found fairly widely over the Highlands where there are extensive woods or stands of Scots Pine.

Our only disappointment in these ancient pine woods, though we could scarely expect it otherwise, was our failure to see a **Capercaillie,** the largest of British game birds and only to be found in the Scottish

Scottish Crossbill

Highlands. In early spring the cock birds produce the most amazing sounds during their 'lek' (courtship display). It has been likened to the popping of corks, plugs pulled from kitchen sinks or, the description we find most apt, someone jumping up and down on a strong cardboard box with increasing rapidity until it suddenly collapses.

To catch a glimpse of these birds it is essential to rise very early on a spring morning in an area they are known to frequent, and to listen for the courtship calls of the males at their lek. Unfortunately the range of the **Capercaillie** in Scotland may be contracting and fewer birds have been discovered lately in their traditional haunts. Research is in progress to discover the causes of this decline. It would be a pity if this species were to become extinct a second time (it disappeared about 1780) after its successful re-introduction into Scotland in the mid 19th century.

In these woodlands of the Spey Valley there is always the promise of other rare and new breeding species. The **Wryneck,** formerly unknown in Scotland, started breeding here around the mid 1960s at the very time that the few remaining pairs were disappearing from their last strongholds in south-east England. A similar fate faces the **Red-backed Shrike,** now virtually extinct in its remaining heathland habitat in East Anglia and southern England. There are signs that the **Shrike** too may establish itself in this part of Scotland with regular summer sightings and some breeding records of birds probably originating from Scandinavia.

At a distance the flat-topped or 'whaleback' mountains of the Cairngorms look less than impressive. The patches of snow, almost ever present on their summits, especially in north-facing corries are, however, a clue to their more gigantic proportions.

We approached them taking the route common to most visitors, via Loch Morlich, itself 1,500 ft (400m) above sea level, and then with the chairlift to the summit.

Snow Bunting More noble spirits will still trudge to the top of Braeriach above the pass of Lairig Ghru, but for those with less time or stamina the chairlift offers an easy option. As we glided effortlessly to the top we discussed the possible birds we might come across on the plateau. It is June but the leaden clouds would indicate a different season.

We alight from the chairlift in a snowstorm which stings our eyes and reduces visibility to a level which puts bird-watching out of the question. After a warming coffee in the summit cafe the weather improves and we move off up the slope towards the Cairngorm summit. The whole plateau maintains this height consistently, enabling the walker to trek with relative ease along the high ridge to Ben Macdui, at 4,296 ft, the second highest mountain in Scotland. Indeed, until the 1840's it was believed to be the highest peak in Britain.

As we begin our walk, deep in the valley below we can see the hazy outline of Loch Morlich like a tiny puddle. We have not gone more than 100 metres when we hear a strange short musical warbling. We stop and prick-up our ears; there it is again! Neither of us recognise the sound as familiar but instinctively we both know it can only be a **Snow Bunting.** We try to locate the bird exactly. It doesn't sound far away. Then we have it: a solitary male **Snow Bunting** in its bright black and white summer plumage, sitting on a small rock and singing, to attract a female maybe? We are left guessing because no other bird appears. It is calling close to the main pathway to the summit, but almost everyone wanders past without even registering its presence. If you are among those bird enthusiasts who depend entirely on their eyes then you will certainly miss such small, quite inconspicuous birds because, despite the male's stark plumage, the few birds to be found here can remain surprisingly well hidden in this vast rocky wilderness.

For the past 100 years a pair or two of these arctic buntings have bred on high Scottish mountains particularly in the Cairngorms. Recently there has been a welcome increase in the **Snow Bunting** population and there could be as many as a dozen pairs now breeding here. In winter **Snow Buntings** are not an unusual sight and can be seen scavenging up here among the skiers and quite often in lowland areas around the coast.

Over the lip of the summit we discover a surprisingly foreign landscape; there are still large areas of snow-covered ground, burns trickle from beneath icy overhangs and a cold winter wind scours the bare backs of the mountains. We could be forgiven for thinking that we had mistaken the month and it was December rather than June.

The most typical bird on these inhospitable tops is the **Ptarmigan,** a northern grouse which reaches greater concentrations in Scotland than in its more northerly habitats of Iceland and Greenland. This is a bird adapted to the frozen snows and belongs to those ice age remnants left behind in the Scottish Highlands where they are still able to hold their own. In winter their plumage changes to an almost pure white, making them invisible on the snow-covered mountains to predators like the eagle or fox. In summer its brown-mottled plumage blends perfectly with the low heather and Bilberry scrub or the gravelly, lichen-marbled rocks.

We trudge through the snow drifts, down the slope towards Loch Avon, deep, cold and black, lying in a rift between Cairngorm and

Beinn Mheadoin. We are soon greeted by the guttural croaks of white-winged **Ptarmigan** as they whirr away over the short, alpine vegetation which clings thinly to the rocks here. One of the birds doesn't fly off but flutters on the ground some 30 metres in front of us, dragging her drooping wings, feigning injury. She is desperately trying to distract our attention from her newly-hatched chicks, crouching in the shelter of some rocks. We allow her to lead us away from her vulnerable brood. Once she has lured us far enough away she gives up her performance and returns to her offspring. Her downy chicks would not long survive the cold without the continued shelter of her warm body.

A blue-white Scottish Hare bounds off over the edge of a low hillock. This species, too, was left here after the ice had retreated and like the **Ptarmigan,** changes the colour of its coat according to the season.

One of the birds we are particulary hoping to come across up here is the **Dotterel,** a bird confined to the highest mountain tops in Britain. The snow-laden sky though, now threatens no more but brings down all its vengeful retribution upon our heads. We are caught in a cheek-stinging, eye-smarting blizzard in mid-summer! We decide to turn back but take a slightly different route and then, not too far from our point

Dotterel

of departure, we put up one, then two shadowy, pigeon-like birds. They land again not too far away and despite the blinding snow we are able to make out their distinctive eye stripes, their chestnut, black-bordered under-bellies: **Dotterel!** Its name, derived from 'dote' meaning silly or stupid arises from the ease with which it can be caught, and also, I surmise because of its habit of choosing to nest on such inhospitable summits. Perhaps this rather uncharitable assessment of such an attractive species reflected our own frozen plight as we struggled to keep the birds under view.

The **Dotterel** are quite well camouflaged on the rock and stone-strewn plateaux where they regularly breed. Only when they run, moving away from approaching strangers do they betray their presence. The two birds blend perfectly as they stand motionless and then run at speed, disappearing behind low grey boulders and re-appearing a second later travelling in a different direction. It seems that they would rather run than fly unless hard provoked. Up here they lay their clutch of four eggs quite late in the season and, it is said that when sitting

Capercaillie

can be approached to within a few feet of the nest, sometimes even allowing themselves to be stroked.

There are about 500 pairs of **Dotterel** in Scotland found mostly in the Cairngorms, Monadhliaths and other mountains with suitable barren, stony plateaux, but a few pairs are found in the Lake District and breeding has been proved in Snowdonia. Recent detailed studies (Watson and Rae in *Scottish Birds* 1987) suggest that there may be as many as 600 pairs in the Highlands which is 4 or 5 times higher than some previous estimates. The accurate calculation of the strength of a species nesting on mountain tops, a day's walk from the nearest habitation, clearly presents problems. The birds we encountered here on the Cairngorms didn't appear to be breeding, but we could not be absolutely sure. Eggs can easily become cold and infertile in these conditions, and we felt it was prudent to make our way back towards base. The going was heavy underfoot where deep snow had collected in large drifts. Time was also running late and we did not relish the prospect of a night spent on the mountain without even a tent.

We breathed a sigh of relief when at last the pylons and cables of the chairlift came into view. We were surprised to hear our lone **Snow Bunting** still vainly warbling away. He flitted from rock to rock and then flew off out of sight, a last and fitting alpine goodbye to the Cairngorms, until the next time!

Occasionally **Snowy Owls** are seen on these mountains but that possibility is something of a long shot in June. **Eagles, Ravens, Ring Ouzels** and **Golden Plover** are all far more probable and should be seen with little difficulty on a good day.

Ptarmigan

IN SEARCH OF
THE HEN HARRIER

Our last trip to Scotland was four years ago and we had been lucky in re-locating scarce species in old favoured haunts. It was encouraging too, because it meant that these birds were at least surviving, perhaps even expanding. The **Slavonian Grebe, Black-throated Diver, Dunlin, Scoter** and **Red-throated Diver** had all faithfully turned up as expected. We had hoped to see a **Hen Harrier** in Argyle but failed, so now we pinned our hopes on a wild moor in the heart of Perthshire where I'd briefly observed a male bird in July six years ago.

(female)
Hen Harrier
(male)

The next day found us on our way back southwards, past Loch Insh and its marshes where such rarities as **Wood Sandpiper** and **Spotted Crake** have bred, while in 1970 a **Bluethroat** was found nesting here. This is the only British breeding record so far but the male bird was never seen.

Through the town of Kingussie, we joined the main Inverness-Perth road which cleaves a broad path through the high country, up the pass of Drumochter and on to the wooded pass of Killiecrankie, famous site of yet another Scottish battle, where the clans fought for the Stuart King, James II against William of Orange in 1689.

We were glad to leave this well-used thoroughfare and once more seek out the more quiet places, but first we needed to replenish our provisions in Pitlochry. This is an old town full of granite charm, one of Perthshire's tourist centres, with its shops brimming with tartans, tweeds, deerstalkers and thistle-decorated cups and plates. It boasts whisky distilleries and a big festival in the summer where traditional Scottish cultural life is put on show.

West of Pitlochry lies Loch Tummel with Queen's View on the north bank, celebrated as one of Queen Victoria's favourite views in her beloved Highlands. Our route today, was via the southern shore of this 10 mile long loch, a more twisting journey along a minor road. On this route we see several pairs of **Redstarts,** which lay their 5 or 6 blue eggs in the holes and crevices of mature Birch trees. From one of the Bracken and Bluebell covered roadside banks we hear the animated call of the **Common Sandpiper** and so stop the car. Through our binoculars we locate the bird on the bank, bobbing up and down and cheeping its alarm and then make out four furry chicks being led away from the road. They must have only just hatched and were now being escorted away from possible danger by the parents.

We also spot a Red Squirrel, the second in three days, springing along a roadside fence before shooting up the trunk of an Ash tree. In previous years we've seen them in Meggernie Wood, Glen Lyon and near Loch Morlich, but never before have we enjoyed such close views from the window of a car.

There are many pairs of **Wigeon** floating in the bays of the loch. Here they are relatively common and along with other water fowl can be found in good numbers on the river and pools between Loch Tummel and Loch Rannoch further to the west.

Rannoch is a wilder loch than Tummel, with a large natural forest on its south shore, bearing the name of 'Black Wood of Rannoch'. Here **Woodcock, Scottish Crossbills, Capercaillie, Long-eared Owls** and many other interesting species are to be found.

Driving past Loch Kinardochy memories flooded back of birds seen hereabouts on previous journeys. A **Snipe** twisting and turning in its typical evasive flight from a clutch of four wonderfully mottled eggs, laid in a wispy clump of reeds by the lochside; a **Peregrine Falcon**

Common
Sandpiper

gliding overhead and then winnowing over nearby Schiehallion, a high conical mountain ; and the bold little **Merlin -** a bird not easily spotted even in its main haunts, looking like a small but sleeker version of the common **Kestrel.** In Perthshire it appears to be relatively plentiful which is probably due to the large areas of heather moor and rich woodland vegetation harbouring **Whinchats, Finches** and **Meadow Pipits.** I remember emerging one morning sleepy-eyed from the tent to see a **Chaffinch** darting and dodging along the course of a tumbling burn, being pursued determinedly and relentlessly by a slate-grey male **Merlin,** both birds disappearing out of sight as the slope dropped away in front of me.

Our quest this time, was for the **Hen Harrier;** a daunting prospect since these birds are not only quite scarce but range widely over the moors when hunting.

At the turn of the century **Hen Harriers,** having suffered like other large raptors, were virtually confined to the Orkney Islands. There they held on until the climate of tolerance changed in their favour, together with the benefits of forestry plantations, providing new nesting sites and cover for the small mammals on which they depend for food. **Hen Harriers** hunt low over the moors and marshes ready to pounce on unsuspecting prey.

The **Hen Harrier** has been one of the most successful birds of prey during this century and numbers have now reached perhaps 700 pairs for the country as a whole. Apart from the Highlands, southern Ireland is the region of greatest concentration.

We arrive at the spot towards early evening and pitch our tent near a small spruce plantation, accompanied by the melodic twittering of **Siskins** and **Redpolls** as they feed in the saplings. We eat a makeshift meal on our less than effective primus; but if putting up with luke-warm congealed baked beans and undercooked bacon allows us to enjoy the relaxing solitude of such a place, then we're willing to make a sacrifice.

After demolishing our meal, we go for a stroll along a narrow roadway which cuts across the heather moor. We pause at an old stone bridge spanning a foaming white burn and watch a dumpy brown-white **Dipper** plunging into the water, jumping back onto a rock, the water streaming from its back as it bounces up and down on spring legs. Suddenly another appears and they both dart off under the bridge-span and downstream like high velocity projectiles. Continuing on our way we catch the now familiar sight of a slow-flapping, **Short-eared Owl** searching the young Spruce plantations and ploughed furrows for its evening meal.

The heather on the moor is interspersed with cropped grass and stony patches and promises to be good habitat for a number of species. The prospects look interesting, and we decide to leave the road and wander through the springy vegetation. The characteristic guttural croak of **Red Grouse** echoes on the breeze and then we hear another familiar bird typical of the high moors, the **Golden Plover.** Its mournful piping is quite close to us so we change our direction towards it. We see it, calling in agitation on a small rise and decide to watch it for a short while. Very soon we can discern two fluffy **Golden Plover** chicks running after the adult bird through the short grass. It would have been fascinating to observe this family for a little longer, but the light was going and we are still vainly hoping to catch a glimpse of the Harrier so we decide to use the car in order to cover a wider area.

We drive along the road bordering the moor and then turn onto a track taking us right onto it and offering a broad vista – it is already past 9 o'clock in the evening, but the sky is still bright. The car comes to a sudden halt and we grab our binoculars: unbelievably, as if by appointment, a female **Hen Harrier** gliding low over the heather comes into view. She hovers fleetingly over a particularly thick patch of heather, interspersed with scrub-willow and then drops vertically into it and we wonder whether we have imagined the whole thing. The moor is transformed once again into an empty vista. We are spellbound until the truth dawns on us; she must have a nest! We continue to

Golden
Plover

watch the spot for several more minutes but there is no sign of movement.

The next morning we return early to the scene. We suspect the Harrier might have small young since it was now nearly the end of spring, and we settle down to await developments. The **Hen Harrier** is not only protected by law but is prone to desert its nest easily so a 'natural' hide such as our car is a good place to observe them. After about an hour the pastel grey male bird appears over the hill. As he nears the nest site the female rises to meet him calling out in a high pitched note. They circle the site together and then disappear from sight. After a further half an hour the 'Ring Tail' (so called because of the characteristic white crescent on her rump) returns again low over the moor, her streaked brown plumage so different from that of her pale mate. With little ceremony she circles tightly over the spot and drops into the heather as before. As we drive back along the road we catch sight of the grey male, his long wings and tail giving a rakish appearance as he hovers and glides low over the distant moor, apparently hunting.

All of this was far more than we had expected and provided us with one of the most memorable highlights of the holiday. It was also an astonishing piece of luck, unlikely to be bettered in what time remained to us in the Highlands.

We were very sad to be leaving this fascinating area but the road south through the soft and picturesque glens of Perthshire, with its lofty peaks and mountain passes consoled us to some extent. We left behind Loch Tay, Loch Earn and lastly Loch Lubnaig. We had no time left to explore the richly rewarding region of Ben Lawers, famous for its alpine flora – the bright pink Saxifrages and Moss Campions – a relic of the ice age.

In our short stay we have seen a generous selection of Scotland's bird species, over 110 during our two-week sojourn and including many of the typical birds of the Highlands.

Approaching Callander, popularly known as the gateway to the Highlands, a melancholy descended upon us. We knew it might be a long time before we again had the opportunity of coming back.

The Highland Line running from south-west to north-east is abrupt, the mountains suddenly disappear as one leaves Callander on the road to Stirling; the more agriculturally developed lowlands, with their neat hedgerows and grazing herds of Fresians communicate an atmosphere of civilised order and mundane existence. How different to the heady, wild excitement those northern, ice-scoured landscapes had given us these last few days.

Great Skua

Arctic Skua

CHECK LIST OF SCOTTISH BIRDS

The Highland boundary fault, running north-eastwards to reach the coast at Stonehaven is a distinctive geological feature, but birds do not acknowledge such boundaries. There are many species whose populations are concentrated in the Lowlands and which are found in smaller numbers beyond the Highland 'Line', in southern Argyle, Perthshire or lower areas of the north-east. Therefore, although the main text deals primarily with Highland birds, the list below includes all those species which breed anywhere in Scotland either regularly, sporadically or exceptionally.

Few species remain in their breeding haunts throughout the year: **grebes, divers** and many species of **ducks** and **waders** move to the coasts in the autumn and winter, where they are joined by large numbers of migrant birds from arctic and northern regions – Greenland, Iceland, Soviet Union and Scandinavia. Some birds move further south within the British Isles, particularly during hard weather. **Auks, petrels** and **skuas** fly far out to sea and disappear in the vast oceans, while **terns, warblers, flycatchers, swallows** and other summer visitors head for warmer climes in the south.

Some species are best encountered on spring or autumn migration as they pass through Scotland on their journeys to and from their main breeding grounds in countries to the north. The strong flying waders are among the most distant travellers. **Stints** and **sandpipers** rest and feed at fresh water stopping places, while huge numbers of passage and wintering **Knot, Redshank** and **Dunlin** flock on the estuaries.

In winter the desolate mountains are almost devoid of smaller birds; the insect-feeding **warblers** disappear entirely from Scotland, while **tits** and **finches** gather together in groups or feeding-flocks in sheltered woods or farmland. **Peregrines** and **Merlins** follow their bird prey to the lower ground, while the **Eagle** stays up in the hills, hunting **grouse** and **Ptarmigan** which brave the Highland winters, or feeds on those carcasses of deer or sheep which succumb to the severe weather conditions. Some other birds are sedentary in their habits, notably the **crow** family, **doves, Black Grouse** and **Capercaillie** and some seabirds like the **Fulmar** and **Black Guillemot.** The **Buzzard** and **Sparrowhawk** also stay close to home, but the **Osprey,** flying south to West Africa, runs the gauntlet of continental hunters who massacre migratory birds on their passage south.

Scotland has a rich heritage of breeding birds, but for people living locally or able to enjoy an autumn or winter break there are many other species observed frequently on estuaries, marshes, coastal headlands and elsewhere. These we have added at the end of the check list. Rare visitors and vagrants, which run into hundreds, are beyond the scope of this book and are not included.

Finally, there are a number of birds, mostly passerines, which are absent from the Northern Isles and Outer Hebrides. In addition to those specifically mentioned in the notes, all species of **warblers** are absent except the **Whitethroat,** the **Sedge** and **Willow Warbler** (both absent from the Shetlands); there are no species of **tits** on either Orkney or Shetland, while there are just a few pairs of **Blue Tits** and **Great Tits** on Lewis, the northernmost island of the Hebrides. Only the **Twite** and **Reed Bunting** are to be found on Shetland, but most of the other **finches** and **buntings** are scarce or absent in Orkney and the Outer Hebrides. The **Mistle Thrush, Tree Creeper, Swift, Magpie, Jay** and **Sand Martin** are other species absent from all three island groups.

Goosanders

1.	**Great Northern Diver**	Mainly winter visitor in north and west but often summers in northern waters. Bred Wester Ross in 1970.
2.	**Black-Throated Diver**	Less than 100 pairs. Caithness south to Argyle. Breeds outer Hebrides and some in S.W. Scotland.
3.	**Red-Throated Diver**	A total of about 1000 pairs from Shetland and Orkney, south to Arran and the Mull of Kintyre with a predominantly westerly distribution. A few pairs in S.W. Scotland.
4.	**Great Crested Grebe**	Breeds chiefly on lowland waters, mostly in central Scotland. Absent Highlands.
5.	**Little Grebe**	More widely distributed than the above species but absent from large areas of the Highlands.
6.	**Slavonian Grebe**	50-70 pairs, mainly in Inverness with scattered pairs elsewhere.
7.	**Black-Necked Grebe**	Less than 20 pairs on lochs with dense vegetation; found on just a few waters in central Scotland. These are the only regular breeding sites in Britain.
8.	**Fulmar**	Numerous on sea cliffs especially in north. Numbers have greatly increased since mid 19th century when it bred only on St. Kilda.
9.	**Manx Shearwater**	Found in island colonies from Shetland to Kintyre, where it nests in burrows. The largest colony is on Rhum.
10.	**Storm Petrel**	Breeds in burrows on island colonies in north and west.
11.	**Leach's Petrel**	Much rarer and more local than above species. Confined to 5 or 6 remote islands. Like the smaller Storm Petrel it is

nocturnal and breeds in
burrows, so numbers hard to
estimate.

12.	**Gannet**	The St. Kilda colony of over 40,000 pairs is largest in the world. Also large concentrations at Bass Rock (East Lothian). Ailsa Craig (Ayrshire), Hermaness (Shetland) and Sula Sgeir, with a few smaller colonies elsewhere.
13.	**Cormorant**	Breeds on sea cliffs in scattered colonies, though scarce on E. coast S. of Caithness. A few pairs nest inland.
14.	**Shag**	Commoner than the above species, are found in good numbers from Shetland and Orkney along N. and W. coasts from Caithness to Mull. Further south and along the E. coast colonies are more scattered.
15.	**Grey Heron**	Resident in all county districts except Shetland. Nests mostly in tree colonies but sometimes on cliffs
16.	**Mute Swan**	Resident mostly in lowlands of central and E. Scotland.
17.	**Whooper Swan**	Mainly winter visitor but has bred on a number of occasions in the Highlands.
18.	**Grey-Lag Goose**	Small number of truly wild geese breed in NW Highlands and Hebrides. Some feral populations elsewhere.
19.	**Shelduck**	Widespread on sandy coasts and dunes, where it breeds in burrows.
20.	**Mallard**	Common resident on waters throughout Scotland.
21.	**Teal**	Familiar on upland lakes and tarns in summer, breeding also on lowland waters. Scarce in parts of north west.

22.	**Gadwall**	Local species breeding mainly in Fife (especially Loch Leven), with a few pairs elsewhere e.g. Uists (Hebrides) and Orkney.
23.	**Wigeon**	Widespread in northern and central Highlands, especially Flow Country (Caithness & Sutherland) and Perthshire. Scarcer in west. Commoner in some border districts of southern Scotland.
24.	**Scaup**	Mainly winter visitor, but occasionally breeds, most commonly Orkney and Western Isles.
25.	**Shoveler**	Uncommon but found in damp meadows, notably in Orkney, Caithness, Fife, Angus and the Uists (Outer Hebrides).
26.	**Pochard**	Breeds in small numbers, especially Perth and Angus, Ayrshire and NE Aberdeen.
27.	**Tufted Duck**	Commoner and more wide-spread than the Pochard. Scarce in Highlands except Spey and areas close to Moray Firth.
28.	**Pintail**	Very scarce, with nesting records scattered throughout Scotland. Most frequent in Orkney.

29.	**Goldeneye**	About 70 pairs now breed in Highlands following first record in 1970, mostly Inverness.
30.	**Common Scoter**	Scarce breeding species, found especially Caithness and Sutherland and scattered lochs in Inverness, Argyle and Perth, also Islay and Shetland.
31.	**Long-Tailed Duck**	Mainly winter visitor to salt waters but sometimes summer in the far north and isles. Last bred in 1912.
32.	**Eider**	Abundant marine species found all around Scottish coast.
33.	**Red-Breasted Merganser**	Very common, especially in N. and W. Highlands and Islands, also SW, but absent in Lowlands and E. districts.
34.	**Goosander**	Common on lochs and rivers in many parts of Highlands and southern county districts e.g. Kirkcudbright and Dumfries. Scarce in far north but absent in N. and W. isles. Breeds in holes of trees or banks.
35.	**White-Tailed Eagle**	A few pairs have now established eyries in Highlands following re-introduction of species in 1975.
36.	**Golden Eagle**	400- 500 pairs are resident in the Highlands and Hebrides. Commoner in W. Few pairs also in Galloway.
37.	**Buzzard**	Fairly common and widely distributed in many parts of Highlands, and Hebrides,. especially in W. Also present in SW.
38.	**Sparrowhawk**	Resident throughout Scotland except Outer Hebrides and Shetland, in wooded districts.
39.	**Goshawk**	Rare resident with local pockets chiefly in the forests of

40.	**Marsh Harrier**	Scarce visitor, has attempted to breed.
41.	**Hen Harrier**	Breeds Orkney, Caithness, Sutherland, central and S. Highlands and Argyle, also on several larger western isles and on plantations and moorland in S. Scotland.

42.	**Osprey**	

About 50 pairs now breed on Highland lochs following recolonisation in the 1950s.

43.	**Peregrine Falcon**	Widely distributed on coastal and inland cliffs in the Highlands, Islands and S. Uplands.
44.	**Merlin**	Scattered widely in most upland areas, but scarce and slowly decreasing.
45.	**Kestrel**	Commonest bird of prey, found in all parts.
46.	**Red Grouse**	Found on moorlands throughout Scotland and especially plentiful in central and E. Highlands.
47.	**Ptarmigan**	Found only on Scotland's highest peaks in S. and central Highlands, but at much lower altitudes in N.W. Sutherland.

48.	Black Grouse	Breeds on lower moorlands with trees in many parts of Scotland. Commonest S. and central Highlands S. Uplands. Scarce or absent much of NW.
49.	Capercaillie	Local in pine woods and forests from Easter Ross through central and E. Highlands, as far S. as Stirling. Commoner in native Caledonian forests but decreasing.
50.	Grey Partridge	Decreasing species on lower agricultural land in S. and central regions and E. coast districts.
51.	Quail	Rare summer visitor to fields and meadows in widely scattered districts; commoner in warm summers.
52.	Pheasant	Resident, but scarce or absent in many Highland areas.
53.	Water Rail	Uncommon and secretive species, widely scattered in marshes and reedlands from Orkney to Solway.
54.	Spotted Crake	Rare and irregular nesting species in marshes with dense vegetation. Recorded Shetland, Outer Hebrides, W. Sutherland, Inverness and Solway in recent years.
55.	Corncrake	Decreasing numbers of this summer visitor. Now chiefly on Orkney, Hebrides and W. coastal districts.
56.	Moorhen	Common resident, mostly in Lowlands., Scarce or absent in most upland districts.
57.	Coot	Generally common except in Highlands and Islands.
58.	Oystercatcher	Familiar species in most parts of Scotland, breeding in all

inland as well as coastal areas.

59.	**Lapwing**	Common resident and partial migrant in most parts of Scotland.
60.	**Ringed Plover**	Common on coasts and shingle-lined rivers. More numerous in W. and large concentrations in Hebridean Machair.
61.	**Dotterel**	Summer visitor to highest mountain pleateaux in the Grampians, where there may be as many as 500 pairs.
62.	**Golden Plover**	Found on moorlands in many parts of Scotland, Commonest E. and central Highlands.
63.	**Temminck's Stint**	Rare breeding bird. A few pairs in Easter Ross and Inverness. Also scarce passage migrant.
64.	**Purple Sandpiper**	Has bred several times in recent years. Otherwise a winter visitor, mainly N. Isles and E. coast.

65. **Dunlin**

Widespread breeding bird in Highlands, commonest N. Isles, Caithness and Sutherland 'Flows' and Outer Hebrides.

66.	Common Sandpiper	Summer visitor to lakes and rivers. Abundant in most of Highlands.
67.	Wood Sandpiper	A few pairs breed annually, mostly Sutherland and Inverness. Also migrant.
68.	Green Sandpiper	Breeding proven in 1959 and suspected on several other occasions. Nests in trees. Mainly passage migrant.
69.	Spotted Sandpiper	Vagrant, but a pair attempted to breed on Skye in 1975 when eggs were laid but failed to hatch.
70,	Turnstone	Often summers in the N. and breeding suspected on a number of occasions. Winter visitor to coasts.
71.	Red-Necked Phalarope	Rare and decreasing summer migrant. About 50 pairs breed on Shetlands, mostly Fetlar. A few elsewhere e.g. Tiree, N. mainland.
72.	Ruff	Mainly migrant and uncommon winter visitor but there are recent breeding records from Hebrides and N.
73.	Black-Tailed Godwit	Scattered breeding records in most years, chiefly in N. Isles or far S. Also migrant.
74.	Curlew	Abundant species on moorland and rough grass, though scarce in parts of W. Highlands.
75.	Whimbrel	Very scarce species, confined mainly to Shetland, with a few pairs in Orkney, Caithness, Sutherland and Lewis.
76.	Redshank	Common in many parts of Scotland, mostly on wet pasture. Abundant on coast in winter.
77.	Greenshank	Less than 1000 pairs to be found in N. and W. chiefly

Sutherland, Ross and
Cromarty and Inverness.
Also migrant.

78.	**Snipe**	Common on marshy ground in most parts.
79.	**Woodcock**	Resident bird in suitable damp woods and copses, but scarce in some N. areas. Absent in Orkney, Shetland and outer Hebrides.
80.	**Great Skua**	Several thousand pairs breed, mainly in Shetland and Orkney, with a few scattered groups on N. mainland coast, St. Kilda and Lewis (Outer Hebrides).
81.	**Arctic Skua**	Scarce — 2000 pairs — mainly Shetland and Orkney, also Caithness, Sutherland and a few in Hebrides.
82.	**Great Black-Backed Gull**	Widespread and familiar bird on most N. and W. coasts. Scarcer on E. coasts S. to Angus and Forth.
83.	**Lesser Black-Backed Gull**	Numerous colonies on W. coasts and islands. Fewer, more scattered colonies in E. and inland.
84.	**Herring Gull**	Abundant and familiar species in most coastal areas where there are cliffs.
85.	**Kittiwake**	Large concentrations at cliff sites, especially N. Isles, Caithness, Sutherland and E. coasts.
86.	**Common Gull**	Familiar bird throughout the Highlands, nesting on lochs, rivers and low-lying coastal sites. Also S. Scotland.
87.	**Black-Headed Gull**	Breeds in colonies on lochs and marshes, distributed throughout Scotland except N.W. mainland, Skye and Mull.

88.	**Common Tern**		Summer visitor to most coasts and on shingle-lined rivers, particularly E. Highlands from Caithness to Perth.

89.	**Arctic Tern**	Most numerous tern in Scotland, particularly in island colonies in N. and W.

90.	**Roseate Tern**	A scarce bird at best, but has dwindled to the point of extinction in its last retreat on Forth estuary.

91.	**Sandwich Tern**	Local distribution Orkney, Caithness, Moray Firth, E. Aberdeen, Tay, Forth and S.W. In total about 3000 pairs.

92.	**Little Tern**	Very scarce with a scattered coastal distribution, mainly Islay, Outer Hebrides and E. coast. Like all terns, a summer visitor only.

93.	**Guillemot**	Large numbers on cliff colonies, especially N. and W. Isles and N. coast. About 500,000 pairs in total.

94.	**Black Guillemot**	More thinly distributed than former species but widespread in W. and commonest in Orkney and Shetland.

95.	**Razorbill**	Similar distribution to Guillemot, but smaller numbers.

96.	**Puffin**	Over half a million pairs, mainly N. and W. Isles, Caithness and Sutherland.

97.	**Wood Pigeon**	Abundant in agricultural country but scarcer in bare Highland areas and islands
98.	**Stock Dove**	Well distributed in Lowlands of E. central and S. Scotland. Scarce or absent in N.
99.	**Rock Dove**	Found on rocky coasts from Shetland, along W. coasts to Arran and Kintyre. Feral birds elsewhere.
100.	**Collared Dove**	Breeds in all counties following its rapid colonisation of Britain in mid 1950's.
101.	**Cuckoo**	Summer visitor. Common and familiar species in virtually all parts. Scarce N. Isles.
102.	**Barn Owl**	Scarce, mostly farmland in central and S.W. Scotland. Absent most of Highlands and Islands
103.	**Tawny Owl**	Common woodland and farmland bird in most of Scotland. Scarcer in N.W. Absent in N. and outer Isles.
104.	**Little Owl**	Rare in Scotland. Breeds occasionally in S. where it extends from its English range.
105.	**Long-Eared Owl**	Local species, easily overlooked. Mainly conifer woods. Very scarce in N.W. except Moray Firth area.
106.	**Short-Eared Owl**	Widely but thinly distributed over most moorlands, scarce in Lowlands and many parts of N.W. Highlands.
107.	**Snowy Owl**	Bred on Fetlar, Shetlands 1967-75. Otherwise rare visitor, mainly winter.
108.	**Nightjar**	Scarce and decreasing summer visitor, mainly Arran and Kirkcudbright.
109.	**Swift**	Abundant summer visitor in

most parts but absent from
much of central and W.
Highlands and Islands.

110.	Kingfisher	Uncommon, but found from Perth and Angus southwards on slow running waters.
111.	Green Woodpecker	Spreading northwards. Scarce but now found in most mainland county districts except Sutherland and Caithness.
112.	Great-Spotted Woodpecker	Now quite plentiful in woodland areas though absent N. and outer Isles.
113.	Wryneck	Rare breeding bird. Mainly Spey Valley and neighbouring districts.
114.	Skylark	Common open ground throughout Scotland, though numbers have been adversely affected by intense disturbance of agricultural land.
115.	Shore Lark	Scarce passage migrant and winter visitor but has bred on a number of occasions.
116.	Sand Martin	Widely, but locally distributed in most of Scotland; scarcer central and N. Highlands. Absent N. Isles and Outer Hebrides.
117.	House Martin	Summer migrant, generally common but absent from similar areas to Sand Martin.
118.	Swallow	Abundant species, except in mountainous districts and N. and outer Isles.
119.	Tree Pipit	Common summer visitor in open woodland and ground with scattered trees in most areas.
120.	Meadow Pipit	The most abundant moorland species. Encountered everywhere on open ground.

121.	**Rock Pipit**	Common on all W. coasts and islands. Less numerous on E. coast S. of Caithness.
122.	**Yellow Wagtail**	Summer migrant. Small number of pairs breed on marshy land in the Lowlands, particularly Ayr and Lanark.
123.	**Grey Wagtail**	Common on streams and rivers, usually where there are trees. Absent Shetland and most of Outer Hebrides.
124.	**Pied Wagtail**	Abundant throughout area, especially near water. Sub-species, the White Wagtail occurs on passage and sometimes breeds.
125.	**Dipper**	Resident on rivers and streams, particularly in hill districts. Absent N. Isles.

126.	**Wren**	Resident throughout the country in wide range of habitats from woodland to cliffs.
127.	**Dunnock**	Widespread in nearly all areas except high mountainous districts. Absent Shetlands.
128.	**Robin**	Abundant throughout mainland and Inner Hebrides. Scarcer Orkney and Outer Hebrides.
129.	**Bluethroat**	Bred once, but mainly a scarce

passage migrant, mostly on E.
coast and N. Isles.

130.

Redstart

Familiar summer visitor to
glens and other open woodland
areas. Absent part of
Caithness, Aberdeen, N. Isles
and Outer Hebrides.

131.   **Whinchat**

Summer visitor. Widely
distributed on rough grassland,
bracken-covered slopes etc. on
mainland, Inner Hebrides and
Lewis.

132.   **Stonechat**

Not uncommon in rank
Heather and Gorse in W.
districts from N.W. Sutherland
to Kintyre including Hebrides.
Also most other coastal
districts but rarely far from
sea.

133.	Wheatear	Summer visitor. Common, particularly upland areas with rock-strewn slopes, short grass, stone walls and bridges.
134.	Ring Ouzel	Thinly distributed during summer in rocky districts, mountains and moorlands in Highlands and S. Uplands.
135.	Blackbird	Abundant and familiar species but more numerous in Lowlands.
136.	Mistle Thrush	Common where there are trees in most parts of Scotland but absent N. and Outer Isles.
137.	Fieldfare	Breeds sporadically from Shetland to Perthshire in wooded valleys and moorland slopes. Only a few pairs in summer but common winter visitor.
138.	Song Thrush	Abundant, particularly low-lying areas or sheltered areas with bushes and trees.
139.	Redwing	Up to 100 pairs breed annually in the Highlands but like Fieldfare much commoner in winter.
140.	Raven	Highest numbers in W. Highlands and Islands scarcer in Central Highlands and S. Uplands
141.	Carrion/Hooded Crow	Hooded Crows are confined to Highlands and Islands and Common Crows replace them further S.
142.	Rook	Found predominantly on agricultural lands in central and S. Scotland and E. coast.
143.	Jackdaw	Abundant in wide range of habitats including coast, farmland and hillsides. Scarce in N.W.
144.	Chough	Very scarce on cliffs only on Islay, Jura and Kintyre.

145.	**Magpie**	Found fairly commonly central and parts of E. Scotland, scarcer in S. and absent most of Highlands.
146.	**Jay**	Local species, concentrated mainly woodland in a band from S. Argyle through S. Perth to Aberdeen. Also areas in S.
147.	**Starling**	Generally abundant. Absent only from parts of N. Highlands.
148.	**Red-Backed Shrike**	A scarce summer migrant but has bred a number of times in N. and N.E. Scotland in recent years.
149.	**Spotted Flycatcher**	Summer visitor to most areas but fewer in the islands.
150.	**Pied Flycatcher**	Very local in woodlands of Spey, parts of Perthshire, Loch Lomond district, Ayrshire and S. counties.
151.	**Tree Creeper**	Found commonly in woodlands most areas of mainland Scotland and also Inner Hebrides.
152.	**Goldcrest**	Abundant in conifer woods in mainland Scotland, scarcer on islands.
153.	**Great Tit**	Numerous in woodland and farmland throughout mainland and Inner Hebrides.
154.	**Blue Tit**	Similar distribution to Great Tit but even more numerous.
155.	**Coal Tit**	Very common, particularly in conifer woodlands.
156.	**Marsh Tit**	Very few breed in Scotland and then only in Berwick, Selkirk and Roxburgh.
157.	**Willow Tit**	Found only in S.W. This is another species common in

Goldcrests

England but scarce N. of border.

158.	**Crested Tit**	The entire British population is found in the Spey and Findhorn valleys, together with neighbouring districts and a few localities N. and W. of Great Glen.
159.	**Long-Tailed Tit**	Widely distributed in woodland and scrub on mainland and inner isles.
160.	**Willow Warbler**	Abundant summer visitor to woodland glades, scrub and open ground with bracken.
161.	**Chiffchaff**	Widespread but local in woodland with sparse undergrowth. Commonest in W. from Argyle to Galloway.
162.	**Wood Warbler**	Local summer visitor to decidious woods with sparse undergrowth, in hills and valleys, notably Argyle, Perth, Stirling and S.W.
163.	**Whitethroat**	Fairly common in scrubland in most districts but scarce or absent central and N. Highlands.
164.	**Lesser Whitethroat**	Very scarce and local but increasing. Breeding noted in several E. counties and Ayr.
165.	**Garden Warbler**	Breeds thinly in much of Scotland but absent from most parts of Highlands.
166.	**Blackcap**	General distribution and habitat similar to Garden Warbler. Found in woodland with undergrowth.
167.	**Sedge Warbler**	Widespread in reed-beds, sedge and scrub but scarce in Highlands.
168.	**Grasshopper Warbler**	Summer visitor and thinly distributed parts of mainland and inner isles but quite scarce in N.

169.	**Hawfinch**	Scarce resident, in woodland, mainly Angus, Perth, S.E., Ayr and Dumfries.
170.	**Greenfinch**	Common in trees and shrubbery, except mountainous central and N.W. areas.
171.	**Goldfinch**	Well distributed but in Highlands only very locally in S. and E. districts.
172.	**Siskin**	Typical and familiar bird of conifer forest in Highlands. Also S. Uplands.
173.	**Linnet**	Scarce in Highlands but common elsewhere, especially where there is rough ground or gorse.
174.	**Twite**	Found mainly N. and W. districts from Shetland to Kintyre on moorland with heather. Small numbers central and E. Highlands.
175.	**Lesser Redpoll**	Widespread and common in birch and conifer woodlands most of mainland and inner isles.
176.	**Crossbill**	Common and Scottish Crossbills are found in E. or central forests from Caithness to Perth. Common Crossbill only, S. Scotland.
177.	**Scarlet Rosefinch**	Scarce passage migrant but has bred and singing males have been observed.
178.	**Bullfinch**	Generally plentiful, especially in scrub-land and young plantations. Scarcer inner isles.
179.	**Chaffinch**	Abundant on farmland and woodland throughout mainland and inner isles.
180.	**Brambling**	Mainly winter visitor but also breeds occasionally in Highlands.

181.	Reed Bunting	Found mainly in reedy places (but also drier areas) throughout Scotland but scarce in many parts of Highlands.
182.	Yellow Hammer	Widespread resident, but absent in mountains and most N. or outer isles.
183.	Corn Bunting	Now scarce and local, mainly E. coast from Aberdeen southwards. Also Hebrides, Tiree, Ayr, Solway and a few other areas.
184.	Lapland Bunting	Scarce passage migrant, particularly Shetland and E. Coast. Has bred.
185.	Snow Bunting	Up to a dozen pairs breed on highest peaks, principally in Cairngorms.
186.	Tree Sparrow	Thinly distributed on farmland in all areas S. of Highland Line and along E. coast districts as far N. as Caithness.
187.	House Sparrow.	Common all areas close to human habitation.

Regular winter visitors and/or passage migrants to Scotland and not included in main list

Red-necked Grebe
Sooty Shearwater
Bittern *(breeds England)*
Bewick's Swan
Bean Goose
Pink-footed Goose
White-fronted Goose
Barnacle Goose
Brent Goose
Garganey *(breeds England)*
Velvet Scoter
Pomarine Skua
Long-tailed Skua
Little Gull
Iceland Gull
Glaucous Gull
Black Tern
Little Auk
Honey Buzzard *(breeds England)*
Rough-legged Buzzard
Hobby *(summer. breeds England)*
Gyr Falcon
Grey Plover
Knot
Sanderling
Curlew Sandpiper
Bar-tailed Godwit
Little Stint
Jack Snipe
Spotted Redshank
Turtle Dove *(breeds England)*
Waxwing
Great Grey Shrike
Black Redstart *(breeds England)*
Firecrest *(breeds England)*
Ortolan Bunting

Useful addresses:
Scottish Ornithologists Club,
21 Regent Terrace,
Edinburgh EH7 5BT

Royal Society for the Protection of Birds,
The Lodge, Sandy, Beds.

R.S.P.B. Scotland,
17 Regent Terrace, Edinburgh

Grey Wagtail

THE EMIGRANTS

The
Emigrants

by
Johan Bojer

Translated from the Norwegian
by
A. G. JAYNE

Introduction by
Paul Reigstad

University of Nebraska Press
Lincoln and London

Introduction © 1978 by the University of Nebraska Press
Copyright, 1925 by Johan Bojer

First Bison Book printing: 1978

Most recent Bison Book printing indicated by first digit below:
1   2   3   4   5   6   7   8   9   10

Library of Congress Cataloging in Publication Data

Bojer, Johan, 1872–1959.
 The emigrants.

 Translation of Vor egen stamme.
 Reprint of the ed. published by Grosset & Dunlap, New York.
 Bibliography: p. xvii
 I. Title.
[PZ3.B6365Em 1978]   [PT8950.B6]   839.8'2'372   78–9813
ISBN 0–8032–6051–2 pbk.

Bison Book edition reprinted by arrangement with The Estate of Johan Bojer.

Manufactured in the United States of America

CONTENTS

PRONUNCIATION OF NORWEGIAN NAMES

The *j* is pronounced as *y*—Bojer (Boyer). Final *e* is sounded—Anne (Ahn-ne). The *ö* is pronounced as *oo* in took (Föll); long *e* as *a* in fate (Per); long *a* as *a* in father (Kal, Karen); long *i* as *ee* in see (Kvidal); long *o* as *o* in rote (Ola); short *o* as *o* in toss (Foss); *ei* as *ai* in raid (Trondheim); *aa* as *o* in horse (Lindegaard); *æ* as *a* in mad (sæter); *y* as *u* in Hubert (Dyrendal); *g* before *i* or *e* is hard as the *g* in pagan (Bergitta). The accent almost always falls on the first syllable.

INTRODUCTION

What has always appealed most to readers of the Norwegian novelist Johan Bojer is his narrative skill; at his best, he is a superb storyteller. They also admire his lyrical feeling for the beauty of the Norwegian countryside and his compassionate portrayal of peasant folk, living out their lives with grace and dignity at the biting edge of poverty. These qualities are abundantly present in *The Emigrants (Vor Egen Stamme, 1924)*, first published in English in 1925.

Bojer was extremely popular with the general public in Norway, but his literary reputation has never stood as high in his homeland as on the Continent and in America. The critics, as Harald Beyer observes, "refused to recognize him as a major writer, on the grounds that his ideas interfered with his art, his characters were insufficiently motivated, and his style lacked artistic cultivation."[1] One is tempted to add that very likely some of them resented the harshness of his condemnation of an entrenched bureaucracy, a cold and formal state religion, and a

---

1. Harald Beyer, *A History of Norwegian Literature*, p. 291.

rigid class system which militated against improvement in the lot of peasant and laborer.

Bojer experienced at first hand the distressing social and economic conditions about which he later wrote. He was born on March 6, 1872, in Orkdalsören near Trondheim, one of the most impoverished sections of Norway. The illegitimate child of a servant girl, he was brought up by a kindly but uneducated foster mother, whose greatest gift to him probably was her inexhaustible store of anecdotes and tales. He received a rudimentary education in the parish school at Bissen, but by his own admission did not discover literature and the pleasures of reading until he was fifteen years old, when he had the opportunity to attend a private school for a few months.

Living at the edge of the fjord, the child grew to love nature. At the same time he recognized both the precariousness of human existence on such primitive terms and the unfairness of the poverty which surrounded him. When he was eighteen he entered the noncommissioned officers' school in Trondheim, not because he was attracted by an army career but because it was a means of obtaining free food, clothing, shelter, and basic instruction. Having so recently discovered literature and the possibility of a literary life, he spent every spare minute reading, attending lectures, or trying his hand at writing poetry and sketches.

Once his military training was finished, he supported himself with a series of menial jobs in order to continue writing. In 1896, when he was only twenty-four, he achieved his first considerable success with *The Procession* (*Et Folketog*), a novel about the sordid political life of a country parish. Moving tentatively into journalism, he was equally successful and became, in his words, "a literary tramp. I lived for years in Paris as a correspondent for Norwegian newspapers, three years were spent in Italy, two years in Germany.''[2] The international success of *The Power of a Lie* (*Troens Magt*, 1903) enabled Bojer to return to Norway, where he settled down comfortably to a long and productive career, writing nearly twenty novels (in addition to many stories and plays), the last of which, *Skyld* (*Guilt*), appeared in 1948. He died in Oslo on July 3, 1959, at the age of eighty-seven.

Bojer has said that his novels fall into four categories: ''[They] describe the lives of plain Norwegian people (*The Last Viking, The Emigrants*), they contain psychological studies (*The Power of a Lie, Our Kingdom*) or lyrical pictures of youth and outdoor life (*Life, The Eyes of Love*). I have sometimes been called a writer of 'ideas' because I have placed my characters in relation to some social or religious idea (*The Great Hunger, The New Temple*).''[3] Today some readers find a number of his novels more interesting and valuable as social, political, or economic history than as imaginative literature, for the total body of his work reflects most of the major issues which confronted Norway during his lifetime: the struggle to organize labor, the growing materialism and secularization of modern life, war profiteering, universal suffrage, women's rights, the mechanization of the fishing industry, and emigration.

Bojer's most memorable novels are those portraying the folk life of northern Norway, especially *The Last Viking* (*Den Siste Viking*, 1921), describing the rigorous existence of Lofoten fishermen; *The Folk by the Sea* (*Folk ved Sjöen*, 1929), dealing with the bondage of tenant farmers; and *The Emigrants*, whose theme is the equality and prosperity to be found in America. In these books

---

2. Quoted in "Johan Bojer," in *Twentieth Century Authors*, ed. Stanley J. Kunitz and Howard Haycraft, p. 157.

3. Ibid.

Bojer expresses the peasant's identification with the soil and the sea and his intense love for his homeland; at the same time he records the conditions which force him to leave it.

Bojer's decision to write *The Emigrants* was influenced by an announcement that in 1925, the centenary of the emigration of the first large group of Norwegians to the New World, the Norwegian government would recognize officially Norway's role in the settling of America. Although his primary concern was not with that particular chapter in his country's history, Bojer saw that the moment was propitious for a novel on the general theme of emigration. Accordingly, in the summer of 1923 he came to the United States and visited the area in North Dakota about which he proposed to write. As part of the research necessary to understand the pioneer way of life on the prairie, he talked with Norwegian-Americans who had been homesteaders and could give him first-hand information.

Before his return to Norway in the autumn, he stopped in Northfield, Minnesota, to visit St. Olaf College, founded by his countrymen in 1874. He was expecting to meet O. E. Rölvaag, who had attained modest fame in Norway for his novels on the immigrant experience. But Rölvaag was in seclusion at his cabin in northern Minnesota working on *Giants in the Earth*, his own novel about life on the Dakota prairie. Having learned of Bojer's plans early that summer, Rölvaag had applied for a leave of absence from St. Olaf to complete the task which had occupied his thoughts, if not his pen, for a decade—the writing of a realistic account, based on his own experiences, of the psychological and spiritual struggle of the newcomer to adjust to life in the New World.

In the winter of 1924, when Rölvaag was in Norway to arrange publication of *Giants in the Earth*, the two writers finally met at

Bojer's home in Oslo. Both men were relieved to discover that although their novels had much in common they differed in important respects. For one thing, Bojer's point of view is essentially Norwegian, as the title suggests, with much of the action occurring in Norway, whereas Rölvaag's is distinctly American, focused entirely upon events of prairie life. A second fundamental difference is that Rölvaag's ultimate concern is the effect, often tragic, of immigration upon the individual, while Bojer's concern—as the novel's last paragraph makes clear—is the devastating loss to Norway of so many tens of thousands of her most vigorous citizens.

Most of the Norwegians in *The Emigrants* are tenant farmers, laborers, or fishermen, drawn to America by the promise of a better life. But the pull of the homeland is powerful, too. Even their simplest possessions hold them back: Morten Kvidal feels affection for the old grindstone behind the hut, "an important personage"; the Skaret boys are attached to the family ax: "A thing like that, which you hold in your hand every day, has a face of its own; it is more than an acquaintance, it is a friend" (pp. 56–57). Still, they feel condemned to poverty in Norway, and to the social class into which they were born. "No, slaves musn't try to be masters," Morten bitterly reminds himself (p. 16). But it is not only the poor who rebel: Else, daughter of the colonel, the richest man in the parish, must run away if she is to marry Ola Vatne, a hired hand and convicted arsonist. Among the other immigrants are Anne Ramsöy, daughter of a well-to-do farmer, who marries a young radical, Per Föll, not because she loves him but because she is pregnant by another man; Kal and Karen Skaret and their brood, the most impoverished of all the tenant farmers; the chronic malcontent, Jo Berg; Anton Noreng, called "Mother's darling," the spoiled son of the town clerk; and Morten

Kvidal, who dreams not only of having as fine a farm as the colonel's, but also of clearing the name of his father, who hanged himself after being unjustly accused of forgery.

These unfortunates form the little group that sails from Bergen during late summer of 1882,[4] the peak year of emigration, when 26,000 Norwegians left for America. Their hopes are high, fed by emigrants like Erik Foss, who returned to the parish with reports of rich prairie soil in the Red River Valley of North Dakota, free for the taking. Moreover, military service is not required; taxes are not collected; no law of primogeniture dispossesses the younger brothers and sisters. In America the young can afford to be young, not as in Norway toiling from early childhood to help their elders wrest a living from the meager soil.

Arriving in America, the group, by now a close-knit family, winters in Wisconsin, then goes by train to Northville (an invented name) in the Red River Valley. From there they proceed by ox-drawn wagons a hundred miles west to the land they intend to homestead. Although Bojer carefully avoids inviting the reader to identify the setting with a particular town or place, we are told that the route is northwesterly and that most of the caravan "followed two ruts worn by the wagons of the Hudson Bay trappers" (p. 77).

To Norwegians accustomed to mountains and sea, for whom at home "the higher [they] climbed, the wider the view became," the fact and the idea of the prairie are profoundly unsettling. Quite naturally their response is expressed in terms of the sea; they think of themselves as having moved across "an ocean of earth," only to be "washed ashore at last" in this desolate place. While Bojer does not endow the prairie with a distinct personality as Rölvaag

---

4. The main events of the novel can be dated rather specifically because of the reference on page 186 to Johan Sverdrup, who became prime minister on July 2, 1884.

does, or probe so deeply into its psychological effect upon the newcomers, he describes its impact upon the group in such lines as "All of them felt as if they were groping for something to hold on to" (p. 77). In the case of Else, "This everlasting plain made her feel so dizzy; it forced her to close her eyes and look for something she could lean upon. And what did she see then? The house at home, the hills and the lake" (p. 79). And the effect of the prairie upon the delicately balanced emotions of Per is devastating; he is finally driven insane.

The newcomers' faith in the possibility of attaining paradise on earth is shattered the first summer, destroyed by heat, mosquitoes, coyotes, and ruinous drought. Largely because of their pride they elect to stick it out; besides, they have too much invested in their enterprise to retreat. As the years go by, their toehold becomes firmer and their sense of possession increases in spite of prairie fire, blizzard, hailstorm, fear of Indian attack, crop failure, and the death of their leader. The settlement acquires a name, Nidaros (the ancient name of Trondheim), and becomes a township. Finally, the town is connected with the outside world by rail, and intercourse with the large cities to the east brings commerce and prosperity.

Throughout it all the Norwegians try to preserve their culture and traditions, although it becomes more difficult as other national origins are increasingly represented among the settlers. Eventually it is required that all teaching in public schools be conducted in English. Following the trend among older children and some of the adults, Anders Skaret Americanizes his name to Andrew. Anton Noreng marries an Irish girl with whom he must communicate mostly in sign language. But the Norwegian language still is preserved in many families; even among the children of the third generation there are a few who lapse into the native dialect when they are alone with their elders. In most homes

cherished possessions brought from Norway remind the inhabitants of their origins—the cracked clock on the wall at Skaret, the
heavy hammer which Olaf and Anders saved from the auction in
the old country, the immigrant chests which were prominent in
the furnishings of the sod huts.

The process of acculturation works painlessly in most of the
settlers, but some of them never feel at home in the New World.
Bojer does not conceive of Morten Kvidal's alienation as being so
profound as Beret's in *Giants in the Earth*; nevertheless, to the
end of his life he feels a stranger in America and—what is perhaps
even sadder—in Norway. Morten is one of the very few new-
comers who are able to go home for a visit. Plagued by homesickness, he returns to his village only to make a grim discovery:
"If you came back, you wanted to leave again; if you went away,
you longed to come back. . . . You had one home out there, and
one over here, and yet you were an alien in both places" (p. 351).

Contributing to Morten's chronic uneasiness is his doubt that in
the long run life in America is better than in Norway. In himself
he can trace the growth of selfishness and materialism:

> He seemed to have drifted so far away, not only from his mother
> and his home, but also from that which had once been great and
> good in himself. Now it was all money, money, and everything had
> turned into business. Did he ever think of anything else? . . . What
> if he had been as humble as his father and had stayed on the little
> farm at home? Wouldn't he have been a better man than he was
> now? [p. 221]

He watches his neighbor Kal, the poorest of the poor in Norway,
who has got his claws into four quarter sections of rich prairie
soil. His only ambition is to plow new land and "turn the whole
world into corn-fields and food." In his craving for more
wealth, Kal has even been willing to "put his name on the next

section-mark to the west. It was illegal, no doubt, but he would like to see any one try to take it away from him'' (p. 180).

But if the prairie brings out the worst in the settlers, it also brings out the best. Ola Vatne, who had been convicted of arson in Norway, behaves heroically during a prairie fire. When Erik Foss is deathly ill, three of his neighbors are willing to travel a hundred miles on skis to get medical advice. Without exception, the members of the community share with and assist one another, and offer the same generous aid to their fellow Norwegians who pass through the settlement on the way west.

The steady stream of immigrants is to some degree the result of the romanticization of the ''America-experience'' in Norwegian newspaper accounts, but it is chiefly stimulated by letters written home which were ''all alike in one respect: They told of the wonders of America, but were silent about the hardships the settlers were suffering'' (p. 198). Bojer makes it plain, however, that if the true story were told, it would contain tragic as well as heroic elements. It would speak of the terrible homesickness and guilt suffered by Morten, who feels he has ''run away from a battle that he ought to have fought to a finish at home'' (p. 52). It would record the suffering and madness of Per Föll, to whom the limitless prairie represents Evil drawing him to destruction. It would include the death of Paulina, the oldest daughter of Kal Skaret, killed in a farm accident, never having had a chance, even in America, to be young and carefree.

If we conclude that the tone of Bojer's *The Emigrants* is in the main cheerful and hopeful, we should also recognize that the book's optimism has no relation to the sentimental view of immigration and the western movement that characterized so much nineteenth- and early twentieth-century literature and history. In fact, Bojer must be credited with treating the Norwegian-

American experience realistically, with hearing its tragic undertones and recording them sensitively.

Undeniably, the novel is flawed in several respects. It suffers from its episodic nature, from its several shifts of setting between Norway and America, and from its lack of a clearly identifiable protagonist, especially in the early stages of the story. And because Bojer lacks an intimate knowledge of prairie life, he is not convincing when he describes a prairie fire or when he ascribes to gophers the habit of raiding the chicken pens. But it cannot be fairly said of *The Emigrants* that the main character is an idea rather than a person, or that the novel is memorable primarily as a social document rather than as literature. Indeed, it gains in importance precisely because Bojer relates so many vital characters to an experience still fresh in the consciousness of both Europeans and Americans, the settlement of the New World. Our understanding of human nature, as well as of the emigrant experience, is enlarged by reading this book, especially our knowledge of the conditions which impelled so many people, at great risk, to break ties with the beloved homeland.

PAUL REIGSTAD

Pacific Lutheran University

BIBLIOGRAPHY

Books

Beyer, Harald. *A History of Norwegian Literature*. Translated and edited by Einar Haugen. New York: New York University Press, 1956.

Bojer, Johan. *The Emigrants*. Translated by A. G. Jayne. New York: Century Company, 1925.

Downs, Brian W. *Modern Norwegian Literature: 1860–1918*. Cambridge: Cambridge University Press, 1966.

Gad, Carl. *Johan Bojer: The Man and His Works*. Translated from the Norwegian by Elizabeth J. Macintire. New York: Moffat, Yard, and Company, 1920.

Haugen, Einar. "Johan Bojer." *Columbia Dictionary of Modern European Literature*. Edited by Horatio Smith. New York: Columbia University Press, 1947.

Kunitz, Stanley T. and Howard Haycraft, editors. "Johan Bojer." *Twentieth Century Authors*. New York: H. W. Wilson Company, 1942.

Articles and periodicals

Lödrup, H. P. "Johan Bojer," *American-Scandinavian Review* 14 (1926): 207–17.

xviii   *Bibliography*

Porterfield, A. W. "America Reads Johan Bojer," *American-Scandinavian Review* 9 (1921): 477–81.
Rölvaag, O. E. "When a Novelist Is in a Hurry," *Scandinavian Studies and Notes* 9 (1926–27): 61–67.

BOOK I

THE EMIGRANTS

I

It was a hot day in summer, and they were building a
new house for the farm-hands at Dyrendal. The yellow
timber walls had risen nearly to the level of the roof, and
in a few days, when the roof was on, the colonel would have
to stand the men a bottle or two, to celebrate the event.[1]
At the moment, only three men were chopping and hammering up aloft. You could see the head and shoulders of
Kal Skaret, a middle-aged crofter with a little tuft of red
beard under his chin; also Morten Kvidal, the best joiner
in the parish, young though he was. And the man who was
just laying another log on the top of the wall was Ola Vatne,
a fair-haired young fellow in the twenties, with a ruddy
complexion and merry light-blue eyes.

Ola Vatne was singing softly to himself. He was not a
carpenter, but the colonel had taken it into his head that
he ought to learn carpentering. He had first come to the
colonel's farm, many years before, as goatherd; now he was
farm servant, as well as fiddler, singer, and bootlegger; a
favorite with every one, above all with the girls. As he stood
up there he had a fine view of the world, with the wide
fiord in front of the snow-streaked mountains in the west,
then nearer at hand the cluster of farms in the level fields
around the church, and finally, quite close, the shining lake
just at the foot of the hills leading to Dyrendal.

[1] A Norwegian building custom. As soon as the roof of a new
house is on, it is decorated with garlands and the owner is expected
to give the workmen a gratuity.—*Translator.*

3

Summer everywhere—and it took less than that to make a man sing! Were not the birds singing as they darted hither and thither above the roofs of the farm-houses? Did not the cow-bells tinkle as the herd grazed along the slopes? And did not the girls hum a tune when they ran across the yard to fetch an apronful of shavings? Why, even that poor penniless devil Kal was grinning up at the sun, in the best of spirits! And there went the tall figure of the gray-haired colonel, striding across the yard to the white-painted house; who knows?—perhaps even he was humming to himself on the quiet.

Ah, there was Miss Else coming up from the garden! The wind was ruffling her dark hair; she had on a pale-blue overall and was carrying a basket filled with the first ripe red currants. "Hullo," she called up, "would you like a taste?" And, holding up a bunch in her hand, she forthwith flung it at Ola, who just managed to catch it. At the same time she sent him a coy little glance, showing her pretty white teeth in a smile, then mounted the steps to the kitchen entrance and disappeared. People said that the real manager of the farm was not the colonel but his twenty-year-old daughter, though nobody really knew much about what went on in the bosom of the master's family.

"See what it is to have a sweetheart," observed Morten, with a wink.

"Sweetheart." Ola went on with his work. Sweetheart indeed, when he came from a beggarly little farm on the uplands, and she was the daughter of the colonel at Dyrendal! Think of all the schools she had been to, and all the countries she had traveled in! Ay, and she was good-looking, too, so that folks stopped to stare when she drove up to the church. Ola's sweetheart indeed! But when he had had a drop too much, he did not altogether mind being teased. He would even wink knowingly, not exactly denying it. What about that time when he was minding the goats?

Was n't she out with him day after day? And last summer while the colonel was away—did not the two of them drive together to the forest to get firewood? And how did they spend the time when they so often went out on the fiord to fish? Ola was not to be drawn out, and never gave away anything; but if any one went too far, there was a row.

Yet people would go on talking about them. There was no denying that Ola was a handsome fellow; the girls called him "pretty-face." But he was none too steady, and he lost his head altogether when he played cards; he would gamble away all he owned—his money, his watch, and even the clothes he was wearing. Out at sea he would sail like a madman. If he went hunting he forgot all about his work, and he would follow the track of a bear for a week at a time.

The very idea of the colonel's daughter . . . and *him!*

Now they were whittling shavings off the timbers, using a plane when necessary. Shavings lay thick on the ground, both outside and inside the walls; the hot air drew out their pungent scent; they seemed to curl themselves up and simply beg for a match! Ola looked down at all this inflammable material; a single spark would—h'm! Queer how his eyes kept on being drawn down to all those shavings; it seemed almost as if they wanted him to do something, as if they were crying for his help, and telling him how they longed to shoot up in a blaze. Ola experienced a sudden craving to light his pipe; but he must n't do that, the colonel had absolutely forbidden it.

Why, there was the colonel himself standing on the steps, his long pipe reaching down almost to his waist, bareheaded, with his big gray mustache bristling on each side of his face. "Ola!" he called.

"Yes, sir." The young fellow straightened up as if he were standing at attention, although he had not yet done his military service.

"When you have finished, this evening, come to my study."

"Yes, sir," answered Ola. The colonel turned and went in again.

Everything seemed so quiet all of a sudden. They went on chopping, sawing, and hammering as before, but neither of the other men said anything more to Ola. They all seemed to feel that this summons boded him no good.

In the evening, when Ola pulled off his cap and stepped into the study, the colonel was sitting at his writing-table, looking at a book. He now removed his glasses, fixed his eyes on the other, and cleared his throat. "Ola Vatne, what wages do I owe you?"

"Oh, only for the last quarter."

"In other words, five dollars. If I am not mistaken, you 've already had the clothes and boots which go with the wages. Well, here is ten dollars for you. And you will leave this evening." Ola stood in a daze. He could make nothing of it. "I don't say you have done anything wrong. And I don't want it said that you were kicked out. You can invent some plausible reason or other. Only, you have got to leave this evening."

"Yes, sir," stammered Ola, staring at the wall.

"I hope you 'll get on well. Good-by, my lad."

Ola stumbled out. He looked about him. Strange to see the farm swept clean of folks, like this! His two mates had gone home. There was nobody about, nobody to feel at all sorry for him. No signs of Else. But as he passed the steps up to the kitchen door he seemed to hear tittering inside. So they were making sport of his being kicked out!

In the old building where the farm-hands were housed he changed from his working-clothes to his Sunday best, shouldered the small wooden chest containing all his worldly goods, and took his departure. As he made his way along the road it seemed to him that mocking laughter was drenching his back like driving spray; it came from the other farm-hands, from the girls in the kitchen, perhaps from Else herself. When he reached the slopes above the farm he turned off the path, flung himself down on the heather, and lay there gazing vacantly before him. So much for the master. So much for Else. And now he would be the laughing-stock of everybody for the rest of his life.

He remembered that in his chest he had a full half-pint of spirits. Hastily unearthing it, he drew the cork, and put the little bottle to his lips. The first gulp did not help much. It only warmed him. The second made the world look a good deal brighter. When the bottle was quite empty, he raised his eyes and broke into foolish laughter. . . .

At bedtime Else went in to her father with the usual evening glass of toddy, and a scene ensued. When at last she came out again, any one could see that she had been crying. The girls in the kitchen exchanged glances. The colonel had shown who was master this time, at any rate.

That night a fire broke out. The carpenters must have been careless about matches, after all, for the farm foreman, who was roused first, reported that it began in the new building. The farm was quickly in a commotion. Men and women hurried to and fro with buckets of water. The colonel, bareheaded and in his shirt sleeves, did his best to direct the work; tarpaulins were wetted and spread over the main building, but the stable and cow-house were burned down. All next day the smoke went on rising from the scene of the big fire.

A fire on a large farm always sends a thrill through the whole neighborhood. People began to talk. Was it a case of arson? The colonel shook his head and expressed no opinion. He had never been one to say too much—at any rate to common folks. But three or four days after this the red-bearded foreman rode up to Ola Vatne's little

home among the hills. Tethering his horse outside, he
entered. He had a knapsack on his back. "God bless the
house!"

Ola sat indoors, making a broom; his father was patch-
ing a pair of boots and his mother was spinning. The foreman was cómically bow-legged, and his hair and beard were
very shaggy. He sat a while, chatting about things in
general.

"That there fire were a bad business," observed the old
man, looking up from the boot he was mending.

"Mercy on us, yes!" the old woman quavered, stopping her
wheel for a moment.

At this juncture the foreman opened his knapsack and
produced a bulky volume. A Bible, leather-bound, with
copper clasps—whatever did he want with that? "Ola," he
said, stepping across the floor to where the lad was sitting,
"can you put your hand on this Bible and swear that you
didn't set fire to the farm?"

Ola sprang up; his father got to his feet, but his mother
looked ready to faint. Dead silence fell in the little room,
broken only by the steady ticking of the clock on the wall.
The foreman was still holding out the big Bible. "You hear
what I say, Ola. Can you put your hand on God's Word
here, and swear that you are innocent?"

Deathly pale, Ola stammered, "Wh-what the devil is this
foolery?"

The foreman persisted. "Swear, Ola. If you deny it
with your hand on the Book, we'll believe you."

But the hands of the other hung limply at his sides.
He tried to raise first his right, then his left hand; but no,
they would not budge. At length he managed to lift his
right hand, but it was only to pass it across his forehead.

"Well, well!" the foreman said. He stepped back, replaced
the book in his knapsack, bade them good-by, and rode off
down the hill. "Ola!" whispered his mother, her eyes fixed

on his face. "Ola!" echoed his father, still standing there with his spectacles on and his awl in his hand. But the boy only stared blankly, in a cold sweat. Clearly, their next visitor would be the sheriff.

But next morning when the sheriff drove into the yard with his assistant and a pair of handcuffs, he found only the old people. He questioned, coaxed, and threatened. But truth is truth. The old couple could but repeat that the lad had made off the night before; and where he was going to, they doubted if even he, himself, knew.

The hunt for Ola Vatne gave the country-side plenty to talk about. The sheriff and his man searched the mountain farms and sæters, the woods and the fields; they carried a pistol and handcuffs, but they could not catch Ola, for all that. Rumors flew from farm to farm. At last they had run him to earth! No, that was all a lie. But what about the goatherd who saw him in the mountains? Yes, three days ago. But the woods and mountains stretched far and wide, and it was summer-time. How did he get food? Would he dare to go near any of the sæters? Days and weeks passed, and still he was at large. The sheriff went on with his search, and by and by a reward was offered to any one who could apprehend Ola Vatne.

Then one night there was a fire at the sheriff's place. It was only his smithy, but rumor confidently asserted that this, too, was Ola's doing. Evidently he wanted to provoke the sheriff, to take a rise out of him. And before long the busy-bodies were spreading the news that Ola had told a goatherd in the forest that he wouldn't be satisfied until every farm in the parish was in ashes.

That put everybody on the qui vive. There was hardly a house now where the inmates dared to sleep at night. At the parsonage and at the houses of the sheriff and the high sheriff, a man with a gun was stationed to keep watch. The Brandts at Lindegaard had two crofters on guard all night, armed with rifles. The scare was infectious; there was hardly a farm where one did not hear wary steps patrolling in the dead of night. What if he came *here* next?

How bright the fiord looked, these soft, light nights! To the east the fir-clad hills showed blue against the higher mountains behind; that was where they were looking for Ola now. Maybe they had shot and wounded him like a hunted wolf, so that his blood left a red track on the heather as he fled from his pursuers. Perhaps he had crept in among the boulders or hidden in a cave, to die there like a wounded bear. Ola, whom all knew and virtually every one liked! Ola, whose playing would set the very stocks and stones capering; who could sing and tell droll stories in a way that would make even the dead rise and laugh! And suppose he was n't guilty, after all.

Meanwhile the sheriff had got some soldiers to help in his search. They went about with loaded rifles. The sheriffs in the adjoining districts also were out with guns and handcuffs, looking for Ola, who might have escaped thither. New stories spread like wild-fire: now the soldiers had pursued him up such and such a hill; he had taken to his heels and they had fired at him, but he had got away. So the hunt went on from day to day.

A girl was sitting on a tussock in the woods, eating her lunch, while the· cattle lay around her, chewing the cud. Suddenly she was startled by the sound of a man's voice: "You there, will you let me have your food?" A wild-looking bearded figure stepped out of the undergrowth, and she gave him all she had. He laughed. "Tell them down on the farms that Ola Vatne is up here now, if they want him. My lair 's a bit farther north on this slope, you can say." And he disappeared again among the trees.

Far in among the farm lands lay the fiord, midnight-blue and shining. A man ran out of the wood, looked about him, and saw that the valley was asleep. Putting his shoulder to a boat lying on the shore, he pushed it into the water, jumped in, and rowed away. Safe. Out in the middle of the fiord drowsed a schooner with hanging sails. He rowed alongside. "Ship ahoy! Do you need a hand?" "That depends," answered the skipper. The man made fast to one of the shrouds and climbed on board. "Where's this boat bound for?" "Denmark." All right, he'd been at sea before. Down in the men's cabin he was given some meat and potatoes, which he devoured ravenously. He was free—safe.

But a few hours later, when the skipper had turned in and one of the sailors was minding the helm, the man jumped overboard; he could not resist the temptation to go back. To be hunted was such sport. To show them a clean pair of heels while the rifles were cracking away among the hills; to hide; to slink like a fox into a cave, and fool them into standing outside to smoke him out, while he slipped away by another opening; to give people a fright in one place while they were hunting for him in quite another—why, it beat even a wedding! He simply had to return and go on with the game.

Now, strange as it may seem, the hotter the pursuit became, the more people began to pity him. Poor boy, they said; a shame that the authorities should go shooting at one of the lads of the parish as if he were so much vermin! And Ola, too, with whom they had chatted so pleasantly time and again!

The summer passed, and still they had not caught him. The sheriff swore, but persevered. The colonel shook his head if any one ventured to allude to it. And now the neighbors were saying that his daughter Else was ill in bed the greater part of the time. But folks still stayed up at night as a precaution, and when the dark autumn evenings set in it was dangerous to go near a farm. At the slightest sound the watchers would raise their guns and take aim.

Then came a rumor that Ola had been taken at last. Not by the soldiers or the sheriff, however, but by two woodcutters who had gone into an empty sæter to cook their dinner. There they had found him lying on the ground, ragged, emaciated, nothing but skin and bones, almost unrecognizable.

"Now then, Ola, up you get!" He went with them quietly, but they had to give him some food first.

One day the Dyrendal crofters were shocking corn when one of them stopped and stared at the road. "Here they come!" he said. The six men strolled out into the road, and stood there waiting.

First came the sheriff himself in a cariole; and he being one of "the quality," they took off their hats to him. Behind him came a cart with a plank across it, and on this sat Ola Vatne, handcuffed, with a man on each side of him. He sat there chatting quite unconcernedly with them both. And, strange to say, the crofters took off their hats to him too, just as if he also had been one of the quality.

Ola turned his head to look at them, and tried to smile. Whereupon his old mates waved their hats to him. But the foreman stopped the cart, and went up to it just to shake hands with him. In doing so he surreptitiously slipped a little note into his hand. Then they drove on.

During the trial the colonel was called as a witness. The stern old soldier felt a queer lump in his throat when he caught sight of his former farm-boy between two policemen. Ola had confessed. But the colonel sang his praises warmly, and went so far as to describe the whole affair as a boyish prank. If he had *his* way, he said, the lad would be let off altogether. The magistrates hemmed and exchanged glances. But it may have been due partly to his recommendation that Ola got only one year's imprisonment.

Late one evening, after the colonel had gone to bed, the door opened and his daughter entered. "Father," she said, "I'm afraid I must tell you something you won't like to hear."

"Well, what now?" He groped for the matches to light a candle, but she took the match-box away from him and sat down on the edge of the bed.

"I wanted to say that the people who had have sent Ola Vatne to prison must not be allowed to ruin him altogether."

"Else, what do you mean by that?" He strained his eyes to catch sight of her face in the darkness.

"I mean that I have made up my mind to marry him when he comes out."

The colonel sank a little farther down on his pillow. There was a pause. At last: "Tell me, child, are you walking in your sleep?"

"I have thought it over well, Father. It is my fault quite as much as his. And if he wants me, we will go so far away that we shall not bring any disgrace upon you. That is what I wanted to say." She passed her hand caressingly over his brow and left him.

"Else!" her father called after her, sitting up in bed. But she slipped quietly out of the room and closed the door behind her. He heard her footfalls die away in the distance.

II

The steamer had dropped Morten Kvidal at the end of the promontory, and now with the fiord behind and the farmsteads in front of him he was striding briskly up the hill toward the woods and marshes around Lindegaard. He was a young fellow of four or five and twenty, dressed in dark homespun and a brown plush [1] hat and carrying a knapsack on his back. His beardless face was less tanned than one might have expected it to be at a time when the spring farm work was in full swing; but then, he had been in town all the winter, working as a joiner.

Whitsuntide had come very early this year; the spinneys on the hills were only just tinged with pale green, while the bare fields still looked black and smelled of manure. Just now, when the snow mountains in the west beyond the fiord were flushed in the sunset glow, the farmsteads seemed to be melting away in a bluish haze, with their windows aflame. When Morten reached the outskirts of the wood and caught sight of the lake lying in the midst of the farm lands, he stopped involuntarily. How strange it felt to come home after being away for so long! As though everything he saw were standing and calling to him, "You are one of our own." The hills, the lake, the farms, were all saying, "Welcome home." He pushed his hat back from his forehead, turned to look this way and that, and forgot all about where he was going. His soul became merged in the landscape whence it had sprung.

Roundabout him lay the big farms, with their brightly painted red and white buildings. And up on the heights

[1] Broad-brimmed hats made of plush were formerly worn by the peasants of Norway.—*Translator.*

14

he could see Kvidal, his own home, where his mother and five brothers and sisters lived; it stood on a patch of cultivated land, but how mean and dingy the little houses looked!

Well, you couldn't make a silk purse out of a sow's ear. Father and son, his forebears had toiled up there as poor crofters, but when the turn came to him he had jibbed. Perhaps it was the fault of the county school. On leaving it he had rubbed his eyes, as it were, and suddenly begun to wonder what the world was really like. He had discovered that it was a pleasure to look at the well-to-do farms, whereas the gray hovels of the poor were merely an eyesore. He could never go near his home without being conscious of a sense of shame. Clenching his fists, he had vowed that some day he would alter all that. The masters at the county school had advised him to go on studying. No, he had answered, books were all very well, but he preferred carpentering and working in the fields. Didn't he write poetry? Oh well, after a fashion, but that would never make Kvidal into a big farm, which was all he cared about.

He had pestered his father so long that at last he had got him to buy his holding. Then they called the place a farm, but the houses did not look any the better for that. He had felt as though all the girls were still saying: "Oh, don't give yourself airs! We all know you come from tumbledown old Kvidal." He had gone on pestering his father till he made him borrow money from the bank so that they might rebuild. One of his neighbors had backed the bill, while another, who could not write, had said, "You can just put my name wherever it ought to be." His father had done so; but later, after he had got the money, this second neighbor, becoming anxious about the responsibility he had undertaken, had repudiated his signature. A lawsuit followed, and his father was convicted of forgery; but when the sheriff came to take him to prison he found him hanging dead in the barn.

The lad stopped again, passed his hand across his brow, and laughed bitterly. No, slaves must n't try to be masters. His father had taken a leap, thinking to rise a bit higher that way—and see what had come of it! The ground gave way. Down he fell. Into the mud. No doubt the big-wigs had laughed and enjoyed the sight. But here stood one in whose breast a fire smoldered, who often clenched his fists in his sleep. He would n't give in! Kvidal should be a big farm yet! His father and his grandfather, and all the slaves before them, should come into their own in the end.

Money—money was the crux. The fishing off the Lofotens had failed four years running. Then he had worked for months as a joiner in the town, lodging in a beggarly back garret, never wasting a cent on amusement, living on nothing but salt meat and dry bread. A life dreary enough to make a fellow cry. Money? He could barely earn the few dollars his mother needed for the taxes, to pay back an instalment of the debt to the bank, and to keep her and the youngsters alive. A big farm, did you say? All right, show us your money. He, Morten, had undertaken to earn it; but could a man do more than work himself to skin and bone?

His face wore the tense look denoting an iron will, and he glanced this way and that, as though searching for a way out of the dilemma. As he strode on, even his foot-steps were firm and decided, like the strokes of a hammer. He must, he *must* succeed some day!

"Hi! What a devil of a pace you 're going!"

Morten turned round and saw close behind him the young schoolmaster, Jo Berg, dressed in a gray homespun suit buttoned up to the throat like a soldier's tunic, and a black bowler hat. A bristly brown mustache stuck out on each side of his face, and his light gray eyes seemed to be always laughing. He had been with Morten when he was fishing off the Lofotens; his home was a little farm on the far side of the lake; and he had borrowed money to train as a teacher. But he never could get a post at any school, because he had ventured to criticize the teaching at the training college. At present he was living on the bounty of his aged father and mother, had to borrow from them even to buy an ounce of tobacco, and jeered at his mother when she whimpered and implored him to think like other people, so that he, too, might get a job some day. Above all, he ridiculed the fools who had gone security for him with the bank, for now they had to pay the interest and the principal into the bargain. He, he! The way things happened in this world made a fellow roar with laughter.

"So you're back from the town," he said. Yes, Morten couldn't deny that. "Did you go and see Ola Vatne doing time?"

Morten told him that he had visited Ola once or twice in the course of the winter. Oh, yes; Ola was as well off as one could expect in the circumstances.

"And have you heard that Erik Foss has come home from America? They say he is a regular Crœsus now."

"So much the better for him."

"You ought to have a talk with him. He wants to take one or two others with him when he goes back."

The very idea made Morten laugh. No, thanks; he hadn't done anything yet which made it necessary for him to clear out of the country. Go to America? Not if he knew it!

"Don't be so sure of that, my boy. Do you think it's such a fine thing to live in this cursed country where you're not allowed to think or believe what you like, if you happen to be poor?"

Jo Berg stalked along stiffly, grinning as he considered the ludicrous spectacle of this topsyturvy world. His fingers were very brown, and the nails much stained, because he would not take the trouble to use a knife to cut his roll of tobacco when he filled his pipe, preferring to tear the plug to pieces with his fingers, a trick he had learned in the Lofoten Isles.

The rumble of carriages overtaking them caused the two men to spring to the side of the road.   First came the magistrate.in a pony-chaise, then the sheriff in a cariole, and lastly the parish clerk in a gig, with his young daughter Helena seated beside him.   All these people belonged to the quality and you had to take off your hat to them.   But they were not all equally important.   The magistrate was the greatest; next to him ranked the sheriff, and finally came the parish clerk.   After all of them came ordinary folk who went afoot, and to these Morten Kvidal unquestionably belonged.   The girl beside the clerk looked round at him and smiled; she had gone strangely red, and the young man looked down. The schoolmaster noticed it and chuckled.   "Ah," he said, "her father thinks no small beer of himself, although he is only a trumpery clerk."

Morten turned pale and quickened his step.   The thrust had gone home.   No doubt the whole country-side knew that the parish clerk would not hear of his daughter walking out with the boy from Kvidal.   He was n't good enough for her.   This added yet another to the burdens poor Morten had to bear.

As he went on alone up the hills he stopped now and then to take breath.   Yes, he thought, there was many an uphill struggle in life; but how good to smell the young leaves and the blossoming bird-cherry!   And the higher he climbed, the wider the view became.   The sun had already dipped in the west, but the glow still lingered upon the mountain snows, as if to bid the whole world a resplendent "good night."   He was home at last.

Cries of "There he is!" came from the farm above.   The first to greet him was the Lapland dog King, which came bounding frantically down the slope, with the youngsters after him. Simen, a fair-haired, sturdy lad of eighteen, cleared the ground with long strides. At his heels came fifteen-year-old Peter, a slouching, hot-tempered boy; then followed the girls and little red-haired Knut. Morten was surrounded; the dog jumped up and actually managed to lick his face, and they all talked nineteen to the dozen, welcoming him back once more.

Each one of them had something to tell. Twelve-year-old Randi, with her flaxen hair flying about her face—what, had she really got a new pair of shoes? . . . So Peter was being prepared for confirmation; were many going to be confirmed this year? . . . And Knut here, with his broad face and sly-looking eyes. Only seven years old, and he'd already begun going to school! . . . But none of them could outdo little Mette, who was just five and shouted loudest of all. Fancy! Dagros had a calf. Well now, that was something like! Morten took her hand and bent down to give her a cake he had brought for her.

"What have you got on your watch-chain?" asked Simen, who couldn't keep his hands off Morten.

"It's a little compass."

They all had to look at it, and of course to touch it, too.

Morten was always rather puzzled at the fuss the youngsters made over him whenever he came home. For he knew very well that when he was there he ruled them with a rod of iron; nothing was done quickly enough or well enough, and somebody was always to blame for it. The thought of this made him feel uncomfortable when he was away, and he always resolved that he would turn over a new leaf next time.

"What a lot you've grown this winter!" he said to the eldest of his brothers.

"Have I? And you're getting to look quite like a town lad."

"With that great fist of yours you'll soon be able to lick the whole parish."

"Ay, look out for yourself!" And he gave his brother a punch. The blow woke up the boy in Morten, too; throwing down his knapsack, he advanced toward Simen with a grin, as though he were going to bite him. "Out of the way, young uns!" They went for each other with a will, hitting out lustily, harder and harder, until they ended by rolling over on the grass, clutching each other by the throat. King rushed at them and tugged away to try to separate them. The elder children screamed with delight, and Mette with terror.

"Bless me, have you quite lost your wits?" came a voice from the top of the hill, and a red-haired woman descended at a leisurely pace toward them. It was Berit Kvidal, their mother.

Then Morten once more approached those aged, gray and poverty-stricken farm-buildings which so often had made him blush, but which were his home after all. There was no place in the world like this. The crazy old house was like a mother to them all, the byre with its green-turfed roof had an air of profound wisdom, and the grindstone at the back of the barn was an important personage: Morten often felt obliged to stand and look at it. On the hill behind the house the Kvidal waterfall was singing its old song, weaving farm, hills, and folk together in a strange harmony; ah, there was no place like this! The latch on the door felt so homely to his touch as he went in, the newly washed floor was strewn with green sprays of juniper, and—dear me!— that clock on the wall had long been on its last legs, yet it was still spelling out the time, as wrong as ever! "Welcome home," it seemed to say. The very air had a peculiar smell of home, of memories good and ill; telling, above all, of the mother who slaved away there, and whose only thought was to do the best she could for each one of them.

Seated at the long and spotlessly clean wooden table, he was treated—like a stranger come on a visit—to thick curdled cream with grated rusks and sugar on the top, to treacle-cake from the local store; in fact, to all the good things she could think of. Meanwhile she herself stood in the middle of the room, red-haired and freckled, thin and bent by incessant toil, but with a glad light in her eyes at the thought of having him back. And the way she pumped him, to hear all the news of the town! Was it true that the king had been there? Had Morten seen him? And was he in uniform?

To Berit the world was full of wonders; there was always something strange happening in one place or another. Her many troubles had left no mark on her; she would shed a tear at the time, but she soon dried her eyes and looked away from her sorrow, and then she quickly found something cheerful which made her forget it. Was it her fault if she had these good spirits which nothing could break? Her mother had been famous in all the neighboring parishes for the tales she could tell about things visible and invisible, and the doings of families who lived in those parts in former days. All about the different clergy and officers, and this sheriff or that magistrate who had lived at such and such a farm —notable folks and notable happenings, real tales of adventure! And her daughter had remembered it all. It was as good as a tonic; many a time when she had been so worn out that she was ready to drop, one or other of these stories had come into her head and set her off laughing, and that had put new life into her. Now and again, when there had n't been a bite of anything in the house for supper, she had put her children to bed and told them story after story till they forgot their hunger and fell asleep.

But why was Morten sitting there with that strained look on his face? Did he mean to do such great things in the world? The boy had a fine head on his shoulders; he inherited that from his grandmother. But she wished he would laugh a little oftener.

The flavor of the treacle-cake was rather spoiled for Morten by a feeling that it must have been bought on tick. He knew that his mother always meant to keep herself in provisions from the store in return for the butter and eggs she sold; but if one of her children looked pale and run down, what could be better than to feed him up on fresh eggs and cream? If Morten bought a sack of flour for her it dwindled away in no time; she had n't the heart to say no to a neighbor who wanted to borrow, or to any poor beggar-woman who came to the door with her bag. It was always Morten who had to pay the piper; goodness knew when he could begin to put by something for himself! And all the while he had such ambitious plans; and money, money was the key to them all.

He supposed there would be the usual Whitsuntide bon-fire to-morrow evening. All very well for those who could afford to be young.

III

Outside the church next day the returned American, Erik Foss, had gathered a little crowd around him. The men stood there with their heads thrown well back, asking him questions, listening and staring. The new-comer was tall and fair, with a brown mustache; and he wore, like the gentlefolks, a collar and tie, a brown frock-coat, and a top-hat and shiny boots. But you could see from his hands that he knew what work meant. Seven years he'd been out there; and though he was only the son of Scraggy Olina, he was a big man now.

Did he boast? No, he just talked quietly and sensibly. Whoever asked a question, got an answer; and if it was something he did not know, he answered straightforward that he didn't know it. If any fool sneered, he pretended he hadn't heard. He had worked as a railway navvy and as a farm laborer, and had himself owned a farm for three years; then the railway came along, prices went up, and he sold out. Now he wanted to go farther west, to the Red River Valley, where the land could still be had for nothing and was very easy to put under cultivation, because the soil of the prairie was free from stones and tree stumps, and you had only to put in your plow and start plowing at once. If any of them cared to join him, they could go in company, and he'd do his best to assist them.

He was quite the center of attraction to-day; when the clergyman appeared, the hats did not fly off so quickly as usual. Erik Foss had just been saying that there were no class distinctions in America; a laborer or a parson—one was as good as the other. His audience could hardly believe their ears. They looked round at Brandt from Lindegaard,—who was so much finer than other folks that he had

23

to have a special pew with a gilded grille, like a little private
paradise, at one side of the church,—and they looked at the
sheriff, taking off their hats as in duty bound, but all thinking: America . . . no class distinctions . . . just think
of that! Then they saw the colonel from Dyrendal coming;
and he was the greatest man of the lot, so they had to make
way for him. Hats off, hats off! But strange to say, Erik
Foss took no notice of any of these great personages: "Why
don't you take off your hat?" one man asked in a scandalized
tone. "I only take it off to people I know," answered Erik.
Ah, it was all very well for an American to talk like that!
Then something singular happened. The colonel stopped,
looked across at the stranger, and went right up to him in
the sight of everybody! The others all stepped back, leaving a clear space round the two men.

"You've just come home from America, haven't you?"
the colonel asked. (Mercy on us! he was talking to Scraggy
Olina's son as politely as if he had been at least a captain!)

"That's right," said Erik; he had raised his hat slightly
when the colonel addressed him, but had put it on again at
once, and now he stood there looking quite as tall and composed as the other. The bystanders heard the colonel say:

"It would interest me to hear a little about the conditions
over there. If you can spare the time, you might look in
one day at my place."

"Certainly I will," answered Erik Foss, in the tone of
one doing a service to an equal.

Then the colonel passed on into the church, but the
others quite forgot to follow as long as Erik Foss remained
standing there. Who would have thought it! When he left
the country he was only a young good-for-nothing, one of
Scraggy Olina's mongrel brats. And now America had sent
him back again as the equal of the colonel at Dyrendal!

Morten Kvidal did not care to stand and listen to the
American; he went straight into the church and up the

gallery stairs to take his usual place in the choir. Helena Noreng, the daughter of the parish clerk, was already seated there amid a number of other girls. He hardly dared look in her direction, though he was vaguely conscious that she was wearing a blue dress. Her flaxen hair was braided in snaky coils round her head, in the way the daughters of the gentry always wore it. Once her eyes slid round toward him, and she colored slightly as the girl beside her gave her a nudge. Now they were singing. He felt strangely exalted at the thought of mingling his voice with hers. When he looked down on the heads of the congregation, and the sound of their singing rose up to him, it seemed as though their voices were all united in a hymn about Helena and himself. He thought no one saw when her eyes met his again; and under cover of the singing she gave him a little smile and a nod. That was enough—a whole letter, indeed. It said, "Meet me you know where."

The farm lands were once more steeped in the pale blue twilight of spring when he left the house late that evening, saying that he was only going for a stroll. His mother smiled as she looked after him. Ah, if the decision had rested only with her!

The young people of the country-side had lighted bonfires along the shores of the wide fiord; flames and smoke were rising into the air from the ridge of Blaaheia to the north, as well as other points on the surrounding hills. The call of the blackcock resounded on the slopes. Morten hurried down the fields to the valley, crossed a piece of rising ground overgrown with alder-trees which was some day to be cleared and converted into corn-fields and meadows for Kvidal, and, entering the birch wood, struck into a path where he knew the going was good. Presently he could see beneath him the parish clerk's farm, with its fields tumbling in a series of hills down to the lake; and here, having reached his destination, he sat down in the heather to wait.

Doors kept opening and shutting at the farm below him, but none of those who came out was the girl he expected. He waited, gnawing at a twig; the sap was rising already and it tasted sweet. He went on waiting. Evening had woven the hills, the farms, and the lake into a fabric of blue; above the moors to the north, banks of yellow and dusky-hued cloud floated in the sky. Should he try to put it all into poetry? But to sit there humming, and let himself be carried away by the gentle murmur of a spring evening, was one thing; to make good poetry was quite another. An evening like this could be expressed in the strains of a violin or in a long prayer to the Eternal, but when he tried to make verses he never could get them good enough. Wouldn't she come soon? Wasn't she coming after all? The sheriff's son was running after her, too, and very likely he would succeed his father some day; that was a long sight better than having one's home at Kvidal, where that poor old man had hanged himself in the barn not long before.

A sound of footsteps, the branches were brushed aside, and there she was, bareheaded, with her kerchief in her hand, warm from hurrying, her face smiling up at him.

"So you 've come, after all!"

"Hush! Just think if any one saw us! Well, how are you?"

They sat down side by side among the heather, and she let him put his arm about her, but every time he tried to kiss her she laughed and turned her head away.

"God bless you for coming! Do you still think of me sometimes?"

"No, I 've forgotten you now." She flashed him an arch sidelong glance.

"Have you been to many dances lately?"

"Rather! But how old you 're getting!" And she stroked his cheek lightly.

"You never write."

"There's too much to write about. But I've got some rubbish here . . ." He opened the little box she handed him, and saw a watch-chain of finely plaited hair, intended to be worn round the neck.

"My word! I do believe it's made of your own hair."

"It took ages to get enough, though; so little hair comes out when I comb it."

With reverent fingers he touched her present; then, brightening: "Can't I have a kiss now?"

"No, you've had quite enough."

"I bought a little thing in town" he said; "but it's only trash." He produced a small parcel. The girl was all inquisitiveness. It was a red silk ribbon to tie round her neck.

"Oh, Morten!"

"It'll be a ring next time."

"I should never dare to wear it."

"But you'll wear this ribbon, won't you?"

"Yes, when nobody sees me."

"You wouldn't mind wearing it if the sheriff's boy had given it you."

"Oh, don't start on that again!"

"All right, I won't if you'll promise to marry me next spring."

Another sidelong glance, but a serious one this time. Did he really think she could go and live with him on his farm, as things were now? She gazed in front of her, a straw between her lips. His eye lighted on the white scar on her temple; she had got that when she fell and hurt herself so badly out skiing on the hills above Kvidal. He remembered how he had taken her home unconscious, on a toboggan.

"Why don't you answer?" he said.

"We've talked all that over before."

"I've got so many plans, Helena. And if only I had you to help me, it would all be so much easier."

"But you've so many to help you at Kvidal."

The words stung him like the cut of a whip. He hung his head. Yes, there was no denying that he had to support his younger brothers and sisters until they could fend for themselves. And now this girl whom he loved had as good as told him that she wasn't going to be mixed up in all that. Oh, she knew what she was about! Her father and mother and grandmother had not dinned all their good advice into her ears for nothing. And wasn't she quite right? It would mean want and misery to marry now. But when? If only he had the least notion of when! . . .

All the same, he tried again. "I know what you would do if you were really fond of me."

She looked him straight in the face this time. "And I know what you would do if you were really fond of me."

"Clear off to the town and settle down as a joiner there for the rest of my days. Leave Kvidal, and Mother, and my brothers and sisters. But you know you wouldn't have any use for such a feeble creature."

They sat a while in silence, without looking at each other. She sighed, munched a blade of grass, and at last got out the words: "Do you think you'll ever make anything out of Kvidal?"

"Wait a year or two. Perhaps three. I've got a new plan now. If only you would wait for me, and not be impatient, Helena!" He took her hand and pressed it.

"Father wants me to go and train as a teacher."

"What! Does your father want *you* . . . !"

"Yes, as I don't seem to be going to marry." She tried to laugh.

He groaned. How he wished she would not talk like that; it hurt so!

How could she tell him the real truth, that she liked

to picture him singing in the choir with that fine clear tenor of his, or flying down the steep slopes on skis, or as the brainy boy at the county school who even stumped the masters themselves by the questions he asked; but that she did not like to picture him at home in those tumble-down houses at Kvidal. She wanted to feel that he was something better than that.

"Do you dance much when you're in town?" she asked with a smile, trying to turn the subject.

"Never. When I'm not at work I stop at home in my den and bury myself in a book."

All of a sudden she jumped up and smoothed her hair. "Goodness! I've been sitting here too long. They'll be waiting for me." A moment later her arms were round his neck. Her face was very near his; she was smiling, but her eyes were wet. "It's a shame that we two can't have each other." With that she kissed him lightly, then set off at a run down the hill.

"When shall we meet again?" he called after her. But the sound of her quick footsteps hurrying down through the wood was the only answer.

High up on the rock overlooking the lake a group of girls and young men had gathered round a big bonfire. Its red glow lit up their laughing faces as they looked across it at one another. Some of them were dragging up fresh supplies of dry juniper branches and throwing them on the fire, which crackled and blazed higher than ever. The sheriff's son—a handsome lad with fair hair and refined features—was there, and Anton Noreng, eldest son of the parish clerk, commonly known as "Mother's Darling" because he never did a stroke of work. The others were girls and young men from the large farms of the neighborhood; they were all in the early twenties, had been at school together, and had been confirmed at the same time. One or two of them had been away for a while, but had come home now for the holidays; and as soon as they met they all felt like children once more; it took them some time at first to realize that they and their schoolmates had grown up.

The hour was not far distant when most of them would have to disperse for good; for in each family only the eldest son had a right to the farm, and the others had to go elsewhere. One fine day they would find out that only children had parents and a home; when they grew up that came to an end, and the safest stand-by of all, their father and mother, turned them adrift. Well, it couldn't be helped; but nowadays when they came together like this their merrymaking had a curious strain of melancholy in it. They met, but only to part again and take up the serious tasks of grown men and women. The happy, careless days were over, and life would never be the same again.

But this evening they were all there together and could be children for an hour or two. Yet somehow a kind of barrier had arisen between these girls and boys, an estrangement they never had felt before. Was it the girls' fault if they saw the boys in a new light? Look at Anton Noreng, for instance. He seemed to have no idea of ever becoming anything; why, his teeth were quite brown from eating sweets—pah! What a difference between him and the eldest son at Flyta, heir to a big farm, and a regular hard worker which made the boy good-looking enough for them in spite of all his freckles. And Martin Skau, with his broad, good-humored face, who had been head boy at the county school. He was attending a grammar-school now, and meant to become a vet. Before long he would disappear altogether into gentlefolks' land; would he take one of the farm girls with him when he went? The sheriff's boy had only to stretch out his hand and take any girl he chose; his father was one of the quality, and he would be too, no doubt, when his father retired; but at present he was doing the work of two on the farm. And Haakon Fagergaard was studying at a training college for teachers; the girls had never taken much notice of him before now, but he had brains and was sure to get on, and that made all the difference.

Now, all these young people belonged to the best families in the parish; if Morten Kvidal tried to join them they would certainly give him the cold shoulder; this he very well knew and therefore would make a detour to avoid them.

"Here come the clerk's little girls," said the sheriff's son.

The two girls whom they saw coming toward them across the green fallow were both fair, but Helena was taller and slimmer than Martha. "Why are you so late?" Anton called out to them; and Martha answered, "Because Helena had to go on an errand for Mother."

Then some one suggested that they should all go down to the fallow and play Odd Man Out. Martin Skau took hold of Helena and fell into position, getting a quick look from the sheriff's son, who was left to be odd man. Couple after couple dashed off, and the hills around echoed with their shouts. But the sheriff's son could not catch anybody, in spite of his long legs. When Helena and Martin ran out, however, he put his best foot forward. They changed places at the last moment, and he caught at Martin and missed. Ha! you wait! Now Helena was in front and he after her, coat tails flying and minus his hat; but he caught her at last in a bush.

The two stood there, recovering their breath. "You've lost something," he said, and went back to pick up a red ribbon which lay on the grass a little way off.

Helena snatched it from him and hastily stuffed it into her pocket, blushing furiously. If only he wouldn't stare at her like that!

A boy who was keeping an eye on the bonfire shouted, "There's a boat coming across the lake." A boat? Well, what of that? "It's the girls from Ramsöy." That was another matter, and they all ran up on the rock to look.

A boat, with its gunwale painted white and a fan of
ripples behind it, was drawing near across the shining water,
in which the red and gray clouds were reflected. Two girls
sat in the boat, rowing side by side; but they never could
pull together, so the boat meandered along in a series of
serpentine curves. This sent the young people on the rock
into fits of laughter. The girls in the boat heard, and one
of them left the thwart and went to sit in the stern. Presently the notes of an accordion floated across the water.
"Anne's the one playing," said one of the group around the
bonfire. "And Bergitta's rowing," said another.

The two girls from Ramsöy had the reputation of being
the prettiest in the parish, but they were such incorrigible
flirts that they furnished the neighbors with endless food
for gossip. Had not their father been chairman of the local
council and a friend of Brandt up at Lindegaard, more than
one might have liked to keep them at arm's length. But
any one could see at a glance that they were used to going
about among well-dressed people. They had a way of wearing their clothes and carrying themselves which made you
forget how flighty they were, and even made you feel inclined to take off your hat as though they were real gentlefolks.

"Let's give them a song," suggested Martin Skau, preparing to conduct. Nearly all of them had learned singing
at the county school, and what could be better than to sing,
on an evening such as this? They formed a semicircle,
and soon their voices rose in the part-song "Sing in the
springtime of youth." The girls in the boat shipped their
oars, laid aside the accordion, and listened to the singing.
When it ceased they cheered, and the choir on the rock
gave an answering cheer. The next minute the boat grated
on the shingly beach.

The group of friends on the rock stood looking down and
waiting. The first to emerge through the foliage was Anne.

She had dark hair, an oval face with a warm sunburnt complexion, and very large, lustrous eyes under long eyebrows. Over her dark dress she wore a belt fastened with a silver clasp; and she was carrying the accordion in her hand. "I say! what a gathering of the clans!" she exclaimed. "We saw there was a bonfire here, and thought we'd row across."

Behind her came Bergitta, who had just turned seventeen. She had been engaged already,—at the time she was preparing for confirmation,—but had broken off the engagement as soon as she was confirmed. She was slighter than her sister, and fairer, with a very delicately molded face, a rose-leaf complexion, and frank, lively eyes. Her green dress had a red collar and her belt was ornamented with a silver watch-chain; she was carrying a little branch off one of the birch-trees, and waved to the others with it.

"Sing another!" she suggested, and threw a look around her, as though she only wished she could gather up the twilight and the landscape into a song. And, having shaken hands with most of the company, the two sisters took their places in readiness to join in the song.

This time it was "The earth is so fair," and again Martin Skau conducted. The fire was burning brightly. The youthful faces became transfigured, inspired by the song. Their voices grew tender, for they were at an age when the heartstrings thrill at a touch—and they were out in the blue twilight of spring, with the trees on the slopes bursting into leaf and golden cloud-lands flaring in the western sky. It was all in the song. Their own dreams and memories were woven into it, too. Now they were together again; to-morrow they would part; some day they would part to meet no more. It was all in the song.

Anne stood with bent head. What long eyelashes she had! Perhaps she was thinking of the young engineer from Bustad who jilted her because she could see that other boys, too, were good-looking; or imagining herself heiress to a certain

big farm in a neighboring parish, where she flirted so out-
rageously with the lads that she was n't allowed to stay on
there; or perhaps her thoughts were straying to that great
big bearded fellow Per Föll, who was always hanging about
her, although any one could see that she was only playing
with him. Well, life was not always easy for a girl whose
feelings were like an accordion, a violin, and a song all rolled
into one! And now she was singing about that too.

Helena was gazing at the far-off western sky as though
she could see her own future there; it was golden, but it was
dark as well: which would come true? And some such
vision rose before the eyes of each of them. But the earth
was fair—and they were singing.

When at last they finished they stood silent a moment
or two; a girl pushed a lock of hair under her head-
kerchief; all of them needed to recover breath, as it were,
before slipping back into their ordinary every-day mood.

"And now let 's play at kiss-in-the-ring!" Anne suggested,
to break the spell and cheer them up again.

"Yes! Yes! Let 's play kiss-in-the-ring!" They flocked
to the field, and the game was soon in full swing. Nobody
gave another thought to the bonfire, but its leaping flames
and blue smoke were mirrored in the still water beneath.

A little way off, at the edge of the wood, a young man
sauntered past; he saw them playing, but knew that he had
no right to join them. It was Morten Kvidal. He was
wandering aimlessly through the wood, striving to walk off
the harassing thoughts that would not leave him in peace.
If it had been only some one particular obstacle; but no,
every way seemed barred to him, and although he was not
much over twenty, he felt as though years had passed since
he was young. When they had offered to help him at the
training college, he had refused: he would not desert his
mother and Kvidal. And now, if he went and settled for
good in town, and became a master joiner some day, per-

haps Helena would condescend to accept him, provided she were still unmarried. But what about Mother, and Kvidal? Betray them? He would never do it. That thought was rooted in his inmost being. But then—what about Helena? Was he ready to give her up? How long did he expect her to wait? He could not answer. All he could do this evening was to walk on and on, and try not to think.

But on a spring night such as this his whole soul seemed aflame. All these buds opening into leaf; the song of the thrushes; the blue twilight which never became any darker up here in the North; the scent of growing things—oh, he must walk on, and on, and on! The sky above Blaaheia had become a wonderland of colored clouds—rivers, crags, and plains, all blue and gold. If only he knew of some country where he could escape from a few of the perplexities that hedged him in here!

He was down by the lake now, and walking along the shore. Presently he caught sight of some one sitting on a stone, staring out across the water. Then the solitary figure stood up—a tall man with a long brown beard—why, it was Per Föll! But his home was right up in the valley: how did he come to be sitting here? Oh, of course; he knew that those two girls from Ramsöy had rowed over to this side. Wherever Anne was, he was sure to be hanging about. "Hullo, are *you* here?"

"Fine evening," said the other. "I see you're out enjoying it, too."

Morten had fallen in with just the right man; they had been chums in the old days at the county school; how well he remembered the strange sight of that huge beard sweeping the school desk! But Per had mastered all the kings and wars in no time, while dates stuck in that big head of his as if they had been nailed there. He had turned into quite a philosopher, too. When they had their school debates he would stand with his head on one side, and hold forth about man's real business here on earth; and later on he began taking radical papers, and made out that there was no need for God now that they had Björnson.

The two men strolled along the shore side by side. But every now and then Per would turn and look back. They were both in the same boat, Morten thought. Per was going about torturing himself, just as he was doing. Ripping up the old wounds, so that they went on bleeding within him. Strange to see such a Goliath so powerless in the hands of a woman!

"Were you at church to-day?" Per asked, casting another glance over his shoulder. Yes, Morten had been there. "What d' you think of the American?"

"Oh, it's all one to me. I've got my hands full enough here, as it is."

They made as though they would turn back, but ended by sitting down on two big stones and staring across the water, each intent on his own thoughts.

Then Per confided to Morten as an old friend that he had made up his mind to leave the country.

"What! When you'll have the farm some day!"

"Some day, yes. But when? If Father were a hundred, he would marry again. We, his sons, will grow old and die some day, but Father—not he! No. But in America you can get a hundred and fifty acres for nothing. There are no class distinctions there, no taxes, no military service; and you're allowed to believe what you like because there's no established church. What about here? Well, you know, yourself, what it's like if you are n't rich and a swell."

"But what about all the changes you were going to make in the parish?" Morten objected. "You used to be always talking about that."

"Ay. Changes indeed! But it's the big farmers and the gentry that run the show here. Universal suffrage, a reasonable distribution of the fruits of the soil—I think I

can see it! There was a time when I thought I could strike
a blow for reform. But nothing came of it. Nothing.
But in America it's all been done long ago. Come with me,
Morten." His eyes sought the brightly colored clouds in
the west. Any one could see that he had come to look
upon America as the country where all his dreams were
awaiting him as realities. And thither he now meant to
go. "You come, too."

But Morten shook his head. He had a new plan now.
He would set up a joiner's workshop in the parish,
engage some journeymen to work for him, and turn out
really good furniture in the old Norwegian style; it might
even develop into a regular factory some day, selling whole-
sale to customers all over the country. He must have money,
and he was going to make it, too! He needed it in order
to develop Kvidal.

"You'll never earn a cent, Morten. That plan'll *never*
work. There's not a man in the place who'll help you."

"The bank."

"Without security! Ha, ha, ha! Put it out of your
mind. Much better come with me to America. You can
earn more in a week there than in a lifetime here."

But all of a sudden he started and gazed eagerly across
the lake. "What boat is that?" he said, and, jumping up,
walked away, quickening his pace, forgetting even to say
good night—bewitched by a boat with two girls in it, on its
way back to the other shore. What was he about? He
could not possibly join them on board. It would be useless
to call to them. No, all he wanted was to be as near to
the boat as he could. To rip up the wound in his heart, and
bleed, bleed, bleed. . . .

The bonfire on the rock had gone out and the young
merrymakers were wending their way homeward. Already
the clouds in the eastern sky were taking on the rosy tint
of dawn. But Morten did not hurry back. Presently he

threw himself down on the heather and lay staring before him. America? Earn as much in a week there as in a lifetime here? That meant deserting his mother and Kvidal. Well, it need only be for a few years, and then he could come back. But what would Helena say? Supposing she promised to wait. Yes, but would she keep her promise?

Leave the country—no, he could n't do it.

IV

Ebbe was a man who went about with two witnesses and levied distress upon the property of debtors. He was a farmer from higher up the valley, a giant in gray homespun, with a big hooked nose and a black wig; his eyebrows and the fringe of beard under his chin were black and bushy, too. The man's face was immovably calm and solemn; the knapsack on his shoulder likewise had a solemn air. His gray homespun trousers were usually rolled high up over his well-greased top-boots, which to-day were gray with the dust of the road. The brown-plush hat on his head was as large as an open umbrella. And such was the respect in which he was held, that the two witnesses always kept several steps in the rear and hardly ventured to open their lips.

On entering a house to perform his duties, he would remove his hat, smile with one corner of his mouth, and shake hands with the inmates; at the same time he always expressed his pleasure at being there again, even if he never had visited the place before. Next he would place his knapsack on the table, extract from it the official register, and seat himself on the best chair. His face was unutterably calm, his register unutterably solemn. Then he would open the book, and begin to read from it with the air of one conducting family prayers.

He knew very well that his coming always threw the household into a state of consternation; but the law had to take its course. He knew, too, that the women-folks frightened their naughty children by saying, "If you don't take care, old Ebbe will come!" But of a Sunday he sat on a front seat in church among the leading lights of the parish; he went to communion twice in the year; and when he was in town and had to tell any one his name and profession he called himself the under-sheriff. To-day he was marching along the road again, trousers rolled up, staff in hand, his knapsack and witnesses with him.

The sheriff, of course, always drove; but Ebbe never did. Not that he had not horses, too, but he much preferred to walk.

The way he disposed of mile after mile of the country roads was wonderful, although he never hurried. When he got past Lindegaard, where the wood opened out on the peat-bog and the long strip of crofters' lands by the fiord, it seemed to Ebbe that the air was different: it smelled of sea, of peat-smoke, and roasted coffee-beans. "H'm! wasting too much money at the store," he thought. Soon houses began to appear on each side of the road; they were weather-worn by the winter storms, but had flowers in their windows and a little patch of cultivated land around them.

"Here's Ebbe coming!" Small feet went scuttling from room to room. "Ebbe's coming!" The windows became alive with faces. "Mercy on us! He isn't coming here, I do hope!"

But when they saw that he did not turn in at any of the houses on the level, they all understood that to-day he was on his way to Skaret, where Kal lived. "Poor Karen and her children!" they said. "He's going to take her cow this time."

Skaret was a croft high up on the hillside. The two little houses were gray, like the rocks behind them. It was the sort of place in which poverty flourishes so well that it blossoms. Two flaxen-headed boys, Anders and Oluf, went about in trousers innocent alike of seat and knees. The two little girls covered their bodies with some nondescript rags that had once been their mother's; never having had any proper shoes, they went flopping about in cast-off slippers many sizes too large; and they never wore anything on their heads.   Karen, their mother, was a pale-faced woman with prominent cheek-bones and big frightened eyes.   In winter, when the icy nor'wester blew right through the house, she had to keep the children in bed to prevent their being frozen to death; and the cow in the byre stood in a pool because the floor could never be mended.   But this white-faced woman never complained, for she had a little secret which kept her from losing heart: there was a brownie living under the floor.   She had seen him in his red cap and knee-breeches and all, not once only, but many a time.   And that was a sure sign: everything was bound to come right in the end.

Sometimes the children would cry for food when there was not a crumb in the house.   On such occasions she comforted them in the cheeriest of voices, and told them that everything would be all right.   Only wait till to-morrow. "Mother, I *must* have some new trousers.   I 've got to go to school," one of the boys would say; and Mother would agree; only wait, everything would be all right.   "What an awful state your cow-shed 's in!" one of her neighbors would exclaim, seeing Karen sit down to milk the cow with her milking-stool almost under water.   "You may well say that," Karen would answer, "but we 'll be putting up another soon; it will be all right."

"Poor Karen," folks said; but nobody thought of pitying Kal.   To be sure, his life was not a bed of roses, but he made so light of it all, with his laughter and jokes.   A bit of a thief and a cheat, perhaps, but no one could possibly call him lazy.   Why, he 'd been quite famous once as a fisherman up in the Lofotens.   Then one black year had followed another, till it had ended in Ebbe's coming and taking his boat and nets.   "Well, well, I sha'n't have any more bother with them," Kal had said, scratching the tuft of beard under his chin.   After that he had tried going shares in boats that other men owned; but the fishing remained as bad as ever. In the spring he came back empty-handed; and at last he could not even get sea-boots or food on tick. "So much the better," said Kal. "I sha'n't get drowned at sea."

His holding was very small, and as he could not get much to grow there, he had to go out as a day-laborer. He was wonderfully handy with a saw, but sawing up wood at twelve cents a day would never make any man rich, and now he was too much in debt, anyhow; if he earned a cent to-day he had to pay it out to-morrow. On coming home tired out after a day's work, when other folks were going to bed, Kal started at once on a new day. Even on the blackest winter nights he would take his sledge and set off up the hills to fetch firewood, wading through the deep snow. Far on in the dawn, when other folks were getting up, he would come plowing down the slopes again with a heavy load of wood on the sledge. As to where he had got it, the less said the better.

Did all this help? No, nothing helped. He became a past master of the art of prevaricating, borrowing, and cheating in a small way. In the light spring and summer nights he toiled, trying to turn little patches of soil among the rocks into corn-fields and meadows; it was n't his ground, to be sure, but all the same he tilled it as best he could, and even carried sacks of earth on his back to places where the soil was too shallow. He was bent at the knees from constantly carrying loads and had acquired a lopsided, slouching gait; his lower lip sagged at the right-hand corner of his mouth as if he were grimacing in an effort to lift something heavy: he seemed to be making a face at himself, and poverty, and the world at large. But he chaffed and swore, romanced and jeered, and screwed up his eyes when he looked at the girls. He had a queer way of forging ahead on the road which put one in mind of a Lofoten fishing-boat sailing before the wind.

To-day he was away doing the statutory work required of him as one of the Lindegaard crofters; for this he received a wage of eight cents a day and his meals; and now Ebbe was coming—and Karen all alone at home with the children.

At the sight of the black-bearded man stalking in with his witnesses the two little girls shrieked and hid behind their mother's skirt; the younger boy, Oluf, picked up a black-and-white cat and slipped into the back room with it; while his elder brother Anders seized a hammer and planted himself in front of his mother: just let any one try to do her any harm!

Ebbe now stepped forward, shook hands, and expressed his pleasure at seeing them again. As for Karen, she could hardly be paler than she always was, her eyes could hardly be redder, or her whole appearance more utterly forlorn. "S-so you're round this way to-day?" she stammered, with a "h'sh" to the children. "Won't you take a seat?"

Ebbe laid his knapsack on the dining-table and took out the book; but he did not begin family prayers yet, in spite of his solemn air. He looked about him. The old wooden bed with some rags on it—he'd valued that once before. There was another in the back room, besides an old packing-case full of straw in the loft, which the boys slept in—none of it worth anything. A cracked clock on the wall, a couple of saucepans and a black kettle in the kitchen—no money in them. Clothes? There were n't any. Kal had no Sunday trousers now, and Karen had no best dress so far as he had been able to discover. No, there was nothing for it but to take the cow.

While he was reading aloud from his register Karen stood with bent back, as though she were out in a hail-storm. At the close he asked her whether she owned any property besides the cow. Karen looked at her children as if she would ward off some evil from them. Many a day that drop of milk was all she could give them for supper! "No," she answered, "we've nothing else, God knows. But—it will be all right." At that a faint smile twisted one corner of Ebbe's mouth; then he resumed his devotions.

The witnesses duly signed. The cow's name was Kranslin; at present she was out at grass. He mentioned the date when he would come and fetch the animal unless the debt and the costs had been paid by. then. And Karen had to scrawl her name in the book, as Kal was not present to do so.

"Good-by." Ebbe shook hands again, put on his hat, slung the knapsack with the register over his shoulder, took his stick, and departed, followed by the witnesses.

As Kal came lurching up the hills that evening four flaxen-haired urchins rushed down to meet him, shouting all together that Ebbe—Ebbe had been there! And soon he was coming again to fetch Kranslin!

"Ah, well, never mind," said Kal, soothingly; "your mother won't have all that bother with milking then."

Those children seemed to have come into the world all atop of one another; only a year between Anders, Oluf, and Paulina, then two babies had died, and then had come Siri, who was only just six years old now.

He took her by the hand, and, bending down, breathed on her little fist as though he were afraid of its getting cold. But when he reached home, and had heard the whole story from Karen, he sat silent on his stool, and his face grew long. His under lip drooped more and more. He had to call Siri to come and sit on his knee: that dratted little thing had such a way with her old dad!

Ride a cockhorse to Banbury Cross . . . sowing-time now . . . and they had no seed-corn. Ride a cockhorse . . . yes, and they ought to plant the potato patch, but they had n't any seed-potatoes. Ride a cock . . . and now the cow was going too!

"I 'll have to go out bread-making as I did before," Karen suggested.

Kal was still riding with little Siri to Banbury Cross. He was thinking that his old woman had her hands full enough looking after the house and the children, but somehow she got time to run round to folks' houses to make their bannocks; six cents a day she earned, and that was something, anyhow. The children had to muddle along as best they could without her; when their mother came home in the evening she had just time to hustle them off to bed; then she could wash and darn and patch in peace till late on in the night.

"Everything will be all right," she murmured as she stood watching her husband and the little girl.

Kal got up and went out to fetch his ax and rope: he might as well take a look round and see if he could find any wood, he said.

Sawing up logs with a pit-saw day after day was the thing to take it out of a man. The folks he worked for always made him stand on the platform at the top; and the man at the top had to pull with all his strength to drag the saw up, and push with all his strength to get it down again. The man who stood underneath at the other end of the saw could at any rate hang on to it by his arms when pulling it down, and that helped, gave one a rest, as it were. But after a time the work made Kal's back and stomach ache terribly, pulling the saw up, up, up, and pushing down, down, down, down through those huge logs. He was tired by evening, and no mistake. Then there was the long tramp home. And now he had to take his ax and rope and set off again up the hills. The sun was going down in the west; 't was getting to be summer up here on the moors.

To-night he went about cutting birch twigs for brooms.

The storekeeper paid one cent for each broom, and that was one cent better than none. By sunrise a huge load was on its way downhill; it consisted of brooms fastened together in an enormous pack, with a rope round it and two sagging legs underneath.

Halfway down the hills he stopped, let his burden slip to the ground, almost straightened out his back, and looked the sun straight in the face. Nobody was stirring yet; there was no smoke rising from the houses. The snow mountains in the west were reflected in the fiord, the windows were blazing. The air smelt nice, he thought—of juniper, and heather, and leaves.

Kal sank down, rested his back and head against the load of brooms, closed his eyes, and sensed the warm red sunshine on his face. He must have had forty winks then, for he dreamed he was in heaven. He was standing before God Himself, who told him to choose the thing he wanted most. Kal asked first that he might lie down on the hay in a barn and sleep for six months or so. And secondly he asked for a Sunday dress for Karen, and for a pair of trousers for each of the boys, so that they need n't be ashamed to attend school.

At last he started up. Lines of smoke were rising up from the houses in the valley now: and to-day he had to go out sawing again. The two-legged load went heaving down toward Skaret.

Karen was already up, and making what she called coffee for him. But the powder she put in the coffee-kettle was really nothing but potato-cake, burned quite black and ground fine with a stone. "You must wait and have a cup too, now you 're here," she said to Kal. . . .

One evening later in the summer the clergyman heard somebody fumbling with the latch of his study door.

"Come in. . . . What! is it you, Kal Skaret? And

what's the trouble to-day?" The broad-shouldered parson
with his long gray beard and bald red forehead leaned back
in his chair by the writing-table and waited.

Kal tugged the red knitted cap off his head and scratched
the bristly tuft under his chin; to-day his knees seemed to
sag more than ever, and he loooked the picture of helpless-
ness.

"It . . . it's only . . . that I'm simply at my wits' end.
Ebbe's been up and taken the cow to-day. We only had
one."

"I see." The clergyman cleared his throat and looked
at Kal, then through the window. "Yes, I've heard that you
find it difficult to make ends meet, but . . ." and the reverend
gentleman went on looking through the window. Lending
money to Kal was the same as giving it. Ought he to do
that? There were so many who came here and complained.
He turned and looked at Kal. When a clergyman could not
give money, at any rate he could give comfort and advice.

"Well, Kal Skaret, I would have you remember that God
sends us trials and punishments. Are you sure that you have
not deserved all this? You haven't got a very good name
in the parish, have you?"

Kal looked down at his cap and shook his head; he would
never dream of such a thing as contradicting the parson.
There was a pause. But all of a sudden the clergyman
bowed his head, covered his face with his hands, and breathed
heavily. What was the matter? Was he ill? Kal waited
and waited; at length he turned to go. At that the clergyman stood up, looking for all the world as though he were
ashamed of something. He came forward and held out his
hand.

"Forgive me, Kal." Kal stared in blank astonishment.
What! He to forgive the parson! "Yes, my man, forgive
me. It is easy enough to preach and admonish. But if
some of us had to bear your burdens, perhaps our reputation

would not be much better.   Sit down, Kal; let's talk it over together."

Kal sank down on a chair, though he felt quite unworthy to do so, in his patched trousers.   The clergyman was walking slowly up and down the room.

"Well, Kal, you're at your wits' end, you say?"   Kal sighed.   Yes, that was just what he was.   Though he'd never shirked work, either. . . .   "No, no; I understand that. But as things are now I suppose you are too much in debt. Even if you work yourself to death it won't help.   It's not your fault.   But . . . but I can see one way out.   What do you say to going to America?"

Kal looked up and almost laughed.   America?   That was somewhere beyond the clouds.

The clergyman continued: "You know Erik Foss, perhaps.   He is going back soon and wants to take some handy fellows with him.   He can get several hundred acres of first-rate land gratis.   Wouldn't that be just the thing for a hard-working man like yourself, Kal?   Think if you woke up one day, on the prairie, to find yourself the owner of a farm bigger than Lindegaard itself!"

Kal could not repress a grin at that.   Did the parson drink? he wondered.

"You must think it over, Kal.   I will have a talk with the American.   Of course you would take your wife and children with you: that'll be a help.   As for the passage money, I expect Erik Foss would lend the necessary money to a few men whom he specially wanted to have with him. I will talk to him about that, too.   If he won't we must try to get you a loan from somewhere else.   For I feel sure you would pay it back when you found yourself in a position to do so."

Kal raised his yellowish-brown eyes for a moment to the clergyman's face.   His brain reeled more and more; he wanted to run away.

"All right. Now go to the kitchen and get some food. Here's a dollar for you; you can send it back to me when you become a landowner."

The clergyman slapped him on the shoulder with his big white hand and chuckled. Then he said a word or two to some one in the sitting-room. Kal made his escape through the door, feeling as though he had had a glass or two more than was good for him.

V

All the talk now was of the expedition to America, and of how Erik Foss was going to take such and such a one with him. But those who met and questioned the American could get uncommonly little out of him. Was it true that Morten Kvidal was going? And Anton Noreng—Mother's Darling? Erik thought a moment, and answered that he was not sure yet. And was it true that the colonel wanted to send Ola Vatne with him when he came out of prison? Erik shook his head. What about Jo Berg, the feckless teacher who never could get a job at any school because he did n't believe as he ought to? Erik Foss only hummed and hawed. And what about Kal Skaret and his wife and kids? Yes, that was quite settled: they were just the kind of people he wanted. And Per Föll? Settled too. "Ah, it's easy enough for folks who can get you to pay their passage money!" But Erik Foss did not understand; he merely changed the subject.

One Sunday later on in the spring the church-goers received a terrific shock: the parson published the banns of marriage between Per Föll, the farmer's son, and Anne Gunnarsdatter Ramsöy, spinster.

The congregation simply could not believe their ears. They stared in blank astonishment; but the parson did not take it back. Moreover, Per himself was sitting there, with that big curly head of his, giving himself airs and agreeing to it all. Surely *he* was n't going to marry the prettiest girl in the whole parish! A fellow who was always mixing himself up with politics and newspapers, for all the world as though he were a member of parliament; and he a freethinker, too! Stuff and nonsense, all of it. And now he was going to marry one of the Ramsöy girls. It was impossible!

They turned to stare across at the women's side of the church, where Anne was sitting. She was hanging her head and would not look up. No wonder, either. Her sister Bergitta was sitting there, too, and she was looking down as though she were ashamed of something. She was thinking of the confession Anne had made to her only the day before. The doctor's son, that reckless boy Klaus Broch, was just such another as her sister; and now Anne had to conceal her shame by running away to America with Per.

Bergitta tried to realize what this would mean. To travel so far, and have adventures, and see so much, was exciting enough to tempt anybody, the very thing for Anne. She even felt tempted to go herself. My word! how different from being stuck here, where everything went on in exactly the same way forever! She'd heard of people who had gone to America with nothing but their two bare hands, and had grown so rich over there that they drove about in glass carriages. No chance of that here. So perhaps Anne was the luckiest of the lot of them, even if she did have to marry Per.

Morten Kvidal had made up his mind at last. He had been to the bank one day to ask for money to start a proper joiner's workshop straight away. He wasn't going to set up in a small way by himself; it was such slow work and you never made any profit to speak of. What he wanted was to make money, the money he needed for Kvidal. On the other hand, if he settled down now on his little farm and tried to put more land under cultivation, creeping along a quarter of an acre at a time, it would take him all his life. A scrap of land added each year, but still no money to build new houses; he simply hadn't the patience for that, and Helena still less. The bank had not refused, provided he could find

good sureties. But who would stand surety for the son of
a man who had committed forgery and hanged himself?
He could n't bring himself to go round and beg them to do
it. Another way closed to him!

Subsequently he had another talk with the girl. "Will
you wait for me if I go to America for three or four years?"
he asked her. "Three or four years? What a terribly long
time! Oh, don't go, Morten!" "Will you come with me,
then?" What! to America? She could never get leave to
do that. Morten left her, feeling ready to cry.

He strode up and down outside the farm, raging inwardly.
The girl was as proud as a peacock, always so high and
mighty, always making him eat humble-pie. But now he 'd
show her: he 'd go to America all the same. He must take
the plunge sometime, if he ever wanted to get on in life.
Poverty on a small farm was little better than slow torture.
There was nothing for it but to go now, stay out there for
two, three, perhaps even four years, and then come back as a
rich man.

But it pained him to look at his mother after he had told
her of his decision. He began to lie awake at night, worried by the thought that he was running away from a battle
that he ought to have fought to a finish at home. It was
such an uprooting; it meant tearing himself away from that
which, after all, was his home, and for four whole years—a
long time! And what about Helena?

One evening he took his brother Simen round the fields.
The lad was hardly grown up yet, but he was the eldest of
the brothers and would have to take his place from now on.
Morten had never told him about all his plans for improving
Kvidal, but to-day he pointed to the large field on the other
side of the river, which his father had secured when he
bought his holding: the whole of this field had got to be
cleared and plowed up. There were seventy acres in all and
the soil was first-rate; it was full of stones and stumps of

trees, of course, but he 'd seen people farm worse land. He
wanted Simen to start at such and such.a place, hire laborers,
clear and plow, using the money he would send home from
time to time. The fair-haired, sturdy young fellow stared at
his brother: these were great plans indeed! If they could
one day bring all that land under the plow they could keep
fifty cows and ten or twelve horses; that would be a really
big farm, and no mistake! It sounded almost too good to
be true, but Morten was no fool.

And before they went indoors Morten showed him the
site where the new buildings were to stand. Here would be
the large outhouses, of such and such a length, with the byre
in the middle, and the stable and barn forming two wings,
the whole painted red, with white barge-boards and window-
sills. And here in front of the old farm-house would be the
new one, of such and such a length, having a kitchen at each
end with a bedroom behind it, living-rooms in the middle,
and a row of rooms upstairs. It would be a handsome building, painted white, with a garden in front, and the flagstaff
placed just there, towering high above everything. They
forgot all about the little gray houses; all they could see was
the big farm. "You must do your bit while I 'm away," said
Morten, "and I 'll do mine when I come back."

Berit Kvidal cried a good deal, especially when she was
alone. Ever since her husband's sad death Morten had been
her mainstay, and now he was going to leave her. For a
long time the boy had been like a mine, and now the powder
had exploded. For several days she was in despair; but that
state of mind never lasted long, and it ended in her wiping
her eyes and looking away from her trouble, when, as usual,
she discovered something more cheerful. Had n't she pulled
through all right when the children were younger? And now
Simen was virtually grown up, anyway; they 'd manage to
rub along somehow. Four years was not a lifetime, and she
did n't suppose she 'd die just yet.

And what if he came back rich?   Supposing it all turned
out like one of her mother's wonderful tales!   He was only
a poor lad from Kvidal, but he'd climb to the top of the tree
yet.   As she sat by the window of an evening and watched
the red-and-gray cloud-lands above Blaaheia, she could see
it all before her.   Well, Morten was being fitted out now
from top to toe,—woolen gloves, socks, shirts,—and she was
so busy that she had to sit up working half the night.

Meanwhile gossip was busy with a fresh sensation.   Erik
Foss was living with his mother, Scraggy Olina, in a little
house high up on the hillside, and a neighbor declared that
he had seen Miss Else, the colonel's daughter, come stealthily
out of the wood one evening and go into the house.   Now,
what might that mean?   Unable to restrain their curiosity,
more than one had asked Erik whether it was true.   Erik
shook his head: how could people make up such stories?

But one thing was quite certain: the colonel had been to
town and had had a talk with Ola Vatne.   And it was also
certain that Ola was going with Erik to America, so now
they'd make a man of him too.   As for Miss Else, she had
just been invited up to the north of Norway to stay with her
uncle the judge, and that would be the best thing for all
concerned.   She was very busy preparing for her journey,
and went about singing in quite her old spirits.

Even up at Skaret, where old Kal lived, there was going
to be an auction before he left!   The very idea of this made
people laugh, for what on earth could Kal find to sell?   However, the neighbors put on their Sunday best and set off
to see; and Ebbe himself was not above coming to hold the
auction.

Now, it is astonishing what will turn up when you start
clearing out a house; there is always something which will
fetch a cent or two.   Here there was the sledge upon which
Kal had dragged home so many loads of wood, a wheelbarrow,
a spade and a fork, a calf, two sheep, a griddle, a coffee-

kettle and two saucepans, two beds and some bedclothes, some tables, and a trough in which Karen had mixed cakes on the rare occasions when she had any flour. Some one bid twelve cents for the lot. "Too little," said Ebbe. "Fourteen cents . . . that's better . . . twenty-four . . . ah, that's more like! thirty . . . bid up, good folks!"

But most of them had come to have a last look at Kal; and though he owed many of them money or goods, they said no more about it. They only remembered all the logs he had sawed up for them, all the loads of firewood he had hauled home at night, all the good stories he had spread abroad even when things looked blackest up at Skaret; and they felt they must go and shake his hand once again.

He was standing at the edge of the crowd, with some of his old pals of Lofoten days round him, grimacing, chuckling, and talking about America as if he had lived there for years. "The earth over there is so rich that you can eat it instead of cream-porridge; and when you sow oats or barley, up come sweet apples or a crop of oranges. The potatoes are as yellow as the yoke of an egg, and taste like raisins, and you can get a square meal whenever you want it for the trouble of stepping outside your door." His friends guffawed, and Ebbe had to call for silence.

God knows where Kal had hunted up that faded homespun suit he had on to-day; it actually was quite whole and clean. He'd a thick woolen comforter round his neck, too, and a sheepskin cap on his head—rather hot for a day in July, but you had to wear something, after all. They were not accustomed to see him decently dressed, still less to see him idle on a week-day. Even Karen had on a black woolen dress, with a sort of brooch at her throat. In the end the older women solved the riddle: 'twas the selfsame dress and finery she'd worn as a bride, and she and Kal must both have hidden their wedding clothes every time they expected a visit from Ebbe.

In the room at the back Karen had spread an apology for a cloth on a table, and was treating her special friends to real coffee and white bread. But where had the money come from? They must have got Erik Foss to lend them a few cents on the quiet. By and by it was whispered that no less a personage than the farmer's wife from Bergheim was on her way to the auction; what would Karen do now? In some magic way she produced a dark shawl with a sprinkling of red spots on it,—immediately recognized by the women as another trophy from her wedding-day,—put it round her, and hurried out to welcome and shake hands with this important guest. Not that she had much to thank her for, but one must n't forget one's manners. "Won't you come inside?" she asked, feeling very generous and hospitable to-day.

They must have got a few cents somehow; or was it because Miss Else from Dyrendal had been there one evening? Why, even the children were running about in new shoes and new clothes, the boys in gray and the girls in blue, the boys wearing new peaked caps and the girls red kerchiefs with pictures of Bismarck and Moltke on them—the sort rich folk blew their noses with! They were full of secrets to-day; Paulina and Siri had quite made up their minds about one thing: they were certainly going to take the black-and-white cat with them to America. Ever since they started turning the place upside down and getting ready for the journey she 'd done nothing but mew and take on, and she would n't touch her food, either; poor pussy! she knew very well what they were up to! She should n't be sold at the auction, no she should n't; and the two little girls kept her safely out of the way.

There were other things that the boys, Oluf and Anders, were sorry to leave, such as the ax they both had used for chopping up sticks. A thing like that, which you hold in your hand every day, has a face of its own; it is more than an acquaintance, it is a friend. And now it had to come under the hammer and be sold; a pity, but it couldn't be helped.

The biggest hammer, on the other hand, which Father had had for mending boots—when there were any boots in the family—and which they themselves had used for all sorts of purposes, was a different matter. They had plotted together to abstract this treasure and take it with them to America. Kal had hunted high and low without finding it, for the boys had hidden it in the rocks above the house.

Among the crowd at the auction might be seen a shriveled-looking man who was Kal's brother Sivert; he was younger than Kal, but looked even more weather-beaten and seedy; he was gray-headed and blear-eyed, and wore leaden rings in his ears. He was going to take over his brother's croft, and carry on the same life in the little gray house.

At length the day came for Erik and his party to leave. It was August now, and the hay had just been gathered; the corn-fields rippled in green and yellow waves, and the fiord shone like a mirror—not an easy day on which to say good-by to one's native place. Just as the cart with the two emigrant chests was ready to drive away from Skaret, Kal discovered that his children had all vanished—dang the brats! He shouted, swore, and ran to and fro looking for them. At last Paulina's voice answered from the rocks above: "The cat's dead."

"Well, what the devil does that matter? You come along, double-quick!"

All the same, it was some time before they did come, for they were just in the middle of the cat's funeral. They had found her dead that very morning; it sounded strange, but it was true, all the same. The boys had dug a grave, and in this they laid pussy, with heather both under and over to make it nice and soft for her; then they sang a little, as well as they could, while they shoveled earth upon the deceased.

A branch did duty for a gravestone. Up among these rocks the children had often built little houses out of the stones; here, too, they had found cranberries, bilberries, and crowberries; once they had even flushed a grouse. It was hard to say good-by to all this. When at length they came down, the eldest boy, Anders, looked rather bulgy about the left side: he had stuffed the hammer into his coat pocket.

Old and young alike said a last farewell to Skaret. When they had got some way down the hills they looked back at the little gray houses tucked under the bare gray rocks. There, at any rate, was something that they knew; but what lay ahead of Kal and his family was hidden in impenetrable mist.

Down at the landing-stage a number of their friends were waiting to say good-by. It was not every day that a whole family left the parish, and now that they were going away forever, more than one felt that he might have helped them a little oftener when they were in difficulties.

But Kal bustled about the beach and carried trunks on board for all the world as though he were off for a jaunt to the town. Karen stood still, looking back at the gray houses at Skaret. Presently she saw smoke rising from the chimney; her sister-in-law had lighted the first fire on the hearth. "Poor thing!" Karen murmured.

Erik Foss stood looking calmly on, but his little shriveled mother held the corner of her kerchief to her eyes all the time. Per Föll was there, too, with his young wife Anne; the huge fellow looked as though he would like to pick her up and carry her: in his eyes the girl was far too good to tread on the ground. Per's bearded face was radiant; he had won her at last! And who should be there but Jo Berg the schoolmaster. So he was really off to America, after all! His wizened old parents were standing near the boat-house, moping; the lad had certainly not been much of a comfort to them. And did you ever! There was Anton

Noreng, Mother's Darling! Was he going to set to work in earnest at last?

On the road above appeared Morten Kvidal, walking beside the cart; Simen was on the other side and their mother was riding in it. The little dun-colored highland mare that he had bought as a foal three years before was badly knee-sprung and its brisk little hoofs went *clip-clap! clip-clap!* Now that the parting had come, they must try to talk cheerfully; otherwise everything would be too difficult. Still Morten could not help thinking all the time about the grindstone behind the barn at Kvidal; folks might call it nonsense, but there was no getting away from it: the grindstone was a real friend. And he'd forgotten to go round to the back and take a last farewell look at it.

"You'd better sow oats in the north field next spring," he said to Simen in as every-day a voice as he could command. And his brother answered in the same tone that he would. "You've enough socks and underclothing for a year or two to come, I'm thinking," observed Berit in an equally matter-of-fact voice. Morten was sure he had, though it would rather depend on whether he was farming or doing joiner's work indoors.

After that they all remained silent for a few minutes. The little horse tripped along steadily, and soon reached the boat-houses where the others were standing. Then, with a little gulp Berit said to Morten, "You'll write, won't you?"

"Yes," answered Morten, looking down and clenching his teeth; it would never do to show any emotion. And yet his voice shook a little as he added, "Of course I will, Mother."

Then he noticed that Helena and her father and mother had accompanied Anton down to the landing-stage. He winced, and only nodded slightly in that direction; he felt he could not bear to talk to her to-day.

A boat was waiting to take the passengers on board, and the women-folks were already tucking up their skirts to step into it; Berit could stand the strain no longer: she tottered back to the little dun mare, and sank down on the cart. She did not even look when the boat put off, and although she knew they were waving, she could not bring herself to wave back.

As Morten stepped into the boat a wet nose touched his face, the Lapland dog King, which had been shut up in the house, had somehow managed to escape and run after them, but had kept in the background till now. "There, there, old man, run along home; Simen's calling you!"

Kal, of course, helped to row the boat, for he could never see an oar without wanting to row with it. He screwed up his face and pulled as though his life depended on it; rowing was his specialty and he might n't get another chance for a long time. Erik Foss stood on a pile of chests and waved his hat to the shriveled little woman on the beach; though she was only Scraggy Olina, she was his mother, after all. The boat had a strangely empty look when it returned. Mothers and fathers, brothers, sisters, and friends remained standing on the beach, gazing after the steamer as it disappeared down the fiord.

Morten Kvidal, who was standing at the side of the ship, saw that Helena was up near the boat-houses; she was waving: was it only to her brother? At any rate, he waved back. He saw his mother and Simen get into the cart and drive away; that little mare was as lively on her legs as ever; they were going home to Kvidal now. Then he caught sight of King tearing along the shore of the bay and barking at the ship. Every now and again the dog would stop and utter long-drawn howls; and then he would set off again. He had noticed the promontory farther on, where the ship had to pass quite near, and was making for that; had the dog lost his wits? On he raced round the bay and out on the rocks, drawing rapidly nearer and nearer; he disappeared into a gully, reappeared, and reached the end of the

promontory just as the steamer was approaching it. Here
he sat down and began howling again; could he have picked
out his friend among all the other passengers?

Morten did not know what to do; he wanted to shout to
the dog and tell him to go home, but his voice failed him.
The deck was crowded with people watching this furry
Lapland dog who was behaving in such a strange manner.
Suddenly the animal gave a leap from the rock and plunged
head foremost into the sea; he went under, came up again,
shook his head, and began swimming toward the ship.
Morten was in despair. The steamer plowed relentlessly
past; already the dog's head was far astern. He was yelping
and struggling on bravely—but Morten turned and walked
away under the upper deck to avoid seeing any more.

VI

The big passenger liner was lying alongside the quay in Bergen, but the screaming of the winches had stopped and the last few emigrants were filing across the gangway, laden with their miscellaneous belongings. A motley crowd of straw hats, summer dresses, and shawls thronged the first- and second-class decks in the broiling sunshine, but the heat did not seem to penetrate the thick homespun clothing of the peasants in the steerage. Some of these country folks had come across the mountains from Valdres and Hallingdal, others hailed from the outlying islands or the inner fiords, and the gaily colored costumes which most of them wore matched the brightly painted wooden boxes and chests they had brought with them.

Erik Foss's party had come to Bergen that night by the south-bound coast steamer, and now stood huddled together in a group apart, overawed by the sight of so much that was new to them. The two or three days that they had traveled together had made them feel like one large family, for their homes were in the same parish, they were bound for the same destination in a far-off land, and they would have to share good and evil fortune alike. The schoolmaster, the parish clerk's son, and the crofter were all equal now; Karen Skaret was as good as Anne from the big farm at Ramsöy; and even Ola Vatne, who was only just out of prison, seemed to be quite at his ease among them. He looked rather paler than the others, after his long confinement, but cheery and self-confident, and nobody could guess from the look of him that he had done anything to be ashamed of.

When he joined them on board they hailed him at once

as an old friend—"Hullo! are you here too, Ola?"—and they
shook his hand as warmly as if he had just come back from
a long journey. "I'm glad you're coming along with us,"
Per Föll said in his kind-hearted way. The only one who was
a little distant was Anton Noreng, who for the fun of the
thing had helped the sheriff to pursue Ola up hill and down
dale like a hunted beast of prey.

It seemed that while he was in prison Ola had learned to
write and do arithmetic, so now he was almost a match for
those who had been at the county school. At present he
was watching the gangway as if he were waiting for somebody; but whom could he be waiting for in Bergen? They
looked at Erik Foss, who was standing a little way off, talking to Morten Kvidal. He was just saying that this was the
last voyage the Bergen Line would make to America: the
Thingvalla and White Star lines had simply knocked the
Norwegian company into a cocked hat, and in future many
people would prefer to travel by way of England instead.
Erik was taller than most of the men, and had the air of a
self-reliant and experienced traveler. If any of his party
questioned him he twirled his brown mustache and was ready
at once with answers and advice to them all.

The ship's bell rang for the third time and the gangway
was about to be hauled in when another passenger hurried
up, a young woman in a dark dress, with a black silk kerchief
on her head, followed by a hotel porter carrying a big trunk.
Erik's party stared in blank astonishment. Surely it
wasn't . . . ? But Ola Vatne was waving his hat and
laughing. "I'm blest if it isn't, though!" gasped the schoolmaster, and Karen Skaret murmured, "Did you ever!"

The young woman glanced quickly round the crowd,
caught sight of Ola, and brightened up. So there was no
mistake about it: she really *was* the young lady from
Dyrendal! And now she came across the deck to them and
shook hands, first with Ola, to whom she gave a beaming

smile and said a few words in a low voice, and then with the others.

"Yes, I'm coming, too," she said; "I hope you don't mind?"

They stared at her in dumb surprise; Kal Skaret scratched his head under the sheepskin cap, and at last blurted out, "We thought you were on a visit up north, miss!"

"Yes, a good many people thought so," she answered with a smile; then, to put an end to the mystery, she added: "Ola and I are going to be married."

A pause. They hardly dared to look at one another. "Well, I suppose one can get married in America, too," the schoolmaster remarked, trying to be humorous.

"Yes, but Ola and I are going to be married on board."

Another pause. "But is there any clergyman on the ship?" asked Anne, at last.

"I don't know; but, in any case, the captain can marry us as soon as we're out at sea."

The men and women looked down, up, at one another, and finally at Erik Foss; but he merely smiled, and did not seem to be quite so surprised as they were.

"Well, I'm sure we're all very glad you're coming along with us," Karen Skaret said, holding out her hand, and the others agreed.

"Thank you, and you must try to put up with me and take me as I am," she said, looking from one to another with a smile.

There was not much of the colonel's daughter about her now. Her plain dark dress and the silk kerchief on her head showed that she had made up her mind to dress like a peasant woman from now on. But Karen glanced at her slender white hands, and then at Ola. "The young scapegrace!" she thought.

"What are they saying?" asked little Siri, squeezing her

father's hand. Kal bent down and whispered, "We're going to have a wedding on board, little lass!"

The liner began to move, and a snow-storm of fluttering handkerchiefs burst over the crowd on the ship and the quay. A babel of voices repeated again and again the words, "Good-by! Good luck! Good-by!" and sobbing could be heard both on land and on board.

Slowly the great vessel glided out into the harbor, to the strains of the band on the upper deck. Here and there a passenger was leaning over the side, gazing back at the shore as though he meant to jump overboard; for even now the great decision could still be unmade. But little by little the crowd on land diminished into a dark line which was fast breaking up. Then the red-roofed town melted into the mountains, and the ship glided out among the islands, past fishermen's huts and country houses on jutting spits or in little green bays. At last the open sea itself came into sight, its smooth oily surface traversed by a path of fire from the red sun which was just sinking low amid golden clouds in the west.

Kal Skaret's children kept close beside their mother, and she held on to as many of them as she could, while they gazed out across the ocean. Where were they all going? Thank goodness she had Kal with her!

As for Kal, he was strolling about the deck, his red woolen comforter round his neck and his sheepskin cap a little on one side, with the air of one who had to keep an eye on everything. He grinned at a couple of longshoremen who were standing spellbound, with a painted wooden box in each hand and their knapsacks still on their shoulders; very likely they'd sleep the night like that and turn up in the same rig to-morrow morning! Well, well, that was their lookout; as for him, he had been to the Lofotens and had seen how folks ought to do things on a voyage.

He sidled up to Ola Vatne, to ask that young rascal a question on the sly without Miss Else hearing it: "I say, does the colonel know anything about this?" Ola chuckled and answered in an undertone: "No, he thinks she's on a visit in the north of Norway. But I reckon she'll have written home to tell about it all."

Per's young bride, Anne, was standing at the side of the ship, gazing with dreamy, wistful eyes at the red path of light on the sea. Somehow she could not believe in the reality of all this: she had only to burst out laughing, or cry, or shut her eyes and sleep it off. She looked round at Per; surely it was only make-believe! But Ola Vatne was there, too, and he'd brought his fiddle with him. And Morten Kvidal was standing next to her; he didn't seem to have said a word to a soul since they left.

Babies were already crying in the cabins below, and when the mate went by, anxious voices asked: "Is it going to be rough? What's the best cure for seasickness?" Else had been down to find out where her berth was. There were five others in her cabin, and you could have cut the air with a knife! She sighed, but endeavored to smile. A new life had begun, and the spoiled young lady must be prepared to rough it now.

When the distant line of mountains began to sink into the sea a strange feeling seized everybody on board. They were losing their hold on the land, and ahead of them lay the wide ocean. Their country would stay behind, while they themselves passed on into the unknown; but what of home, of mother and father? Even Jo Berg looked depressed now, though at other times he went about boasting that he had turned his back on his rotten country forever—no more Norway for *him!* His pipe had gone out and he quite forgot to light it again; he was thinking of his shriveled old mother and his tall, white-bearded father. They had come down to the landing-stage with him and had actually been sorry to lose him, though he had always gone against their wishes in everything.

A faint shadow still darkened the horizon; soon that too would vanish. When would they see their country again? Men and women stood straining their eyes to catch a last glimpse; they climbed on boxes and bales to see better, and mothers lifted up their children. "Look, look! the last sight of Norway!" A lump rose in many a throat; it was bad enough to part from one's mother and father, but this was almost worse.

The band struck up the national anthem. One or two began to sing and soon the whole ship joined in, their voices hymning it slowly and sadly, as though they were in church. Singing had never been in Kal Skaret's line, but he felt that the occasion required him to do something. "H'sh!" he said to the children, who were standing perfectly still. "H'sh! don't you hear they're singing?" And to keep them quiet—though they were as quiet as mice already—he gave them some buns with which he had filled his pockets before leaving Bergen.

Then the last trace of old Norway faded away in the distance, and the great liner with its strange freight of human destinies steamed on across the golden evening sea as the sun dipped in the west.

BOOK II

I

"Get up!" Erik Foss would shout to his oxen as he drove across the prairie at the head of his caravan of six wagons. Thereupon Kal Skaret would call out, "Get up!" to his own beasts, for he knew that this meant they had to push on a bit faster. "You damned rascal!" Erik would yell at the off bullock, cracking his whip over its back; and immediately Kal would roar, "You damned rascal!" at one of his, proudly conscious that he was calling it a lazy devil. And in this way Kal picked up a good deal of English. He found that the oxen in America had a number of different names, such as Jim and Buck and Tom; but, for all that, he secretly nicknamed one of his own "Ebbe."

They were traveling over the wide plain of the Red River Valley, with nothing anywhere in sight but sky and level ground under the burning glare of the sun. Kal was seated in the front of his wagon, still wearing his sheepskin cap and thick woolen comforter, with little Siri perched beside him in her blue dress and red kerchief. Folks said there were rattlesnakes in these parts, so he thought it best to keep her near him. Five of the wagons were emigrant prairie-schooners of the ordinary type, a little four-wheeled house with a canvas cover. Inside was a small room with a stove, and here Karen could sit with her sewing and darning, while Oluf and Paulina sat on the bed and repeated their Bible history to her; it really wouldn't do to idle away the time day after day.

Behind them came Per Föll's team, but he himself sat inside, looking after a black-haired baby with brown eyes,

71

a lively little creature which had made its appearance that winter in Wisconsin. Anne and Else were walking together beside the wagon, their heads swathed in kerchiefs to keep the mosquitos off, their faces tanned dark brown and blistered by the sun.

It seemed strange to them that they had had so little to do with each other in the old country. Nowadays they always had so much to talk about, and Else could not help wondering why Anne had had such a bad reputation before she married. Of course she had high spirits, but she never said anything silly, could talk very sensibly indeed, and tried to learn what she could from her friend. Both of them were tall and slender, they were just the same age, and they both had to make the best of the strange life to which Fate had called them. Just now they were exchanging reminiscences of their girlhood, and finding plenty to laugh at. Now and then Jo Berg would come and join them; he seemed to be rather hanging about Else, lately. "You 're a peasant woman now," he said to her, "but you have n't learned to talk like one yet."

"No; I think I might be allowed to speak in my own way."

"Ola's countrified talk is n't good enough for a colonel's daughter, eh?"

"Of course it is, but I think my own is good enough for me, all the same."

"What does Ola say to that?"

"He says it 's nobody's business but ours."

Ola Vatne sat in the front of his wagon, singing softly to himself. He had got a black eye in a fight outside the lodging-house where they had camped for the night; not that it was his fault, even Else admitted that, but the two damned Yankees had picked a quarrel with him. It was n't all plain sailing, though, to be married to a gentleman's daughter, for almost everything one did seemed to be wrong, even if she did n't say it in so many words. But no doubt he 'd have to go on thanking her all his born days for what she had done. Well, well! it could n't be helped; better sing and make the best of it.

> "Oh! Susanna, oh! don't you cry for me!
> I 'm goin' to California wid my banjo on my knee."

The oxen plodded along so slowly that the wheels scarcely seemed to turn. Anton Noreng and the schoolmaster owned a wagon and oxen together, and to begin with they meant to share a hut and farm the same piece of land. At present they were sitting inside, playing cards to pass the time. Behind them came Morten Kvidal, sitting with closed eyes for long periods; he had staked everything in a lottery, and now he could only wait and see what would turn up. Last of all came the baggage-wagon, loaded with all their scythes, harrows, plows, seed-corn, sacks of flour, planks, and tools. A couple of cows walked behind each wagon, with that important personage the bull behind the last. The emigrants would have no neighbors within a hundred miles of their new home, so it would not do to forget anything.

They had been in the country for nearly a year. During the autumn and winter they had worked in Wisconsin; the men had found employment at a sawmill, and the women had done washing and cooking for two or three families besides their own; they could n't get on without a little money, even if they were going to start life on the prairie with nothing better than sod huts and oxen. Then, a week ago, they had come on by rail to Northville, in Dakota, and, after making ready their outfits, had started on the long journey to their new home in the West. Where they were going, and when they would reach their destination, not one of them knew, but they left that to Erik.

For two or three days they had passed through Norwegian settlements; here they had seen much that seemed strange to them, but they had been able to talk Norwegian to all the people they met. They saw crippled veterans who had fought in the Civil War, and heard stories of Indians killing and burning in these very parts; that had been some years back of course, but—who knows?—they might make another raid. You could see that folks had not got over their fright even now. If the emigrants stopped to look at a church, they saw nothing but Norwegian names on the gravestones—an odd thing, when you came to think of it, but true all the same. Many an Ola, Per, Gunhild, or Maren had traveled all the way from the old country to find their last rest here. It gave the new-comers a homelike feeling; but they had still a long way to go.

Erik Foss sat whistling impatiently, with his straw hat pulled down over his eye. This was darned slow! An ox could never move a foot without thinking twice about it. Early in the spring he had gone on ahead of his party, to explore the country. He had had to go a long way before finding the best land, but what matter? Provided you began in the right place, the railway was bound to come and hunt you out before very long, and then flourishing settlements and towns would spring up; that always happened here now. Only, you had to be first in the field to secure the best land.

The settlements they were passing through to-day were becoming more and more scattered, and presently they would enter the wild prairie itself. A lonely farm could still be seen here and there, but even if the houses were two stories high, they looked hopelessly lost in the wide stretch of plowed land around them, and the lofty haystacks reared their heads in vain, for the vast surrounding plain seemed to flatten them to the ground. The settlers here were plowing with light-footed horses; yet they too had begun in the stone age, only a few years before, with nothing but oxen and sod huts. And now his own party was just entering upon the stone age.

Erik Foss whistled a tune; there was time and to spare for thinking. His thoughts went back to his childhood, when Scraggy Olina's little boy had had to go out minding the neighbors' goats from the time he began to clatter about in his little clogs; hungry and cold, bullied and beaten, he had soon learned to hit back, but had always been knocked about because the others were so much stronger than he. In later life he had often dreamed of revenge, but his plans had changed a good deal as the years went by. Revenge? Supposing he could manage to get other people in his power, would not that be a sort of revenge? Many a slave from the old country had founded a settlement in the wilds, built towns, hospitals, churches; it wasn't a new idea, but couldn't it be done again? But Erik would not found a kingdom of riffraff; no, much better to have boys and girls from the big farms at home, and then folks would say some day that they had grown rich by his help. Would not that be a sort of revenge? And now he had them there, driving in the wagons behind him, and his wonderful plan had succeeded.

Never had he dreamed that he would get one of the daughters from Ramsöy to come, still less a swell young lady from Dyrendal; yet there they were behind him, not in jest but in sober earnest. Was not *that* revenge? Already they were completely in his power, and he had to act the part of Providence toward them all. The money they had earned in the winter had not nearly paid for their outfit, so they had had to borrow from him; and why not? "Don't let that worry you," he always told them; "we shall all be rich one of these days." He merely wrote the name and amount in a little note-book, got them to sign it, and that was all.

His revenge? That could wait. Nobody else had been

initiated into his visions of the future—the towns and churches and high schools.   Why use three words where one would do?   But the queer part of it was, that the more he got these fellow-countrymen of his into his power, the more his triumph melted away; new, unsuspected forces welled up within him—concern for the children and untiring care of all the rest; plans and still more plans about every little detail, about what was best for each one of them.   He could not help laughing at the whole thing, but there it was. Well, there were more ways than one of taking one's revenge.

No more flocks of prairie-chickens rose now; he had noticed that these birds kept close to the cultivated land.   Nor were there any more of the blackbirds which devoured the farmers' corn.   It was so still here; not a sound to be heard but the soft rustle of the prairie wind.   A hare dashed off, arching its back, a rabbit scurried away to one side, a prairie-dog looked out of its burrow to yelp and swear at the intruders.   "Keep your eyes open!"   Erik shouted back to the emigrants; "there are rattlesnakes about where you see that little fellow."   Kal shouted to his youngsters to look sharp and get up into the wagon.

The sun's red disk was sinking slowly down toward the plain in the west; it was time to camp for the night, and as soon as they reached a stream Erik shouted, "Whoa!" to his oxen.   "Wo-o!" shouted Kal to his own team, knowing that this was the English for "pr-r-r!"   It stood to reason that one had to talk differently to American animals.   The wagons rolled up, the oxen were unyoked and, after being watered, began grazing on the prairie.   Certainly there was no lack of pasturage here.   One of Erik's oxen had been yoked with one of Kal's when they belonged to a previous owner; the two animals were still friends, and did not like being separated; so now they joined forces again, and after licking each other went off to graze a little apart from the rest.

"It's Anton's turn to fetch water for the women to-day," said Erik Foss. The men had to help with the cooking arrangements and to fetch water, but Mother's Darling always shirked, and Erik had made up his mind to put a stop to this. The three women had to milk their cows before they could attend to anything else. Morten, Erik, and the schoolmaster milked their own, Kal's work was to put on the kettles of porridge to boil for supper, the youngsters had to get out the plates and spoons, and, as the whole party ate together, it all worked out very fairly. But what about wood? There was not so much as a dry branch anywhere. "Where can we get something which will burn?"

"Get some dry prairie-grass and twist it into a rope," Erik called out from where he sat milking one of his cows. Here was a job for Kal and the children. Queer sort of firewood, though! But, sure enough, here was some old grass as dry as a bone, which they could twist and press tightly together. They would want a lot of it, though, if it were going to be of any use at all. "Look alive now, young uns!" said Kal.

At last everything was ready for supper; but instead of sitting down they stood staring about them. It struck them now for the first time that they had got so far out into the wild prairie that they could no longer see a soul. Every trace of man had vanished. Up to now they had followed two ruts worn by the wagons of the Hudson's Bay trappers who every year sent their caravans across the plains of the West. Now even these had disappeared. They stood stock-still, gazing at the scene; even the children from Skaret stared, finger in mouth. None of them but Erik had ever seen anything like this; they had never imagined that the earth could be so big or the sky so limitless.

Per Föll put his hand to his head, and all of them felt as if they were groping for something to hold on to. If only there had been a tree or a hill! But there was nothing but this ocean of earth, undulating in heavy, long-drawn waves, on and on into the blue distance, till the last wave spent itself somewhere beyond the sky-line. If they got lost here, no one would ever find them. Could they see a hundred miles westward, or was it more? Whichever way they turned, the view was the same; and the distance became greater and greater the longer they looked. They might travel on for days toward the horizon, and still it would remain as far away as ever.

The emigrants stood motionless and silent. The sun's fiery ball sank down toward the prairie sea and cast a red glow upon their faces. They seemed to be straining their eyes in a last frantic effort to see the mountains, fiords, and forests, the smiling lakes and green hillsides of their native land. But gaze as they would, they could not see them out here on the prairie. The vision of Norway which still lived on in their minds clashed with this desert plain, and made their brains reel more and more.

But the tide had carried them here, and it was too late to turn back. To-night they would sleep in this bewildering prairie desert, and to-morrow they would journey farther and farther on into it. Here they would live for the rest of their days. Here they would die when the time came. As for the old country, they would never see it again.

At length they sat down to their porridge, but no one seemed to have much appetite this evening. The women-folks climbed into the wagons to go to bed, and the men sat on, smoking, round the fire. For once Ola forgot to get out his bottle and give the others a drink. He sat gazing moodily into the fire. Else had been going about by herself all day without a word; what did she mean by that? The schoolmaster and Anton Noreng were discussing their favorite subject—how shockingly bad everything was in Norway, and how splendid everything was here. Morten did not contradict them, but his face wore a sarcastic expression; with Jo he always disagreed anyhow, while Anton was Helena's brother, and they rather kept each other at arm's length. When the sun sank below the horizon they heard a sad, plaintive singing in the far distance. "What sort of musician may that be?" asked Jo.

"It's the coyote, or prairie-wolf, which is a little smaller than the real wolves," Erik explained. "You'll often hear it howling like that at sundown."

The darkness was closing in rapidly; soon the great dome above them would be glittering with stars. Well, it was high time to go to bed. They usually slept under their wagons, rolled up in the warm sheepskin rugs which they had brought with them from home, their caps pulled down over their ears. Kal's two boys slept beside him. Tired after the long monotonous day, all soon closed their eyes and fell asleep. Overhead stretched a vast expanse of starry sky, and the prairie lay silent and still.

Presently the form of a woman came cautiously out of one of the wagons, moving with scarcely audible footsteps. It was Else. She had a shawl about her shoulders, and paused for a moment to gaze out into the darkness, then, making her way to what was left of the fire, she seated herself beside it and gazed into space again.

She could see nothing, except the faint glow of the embers and the myriads of stars above her; but what a relief to be quite alone!

Fate—what did fate mean? To be sitting here, thousands of miles from her own people, married to Ola the farm servant—surely that was fate? This everlasting plain made her feel so dizzy; it forced her to close her eyes and look for something she could lean upon. And what did she see then? The house at home, the hills and the lake. How she loved to recall it all now! She could see her father, too, and the happy days of her girlhood. Ola the farm servant —how had it all come about? And what did fate mean?

The colonel's daughter—yes, but country-bred all the same. She had lost her mother as a child, and had run about as she pleased in the woods and the fields, among the farm-hands and the animals. She had liked books, but it was much more fun to milk the cows. When her mother died, the grown-ups had mourned in their fashion and she in hers, but nobody had known how to talk to her about these things except one, and that one was Ola Vatne the goatherd. They used to go for walks on the hills, and the grown-ups said that the two children were playing together. Ah, that was all they knew about it! By and by she had become a young lady with a long plait hanging down her back, and he had become the farm servant. Ought they not to break it off now? Sometimes he had been wild and head-strong, but was not that because he feared that the rich farmers' sons would take her away from him? He had be-come a fiddler, but were not the gay or the plaintive strains of his violin a call to her?

Then she had had to go to the town, to schools, to dances. But what about the young men she met in the town? There was something she missed in all of them; what was it? They were too "townified," as if they had had no landscape behind them. Their character was marked out with a pair of compasses; their opinions were nothing more than the last newspaper article they had read, a set of mathematical rules for good and evil. It was like the plain—smoothed out, dull, and featureless. How could she help thinking of Ola? What did Ola stand for? Forest-clad hills, the note of the herdsman's horn, green slopes, tinkling bells, the scent of turf and leaves. That was how it had come about; at least, so it seemed to her now, as she sat here trying to unravel it all. With Ola she could really settle down and live her own life. Headstrong? But who would marry a man in whom there was nothing sheer, incalculable, dizzying?

The more she had seen all the obstacles mounting up,

the greater the temptation had become. Her father had
shown signs of wanting her to marry some one else—and
what came of it? The soldiers had hunted Ola like a wild
animal up hill and down dale—and what came of that?
She had seen him driven past her window in chains—and
what had happened then? If Ola had been drowning, and
she unable to swim, would not she have jumped in at
once to save him?

Everybody was asleep, in the wagons or under them.
The sky looked very wide and bright with stars, the night
was very still. She was beginning to see some things a little
more clearly, but fate—who could understand fate?

Well, she had run away from her father and her home
and had married Ola; what would come of that? What had
it cost her already? Her father had written to her once,
a horrified letter full of suppressed agony. He had retired,
his disgrace was the talk of the country-side, he had left
Dyrendal and had sold the house, her home, to a peasant.
She gazed ahead of her and sighed. Ah, it was too late
to repent now! There was nothing now but this immense
plain, the ever-receding prairie ocean, which would neither
shield nor support her, but forced her to shut her eyes and
flee away—only to meet all her troubles again. Would she
be strong enough to stand the strain out here?

Ola—what would it be like to be married to Ola for the
rest of her days? She sat motionless, staring into space.
The fire had gone out now; the sky looked supernaturally
vast. What a wonderful night, with all those stars! Ola?
How would it all end?

The sun lifted its glowing red disk above the horizon
again, and the coyote greeted another dawn with its melancholy wail. Inside the wagons cocks began to crow and
young pigs to grunt. Fancy having *them* here!

Another day. The caravan was in motion once more: the
prairie was steaming after the night-dew, shadows of oxen,

men, and wagons glided noiselessly alongside, Ola had started singing again. Wild ducks were quacking on a little pond. The wagons rolled along over the sea of grass; there was no trail now, perhaps no foot had ever trodden this path before. Erik was counting the section marks and looking at a map. Only a couple more days and they would be there.

The summer heat had set in, but the snows had melted so quickly that spring that large lakes had formed; the caravan had to go round them, and often the oxen sank deep in the mud and the wheels were in danger of sticking fast. "You damned rascal!" Kal would roar, cracking his whip over Ebbe. But Ola sang on unconcernedly.

How long had they been traveling, and when would they get there? Well, luckily they could trust Erik. Per Föll went and climbed up beside him, and this huge fellow with the prophet's beard looked strangely pale, as if on the point of fainting.

"Why, whatever's the matter?" Erik asked.

"For God's sake, tell me: aren't there any hills where we're going?"

It sounded like the cry of a drowning man. Erik smiled. "You'll get used to it, Per; don't you worry."

That night they were roused by the howling of prairie-wolves. Morten started up and seized his gun. The oxen and cows came running back to the wagons, then turned round and glared out into the darkness. It seemed strange to Morten to be standing there straining his eyes to catch sight of these wild animals—as if something deep down in his nature had found satisfaction at last. He was in his element now; he had been waiting for these howling wolves all along. Even when he was at Kvidal they had seemed to call him. What was this longing to see the world? He thought he could understand it better now.

The last day! The oxen lumbered meditatively along,

shoulder-high in the prairie-grass; they were wading in food all the way, and they tore off mouthfuls of it as they went. Away ahead, the grayish-yellow plain stretched on and on, a sea of grass rippling in the prairie wind. By and by they came to a belt of bare, light-gray earth, too alkaline for anything to grow there, and then to a plain of flowers— prairie-roses, lilies of many colors, an immense garden filling the air with its spicy scent. "Oh!" cried the women. Anne and Else could not resist the temptation to stay behind and pick some; they called to the others to wait, then ran after them with their arms full of flowers. "Is *our* place like this, Erik?" Erik looked round with a grin: "You wait and see." Larks were trilling high up in the blue sky above them. There were birds here, then, after all.

On again, and to-day they cut short their midday halt. Then at length Erik pointed with his whip and cried, "There it is!"

At last. They had reached the end of their journey.

Toward evening they halted; the wagons drove up, the oxen were let loose, and the emigrants stood looking about them. Was this the place? Had they really arrived at their new home? Not a house, not a tree, not a hill anywhere. Nothing but an ocean of earth with the sky above it, just as it had been all along. They had always thought that they would reach something definite. Surely it could not be here?

Now, for the first time, they seemed really to understand how far Erik Foss had taken them away from civilization. They looked at one another, then fixed their eyes on the interminable plain, unable somehow to grasp it. Was this really the place?

They made the usual camp-fire of prairie-grass, milked the cows, and then sat down to their customary supper of porridge. Nobody said much, and their eyes had a far-away look. In face of the vast distances that separated them from other human beings they seemed to huddle together for protection. From now on their next-door neighbor would be the endless plain. So this was where they had been washed ashore at last!

The yellow rim of the moon appeared above the sea of earth. At any rate the moon seemed to be the same here as in the old country.

They sat on round the fire for a while before they cleared away the pots and pans. To-morrow they were going to make a new beginning, for to-morrow the party would disperse to their respective lots. Well, that would be a change, anyhow.

At length Karen Skaret suggested that they should sing a hymn.

It was a very long time since they had been to church, and it would be many a long day before they went again. But several of them had once been in the choir, and Ola Vatne was something of a singer. Jo Berg began to hum one or two tunes, and presently hit upon "A Fortress sure is God our King." They all knew that, and one after another took it up, singing in subdued tones but with deep feeling. The women joined in; and Kal made signs to the children to keep still. Softly and reverently the little choir sang the hymn through to the end.

By now the moon had climbed high up into the sky, and its yellow face was gazing down wonderingly at the desolate land below.

II

Next morning the six men were afoot at daybreak; first they had to divide the land among them, and then they would all have to set to work and plow if they wanted anything like a crop the same year.

They started off at a brisk pace across the prairie, all flushed now in the sunrise. As they waded through the tall grass, they left paths in the dew; and big light-gray clouds, floating across the sky, threw wandering shadow landscapes on the plain around. Land, land, rich meadow-land right on to where it met the sky in the blue distance. They stopped to look at the bleached skeleton of some huge animal; now, what might that be? A buffalo, Erik answered; and went on to tell them how great herds of these stateliest animals of the prairie had once fed there, until European sportsmen had come with their rifles, shooting, killing, and butchering them, without rhyme or reason. So the buffalo had been exterminated; and this was the skeleton of one of them.

Then he began to point out and explain about the land he had got for them. When exploring the ground in the early spring, he had sampled the soil in numbers of places, but this was far and away the best. The chief difficulty on the prairie was to get water, but they could dig wells here, for there was plenty of water about. In other parts the melting snows often washed away the houses, and formed lakes many fathoms deep; but here the land sloped sufficiently toward the south for the water to drain off at once, and the houses at the top of the slope would be perfectly safe. At the Northville land office he had taken a claim on a quarter-section—as much as any one could get gratis—for each of them; that meant one hundred and sixty acres,

which, again, was the same as six hundred Norwegian *maals*.
But some day that would be too little—for a clever fellow
like Anton Noreng, for instance. Well, on that account
he'd arranged for a vacant quarter to be left between each
settler and his neighbor, and this they could buy later on,
as preëmption land, at a dollar an acre—dirt cheap. So
for the present they'd each three hundred and twenty acres
to play with, and when they outgrew that—eh, Anton?—
the prairie was wide, and they could get a section, two, three,
five sections; why, there were Norwegians in America who
owned as many as ten or twenty sections! Ragna Adilsdatter's kingdom could n't have been much bigger than that.

Their eyes met. Kal thought of the days when he had
carried loads of earth on his back up the rocks at Skaret,
to try to make the soil deep enough for sowing. Here he
saw before him a whole world of splendid earth, not so much
as a tree stump or a stone in it, covered with grass six
feet high—enough to feed a million cows. Take your choice,
Kal: a hundred and sixty acres to-day, and double as many
to-morrow! Ha, ha! They'd call that an estate in the
old country. He must be dreaming!

Now they could choose as they liked, and settle the matter
among themselves. Erik looked from face to face. The
lots were equally good, he said, so they'd only to say which
they preferred. The emigrants looked this way and that,
and wandered about from one "quarter" to another. Was
there any difference between them? At all events they
made up their minds in the course of the morning. Kal
chose the lot farthest to the west. "Precious seldom I go
to town," he grinned.

"Sly old dog!" said Morten. "There's something behind
that; see if there is n't!"

Erik took the lot next to Kal's; then came Anton Noreng,
Jo Berg, Morten Kvidal, Per Föll, and lastly Ola Vatne.

"Yes, you'd better be nearest the town," said the school-

master, caustically, twirling his mustache with his dis-
colored fingers.

From where they stood they could no longer see the camp,
but only the smoke rising from it. No mistake about their
being in a new country now, where property was on a
large scale.

Returning toward the camp at dinner-time they became
aware from some distance of a smell of fried bacon. The
women-folks had their hands full, one making butter, another cakes, Anne washing clothes in a little stream. It was
odd to see all this housework going on in the open air!

Kal Skaret wasted no time; he moved on to his own ground
the same day.

In the course of the long journey his prairie-schooner
had collected various odds and ends which were fastened
on the outside—an old harrow, a plow, a table, a chair, in
such a condition that he had got them for nothing; a wheelbarrow, a kettle which some one had thrown away, and even
an old grindstone which might come in useful in a place
where you couldn't get anything. Kal had tied on one ac-
quisition after another, till the wagon bristled like some
strange monster. Finally he had hoisted to the top an
old *kubberulle,* a wagon on four solid wheels sawed out of
a huge tree trunk—just a beam with two wheels on each
side of it and a couple of planks placed lengthwise. This
was the emigrant's first conveyance: on this he carted his
crops, drove to town or to weddings, and some day journeyed
in his coffin to the churchyard. Kal had seen one of these
cast-off *kubberulle* lying about, and had forthwith annexed it.

Now he loaded it with his sack of flour, plow, harrow,
tools, and planks, together with a number of boxes of various
goods which Erik had given him as his share, and fastened
it on behind the schooner. "Get up! Get up!" Well,
good evening and good luck, all! The children led the cows
by their halters, while Karen sat in the wagon with the

fowls in their hamper and the pig in its box. She was feeling terribly dizzy, did n't know what to do about this headache! Kal drove his two oxen, Jim and Ebbe, over the others' lots, and finally arrived at his own. Of course he 'd had something up his sleeve when he chose the one farthest away: it gave him the open prairie on one side, and he could help himself when the time came, and keep his land all together.

The procession halted, the animals were let loose, Karen got out, and the whole family stood looking about them. A hundred and sixty acres, all their own! And in the middle of their land stood the wagon, a little room on four wheels, their first house out here. The grass reached high up its sides, and Kal's first job must be to get a scythe and do some mowing, to make a bit more elbow-room.

Soon he was swinging his scythe vigorously; yes, this was the sort of stuff to feed animals on! He wished he had a thousand cows! And houses for them, and folks to look after them. While he mowed till the sweat poured off him, Karen sat brooding. The children gathered round her, and little Siri climbed up on her knee. Kal looked round at them. "Anders and Oluf, set to work, now, and put up that netting for the pig and the chickens," he shouted, and went on mowing. What the deuce was wrong with the old woman?

The little girls were talking about Indians; they had heard such a lot about them since they came to America. What if they should come to-night? But the men had all brought guns in case of need. Their mother took no notice; she only sat there staring ahead of her.

"Well, now there 's room to turn round, anyway," Kal panted, laying aside his scythe. He had mowed a little patch, on which the grass lay in long swaths. It was their first farm-yard.

Now he supposed he must help those young cusses with the netting. Here were some posts to stick into the ground;

Erik had thought of everything. And there was the netting. Those coyotes were fair devils for eating young pigs
and chickens, and maybe there might be wolves around, one
of these nights; a run must be put up, strong enough to keep
them out.

The next thing was to find water. He tramped heavily
backward and forward, till presently he heard a queer squelch-
ing sound under his feet. He stuck in his spade—no, nothing there. He went on tramping about. You couldn't
expect to find it all in a moment. At last he discovered
what he wanted: there certainly was water here! He tore
off his cap, and started digging. Karen and the youngsters
were still sitting there. "Go and look for something to
make a fire and cook the supper!" he shouted to the boys.
He went on digging; now there was a good-sized hole, water
was oozing in, he'd made a well. "Hi! old woman, come
along and have a drink!"

But Karen did not hear. Her eyes saw nothing but the
plain, the same everlasting plain. Even their fellow-
travelers seemed so far off now. Lucky they had the wagon,
anyway. A sort of little home on wheels. Skaret wasn't
much to boast of, but *this* . . . and she sighed.

The children were coming back with dry grass for the
fire; she must put on the porridge to boil. Why, the chickens and the pigs were very lively now they'd got into their
fine new house, and that made things cheerier all round!
Presently they all sat down to supper together; they had not
had a meal by themselves since they sat round the long
table at Skaret. They looked at one another; well, here
they were at last.

To-night Kal meant to sleep in the wagon with Karen;
owning a hundred and sixty acres was not a thing to be
sneezed at, and the first day was rather like a wedding-
feast. The air was cooler now the sun had gone down.
To-night the boys and girls could sleep underneath the

wagon. Kal wrapped them up well. "You'll be nice and warm here, Siri lass." Then he lay down beside Karen, breathing heavily, with closed eyes, after the hot and eventful day.

Heavy footsteps sounded outside. "Moo!" said a voice; why, here was Erik's Buck come on a visit to his pal Jim! . . . Kal's thoughts wandered, first to his acres, then to the little gray houses at Skaret. By and by he groped for Karen's coarse, toil-worn hand. "Well, old girl, that's something done."

"Yes, Kal. 'T was a long way."

They lay thinking about it until presently their breathing became very regular. At any rate, they were together. And they fell asleep so imperceptibly that they quite forgot to unclasp their hands. . . . Outside, the lofty sky was glittering with stars, and the night was cool and still.

III

Kal had no watch, but he woke early, rubbed his eyes, and sat up. It was no longer dark, and the cock was crowing; trust that chap to know the time! He crept out of the wagon quietly; Karen would be all the better for a bit more sleep.

Outside, an orange-rimmed sun was rising above the sea of earth. Well, here was another day! He'd been early afoot many a time in the old country when he'd had to go out working on the farms, but things were different now: his time was his own, the ground was his own, he was a landowner; it was a new life altogether. He stood there bareheaded, with bits of straw in his hair, screwing up his eyes as he surveyed the world around. There'd be a scrap of porridge and a drop of milk left over from yesterday, he thought, and he went to look in the big packing-case near the wagon, which did duty as larder so long as they had nothing better.

He ought to set about plowing now, but it would do the oxen good to have one more day's rest; besides, there was the grass. Why, a man would need a heart of stone to go and plow down all this splendid fodder! No; first he must do a bit more mowing. Gosh! what a field of hay! He swung his scythe strongly, cutting wide swaths. When the children woke up they saw their father hard at work, his head streaming with sweat; already he had laid down the grass on a strip of ground as large as the whole field at Skaret.

"There's Dad mowing!" said Anders, and Oluf was wide awake in an instant; hadn't they begged and prayed to be allowed to bring a little scythe each? They got these out quickly, and without stopping to eat anything ran off to join their father. Cutting their way into the rank grass, and each mowing his own row, they tried their hardest to keep pace with him, but in vain.

Here was a chance for little flaxen-haired Paulina to use her new rake! Sleepy-eyed, she came trotting after them and began spreading out the hay. With this hot sun it would be dry in a few hours. What fun this was, tedding the hay just as the grown-ups did! To-day she was the daughter of a big farmer; she hadn't been that yesterday.

And sure enough, the hay was getting dry already. They piled it up in stacks, for in this country nearly all the crops were piled in stacks. When Karen came out, the haymaking was in full swing. Did you ever! Fancy her lazing away the time in bed like that!

But the really great event took place on the following morning. Kal had yoked the oxen to the plow before day-break, and when the sun began to lift its golden rim above the plain, he stood there ready and waiting. Now he could start plowing.

The plow was rusty from lying out of doors all winter; nice way they looked after things in this country! He had marked out a straight line right down his piece of land, thinking it would be fun to plow it from end to end, and now he put the rusty coulter into the ground. "Get up!" The plowshare buried itself in the earth, but immediately sprang up again, forced out by the matted turf, which was as thick as the palm of a man's hand, and as tough as a tarred rope. He tried again. "Get up, get up! You damned rascal!" and down came the whip on Ebbe. Kal toiled till the sweat ran, cursed in English and Norwegian, struggled on. No one could plow a straighter furrow in the days when he used to work at Lindegaard, but here he was only making a mess of it. He must get that young rascal

Anders to come and sit in front, on the beam, to keep the share down. He shouted as if his life depended on it, and Anders rushed to the rescue.

"Sit there in front, you young rapscallion." Anders had ridden in many different ways, but never like this. The plow jerked him up, and he bumped down and nearly lost his hold. His father fumed and pushed with might and main—they were getting on fine now! And here was Kal breaking up prairie land till the sweat fairly rained off him! A dark-brown wave was rolling up behind him. Precious slow work plowing with these darned oxen, but anyway they were going forward and not backward. Hi! Get up!

At last he could turn and look back along his first furrow. Well, that was the first. And something like earth, too! Rich, dark soil. He took up a handful and smelled it, and his face softened; somehow it reminded him of the smell of cream-porridge. Ha, ha! This was earth, and no mistake!

Turning the plow, he began another furrow. As the soil curled over, it gleamed in the morning sunlight. For thousands of years this soil had lain here waiting for him, and now he had come.

Erik Foss had also moved on to his own land, but his first concern was to see that the others got to work. There was not even a wagon on the ground of his neighbor Anton Noreng, for Anton lived in Jo Berg's. When Erik went to look them up he found the schoolmaster sitting inside, reading a book, and learned that Anton had gone out with his gun to try to shoot something.

"Kal's hard at work plowing."

Jo Berg grinned. "You need n't come and tell me that," he said.

"Well, you 'll have to take life seriously out here. If you want to live at all, you 've got to work," Erik answered, and passed on.

Morten Kvidal was plowing. He was not so tender-hearted toward the hay as Kal was, but plowed it down without mercy, knowing that there was more than enough all around them. It was hard work for him alone, for the turf was stiff and intractable here too. Yet the first furrow affected him strangely, making him think of the little home thousands of miles away. Here was he, plowing up new land, not at Kvidal, but on alien ground. Things didn't always go as one would like them to. How was Mother getting on, and were they at work now on the hillside at home? Ah, he had run away—had deserted them!

Well, the thing was done now. But he hoped it wouldn't be too long before he could get back to plow the hillside at Kvidal.

"You go at it like a man," said Erik Foss, stopping to watch him. He felt like a sort of inspector going round to see that everything was being done properly.

"It's damned hard work!" and Morten mopped his face.

"There's many a settler has said that before you. You must remember you aren't the first!" Erik chuckled and strolled on; Morten was one of the best of the lot, he said to himself.

Farther on he saw the stalwart Per struggling along with his plow. Erik pulled up short: could he believe his own eyes? Some one helping Per? Who could that be? A woman was sitting in front, on the beam; it must be Anne! Look at that, now! Who'd have thought she had it in her? But folks soon showed what they were made of when they got out here on the prairie.

"Bless the work!" he greeted them.

Anne, who had not seen him coming, jumped off with a little scream and an embarrassed laugh.

"You've got a real helpmate there," said Erik to his friend.

"Helpmate—yes, that's just what I always say!" Per

answered, looking round as if challenging anybody to deny it.

"Yes," said Anne, "he was making such a to-do, complaining that he could n't get on at all, so I thought I 'd best try and help. Baby 's in the wagon—crying, I expect."

"No. I passed close by, and he seemed to be asleep."

Erik walked on. Quite promising, this! If only they 'd stick to it. But what should he do with those two ne'er-do-weels, the schoolmaster and Mother's Darling? Give them a hiding? It might come to that if they did n't look out.

None of them, however, was in such a furious rage as Ola Vatne. He, too, was plowing; bareheaded and naked to the waist, he was urging forward his plow and his oxen, cursing, sweating, and looking as if he wanted to smash the whole lot of them. A nice state of affairs, this, for one who had always done well at everything—whether it were cards, or dancing, or fighting!

"What sort of damned land is this that you 've palmed off on us?" he shouted, as soon as he saw Erik coming. Erik gave a chuckle and stopped to watch him.

"You ought to get some one to help you; some one to sit on the beam."

"All right; take a trip to town and hire me a lad!"

"Ha, ha! Per Föll's wife is helping him, although she 's got a kid to look after."

"What! Anne?"

"Anne 's her name, I believe."

"Well, I 'm——!" said Ola, and drove his oxen on. If Erik dared so much as to hint that Else thought herself too grand to come and help him! But luckily Erik said no more, and strode on into the prairie.

When Ola mentioned this to Else in the evening, she cried, "Oh! How stupid of me not to think of it!"

"You? Ha, ha!" The notion tickled him.

"What! Don't you think I can do it as well as Anne?"

"I don't know if you can, but I do know I won't let you."

"D' you suppose I shall ask your leave?"

He did not dare to remind her nowadays that she was a colonel's daughter; more than once she had given him a little box on the ear for doing that. Next morning she got up at daybreak like himself, and went out plowing with him. It went far better after that.

"I 'll be hanged if I ever saw such a woman as you!" Ola said admiringly.

No doubt the others were only waiting to see him come to grief. Who could expect anything else of a convict coming to the prairie with a gentleman's daughter? Let them wait. Not that it was easy to be the husband of a colonel's daughter. But that was his own fault, for where could you find a woman fit to hold a candle to her? If only he could learn to please her! It had been a long sight easier before, when they met on the sly in the hills or in the outhouses at Dyrendal; in those days she used to say she liked him best as he was. But how had it been since? He was always feeling ashamed of himself, somehow.

He had run amuck and burned down one of her father's houses; but was n't she always telling him that that was *her* fault? Had she ever complained that she had thrown herself away on him? No; on the contrary, she worked as if she 'd been born and bred in a crofter's hut. When he had gone on a spree now and then, in the winter, she had n't scolded him once. No, she 'd only looked surprised, and kept her thoughts to herself! What could one make of that sort of thing? She always made him feel so uncomfortable and ashamed of himself. If only she would scold and bully him, to give him an excuse for being angry! She never even said, "Wash your hands before you eat." Not a bit. She just washed her own and showed him how clean they got.

Ah, he had no chance of living up to *her!* Heaven help

the man who had a wife who was so perfect from top to
toe! Ola felt as if he were a bull in a silk halter; the hand
that led him was a weak one, but if he broke away one
day to enjoy a taste of liberty, he knew he would want to
hang himself afterward for very shame. And yet, and yet
—something kept surging up inside him. Was it obstinacy?
No! It was a rebellious longing to break away—and run
wild. Ugh! Plow, plow! But the longing grew worse
and worse, surging up inside him all the time. Heigh-ho!
how he wished he were back in the hills, running for dear
life with the rifles cracking behind him! But he must n't
say anything; he must choke it down and go on plowing,
plowing, glad that he had the prairie to wrestle with, anyway.

Erik Foss had n't an easy time, either, for he felt himself responsible for all of them—and what if the whole
scheme failed? If they were unhappy here, it would be his
fault; if the crops failed, he knew they would put the blame
on him. Already it had come to his ears that Anne could
not sleep, and lay awake all night crying. But there might
be more in that than dislike of being here; perhaps she 'd
just discovered that marrying Per was not such a joke after
all? Then there was Karen Skaret, who complained of
dizziness and could n't eat or sleep properly; she said it was
all the plain, this everlasting plain.

One day he drew Anton Noreng a little apart from his
mate, and when they were out of ear-shot he stopped abruptly
and faced him. "You have n't done any plowing yet," he
said.

"No. Maybe I 'll start to-morrow."

"To-morrow, eh? That story 's getting pretty stale now.
You 'll start plowing your own land to-day. Is that plain
enough speaking?"

"Yes, but—I 'm thinking of returning home."

"And I 'm thinking of giving you a hiding. I 've promised

your father to try and make a man of you. So either you do as I say, now, or you get a hiding."

"It's no business of yours."

"If you say that again, I'll knock your head off."

The retort on the tip of Anton's tongue—a reference to the opprobrious nickname of Erik's mother, Scraggy Olina —stuck in his throat, for he saw that the other was in dead earnest.

After a moment's silence Erik continued: "Remember that out here you can't hang on to your mother's apron-strings. There are no public authorities. I'm boss here. You and Jo can't be allowed to spoil everything for the rest. So you'll begin to-day; you can borrow a plow and oxen from me."

Erik Foss turned on his heel. Anton stood staring after him. Should he cry or laugh? It was so confoundedly hard to settle down to any work. At home he had never been able to go on long with anything he began; everything seemed so dull after a bit. Then he had taken it into his head that all would come right if only he went to America. And now they actually expected him to slave here, too!

Was he afraid of getting a thrashing from the son of Scraggy Olina? Yes—and no. At home he could have shut him up merely by saying something witty about his mother. But out here nobody would laugh. Erik Foss seemed to have sprung up out of the prairie itself, and so did the others; there was no difference between them, whether their father was a clerk or a colonel, and the prairie was equally stern to all of them. Was he going to let Erik thrash him, and give the rest something to laugh at?

At dinner-time he said to Jo: "To-day I'm going to start plowing my land."

Jo slapped his thigh and laughed. "What! Are you going to plow with mosquitos, my son?"

"No. I'm borrowing a plow and oxen from Erik." And Anton squared his shoulders and assumed an air of importance. "I can't go on wasting time like this," he added.

On every lot but the schoolmaster's there was soon a dark-brown patch of plowed land. Erik had been hard at work with his own plowing, but he managed to go and have a look at the others' at least once a week. Having owned a farm farther to the east, he could give them the benefit of his experience. Flax was the best crop the first year, and ought to be sown in one way, while wheat should be sown in another. His mates had never grown either of these at home in Norway; but Kal would show them what was what when it came to sowing oats! It was some time yet to midsummer; with luck they would get a crop this year, after all.

One day one of Kal's oxen went lame just as he was harrowing in the seed, and of course it was that artful cuss Ebbe. What did Kal do then? Why, he yoked one of the oxen, and instead of the other he harnessed himself, Karen, the boys, and Paulina by a rope at which they hauled and tugged in a long line across the field. Little Siri sat on the harrow, wild with delight, shouting, "Get up!" and trying to imitate the voice in which her father said, "You damned rascal!" All in the day's work. They used to do this sort of thing at Skaret, too.

Jo thought it was cowardly of Anton to let himself be frightened by Scraggy Olina's son. Just let Erik come to *him:* he'd soon tell him what he thought of him for enticing decent folks into this desert where there wasn't so much as a stick to make a fire with! Anton and he had agreed to milk the cows and do the cooking on alternate days, but now Anton always came in as hungry as a hunter and expected to find dinner ready. Jo couldn't prevent him from sleeping in the wagon at night, though they had decided to send each other to Coventry for a week. What

should he do with himself? Why had he ever come out here
into the wilds?

He was getting used to being a martyr. Lounging about
with his pipe in his mouth and his hands in his pockets, he
stared this way and that. It was just the same everywhere:
not a thing to be seen but earth and sky. For years he had
comforted himself with the thought that it was not his own
fault that he could not get on; he was living in a narrow-
minded, reactionary country where a free man had no chance,
however talented he might be. For instance, look at the
way the authorities had treated him. Did they let him get
a post in any school? Did they let him believe what he
thought it common sense to believe? He had got used to
lying in bed at home, smoking, reading the papers, and
grumbling about the state of the country, till he had grown
fat and lazy doing nothing.

Then had come a gleam of hope—America, the land of
the free; a chance for him at last! Well, he was there
now. In Wisconsin he had worked as a day-laborer; and
he'd had to stick to it, too, or get the sack. The capitalists
in this country were the worst of all for exploiting the
workers who slaved for them. But he had hung on because he wanted to save up enough money to come here
with the others; Erik had said it was such a fine place—
all the land you could possibly want, vast fields of wheat,
wealth in whatever direction you turned your eyes. Well,
he'd got the land, but now he had to start slaving again.

Work, work, work! Worst of all, he couldn't blame the
authorities this time. As far as he could see across the
prairie, he couldn't find a trace of any authorities at all.
The State? No doubt it was the duty of the State to give
bread to its children. But, however much he strained his
eyes, he couldn't see a sign of the State—nothing but the
earth, the sky, and himself. Work! Swim or you'll sink:
who could make any sense of a cynical law like that?

He could go in and out, or wherever he liked, but he had no one to blame, no one to rebel against; all he had was his land, which would never yield any wheat as long as he did n't plow and sow. It seemed to lie there and mock him. That made him think of the farmers at home who had gone security for him with the bank, and who doubtless thought they would soon get some money from America. Ha, ha! His mother and father had often said to him, "Jo, you 'll always have a grievance, wherever you are." And it really began to look as if they were right. The thought vexed him. Were the old folks going to be right about that too? He could see them holding up their hands in horror, and feeling themselves in the right. And for all that, they were sure to expect him to write and send them money.

Then one fine day he had no more tobacco—another trick of his enemies. But he could n't exist without tobacco, so he went to Erik Foss. None of your newfangled stuff in a packet, thank you, but a proper roll which he could pull to pieces with his fingers. "Right," said Erik. "When you 've plowed ten acres, you shall have some."

Jo stood stock-still, gaping. Should he tell Erik what he thought of him? But Erik went on:

"And when winter comes, and you 've no food, you can starve or live on your own fat, for you 'll not get a crust from any of us." This was holding a pistol to his head, with a vengeance!

However, Jo did not tell Erik what he thought of him. He went round to his neighbors instead, and managed to get a little tobacco from each of them; but they told him that they had only just enough for themselves—an unmistakable hint. He began to think of going away. Only, where should he go? To the town? But there a misguided social system would force him to slave again. Back to the old country? No, not for the world!

The upshot was that Jo started plowing, but not until the crops were already coming up on the other lots. Anton was part owner of the oxen, but never dared to take them if Jo wanted them. Jo's plowing took a long time; it made him uncommonly stiff, and the obstinate turf reminded him of his teachers at the training college, but he wasn't going to give it any quarter now. Before long his appetite improved wonderfully. He slept like a top. He even began to talk to Anton again, and became quite sociable. As for his oxen, he had almost a brotherly feeling for them; he would stand by the hour scratching their backs and talking English to them, and once he very nearly said that all toilers ought to make common cause. He had given them new names, and called one Luther and the other Garibaldi, both champions of liberty.

Meanwhile the settlers had advanced a step farther and had begun to build themselves sod huts. Of course they all went to Erik to ask how they should do it, for none of them had ever built a sod hut before. Neither had Erik, for that matter, but he did not consider it necessary to tell them so. "First of all, you must have a good cellar," he told them. "It's pretty cold in winter on the prairie, and you must have a place where you can keep the food and milk."

Four of the neighbors had dug out gaping holes for their cellars before Anton and Jo had finished working in their fields. The two men had made friends again and exchanged a few sentences morning and evening. But if Anton started running down "that rotten country" Norway, the schoolmaster soon shut him up; he had heard that story a hundred times.

One day the two boys Anders and Oluf set off barefoot on a secret expedition into the prairie, their object being to go so far that they could no longer see any smoke. What a lark if they should get lost, or were caught by Indians and carried off to be tortured! Anders had prominent cheek-bones and large eyes, like his mother, with an enormously wide mouth which seemed specially made for calling the cattle on the hills. Oluf was shorter, but more thick-set, with very wide-awake eyes—a regular rogue.

They ran on at a brisk pace. Presently they came upon a queer-looking grayish-brown animal with a pointed snout, and it smelt so awful that—faugh!—they had to hold their noses! Anders swore and Oluf spat. They must have walked miles by now! What if they could n't find the way home? But still they ran on, often through prairie-grass that reached up as high as their chests. All of a sudden they fell head over heels into a little river; they struggled out dripping wet, and stood panting on the bank, staring in bewilderment at each other and the water. Then they noticed that there was sand there, and stones too. "Look!" cried Anders, pointing, "here's a lot of stone, the very thing Father wants."

There was driftwood, too, left on the bank when the water had been higher, and as dry as a bone—the very thing for their camp-fire.

When they got home, full of their great news, Kal gave a meaning glance in the direction of his neighbors and told the boys to keep it dark. Then he went and yoked the oxen to the *kubberulle,* seated himself on it with the two boys, and drove off, swaying and bumping over the prairie. Kal could not help laughing at his wonderful cart: its wheels reminded him of grindstones, and the wooden axles clattered like clogs. But it got along somehow. Some stones to support the cellar wall were just what he needed, and here were enough for himself and plenty for the others as well.

The boys were delighted with the little river they had discovered, and began to wonder whether there were any fish in it. If only they could get some fishing-tackle! They talked it over in secret, and did not breathe a word about their plans even to the two little girls. Surely there was no harm in stealing a darning-needle from mother, and holding it in the fire till it became pliable enough to bend into a hook? They found a long piece of string tied round some packages, and as for bait, there were sure to be worms under the stones near the river. As soon as their father settled down for his after-dinner nap the two boys stole off again.

Kal swore when he woke up and found that they had disappeared; those tarnation boys had n't finished planting the potatoes! In the evening he caught sight of them coming back across the plain, and vowed that if they had never had a thrashing before they should have one now. But what the dickens were they carrying between them? He stared in amazement. Fish, as he was a sinner!

"Well I 'm blest!" cried Karen. None of them could tell what sort of fish they were—certainly not trout. "They must be pike," Kal declared, though he knew precious little about fresh-water fish.

Another day the boys were fishing up the river when they suddenly made a new find—some trees. They were growing in a hollow, almost like a little valley, too far away to be seen from the camp. And now those who wanted more roof-beams could get them.

Soon the huts would be ready. There was only one room in each, but perhaps they could build on another next year. And the oxen and cattle must have a roof over them in winter, too. But not even Erik had remembered everything when he bought their outfits; he had forgotten all about window-glass. A "house" consisted of four walls of prairie sod piled layer upon layer, a door, two holes for light, a roof of elm poles overlaid with brush and "shingled" with sod—and that was all. For the present the windows had to be covered with paper. "Just like a fisherman's hut," said Kal.

He did not pretend to be much of a carpenter; but, then,

he was n't making the furniture for an exhibition. There
were bedsteads against three of the walls, one for the girls,
one for the boys, and one for the old folks. The stove, with
a pipe which went up through the roof, stood in the middle
of the floor, where it would warm the whole room, Erik
said; they 'd be glad of it when the prairie winter set in.

They were busy enough all the week, but Sunday was a
long day.

It was no use gazing out over the prairie, for they could
not see a church spire anywhere. Kal Skaret made a point
of getting up at daybreak even on Sundays, and worked
away as usual until he saw that the others were beginning
to stir. No doubt the Lord could see him; but, then, He
was not so particular as one's neighbors here on earth.

The settlers would wash and make themselves smart in
their Sunday best, and then seat themselves outside their
huts, staring across the level plain that stretched on endlessly
till it vanished in the quivering sunshine. Visions of the
old country would rise before them. It never occurred to
them that there might be a difference between the time there
and here; the church bells would be ringing out over the
valley now, they thought, and all the folks would be driving
or walking to church. What would the parson's text be to-
day?

Or husband and wife would go for a stroll round their
fields to see how the crops were getting on and talk over the
prospects. The land would be all the better for some rain
now. The broad-bladed wheat was peeping up all over the
large square patches, and the oats looked as even and fine as
velvet. When they went out into the prairie they could see
their fields from a long way off, cabbage-green against the
brownish yellow of the surrounding plain. After all, this
ground that they had broken up was making them feel more
settled and contented. So they kept Sunday by walking
round it and wishing good luck to the seed they had sown.

Sunshine and rain were their Providence now, and the fields were a kind of home.

Already they had begun to call their land after the farms in the old country: their lots and their huts had come to be known by the names of Skaret, Foss, Vatne, Berg, Noreng, and Kvidal. "Let's go round to Skaret and see how Kal's getting on," the neighbors would say. The bestowal of these names seemed to consecrate the huts, and called up a sort of mirage of their homes in the old country.

One day Karen Skaret had a strange experience. The hut for the cattle had been built and the animals had spent two or three nights in it; then one evening she had gone round in the dusk to milk the cows and had seen—the brownie from Skaret! Dreamed it? Not she; it was the sober truth. As if *she* didn't know that little fellow! Why, the sight of him struck her all of a heap, and she had to hold on to the door. Fancy his coming with them all this way! Well, after this everything was sure to come right.

She did not dare to tell anybody, though, for that might bring bad luck on both man and beast. But from that day on she felt better. Her dizziness passed off, and she no longer got a headache from looking at that tiresome plain. It seemed as if all she had cared for at Skaret had accompanied her here—as if she could even smell the hills and the fiord again. Often the children and Kal would look at her in surprise. She had become quite her old self now, just as they remembered her going about at Skaret.

IV

Another Sunday afternoon. Else and Ola had been for
their usual walk around the fields, and now they were talking,
seated on some soft hay in the shadow of their hut. Ola
was bareheaded—his mop of fair hair was very thick—and
every now and then he strummed a little on the fiddle that
he held in his hands. Else asked him to play a country-
dance and he did so. But somehow the tune seemed to float
away and lose itself in the endless plain, and Else felt that a
dance like that had nothing in common with the landscape
here. It called up visions of waterfalls and steep mountain-
sides, of wooded hills and clear summer nights. A tune to
make any one homesick, even if she were not so before.

But Ola had not a good ear. He played carelessly, and
very often out of tune, too. She herself had had music lessons and had learned to play the piano. Taking his fiddle,
she tried the strings; she could not play, but she tuned it,
drew the bow across the strings, then tuned it still better.
"See whether that does n't sound nicer now," she said, handing it back to him. He tried it with the bow, and agreed
that she had improved it. And once more he realized that
she never liked finding fault with him; she had given him
the benefit of her finer ear, and that was her way of teaching him. Only Else would do that. But now he began to
doubt whether his playing was good enough for her: ought n't
he to give it up?

While he was having his afternoon nap Else strolled off
across the prairie to see Anne. The neighbors had gone this
way so often, on their visits to each other, that they had
worn a little path. To-day the sun was as blazing hot as

107

ever, and bluish-red heat-waves quivered on the distant plain. The cattle feeding there looked no bigger than ants, as if they were miles and miles away.

Else knew in her heart that she was seeking something which she could not find by visiting Anne. Why not be honest and admit it? It was not only the dark uneasiness in the under-world within her—the agonizing fear that she had killed her father, brought shame on her two brothers, and so disgraced the family name that they all hated her. No, it was not only that. Such things could be forgotten if one worked hard all day; one's senses grew blunt as one's back and arms became tired. But there was something else, something that she missed; and why not admit it? Birth and education—did they count for nothing? Could one throw them overboard so easily, after all? Was it enough to love a man, to give up everything for him, and bear part of the burden of his crime in order to make it lighter for him? Was that enough? It might give one a certain happiness, but would it suffice in the long run?

How she longed to hear real music again—a sonata of Beethoven, a nocturne of Chopin, or one of Schumann's songs! Never till now had she guessed how much it meant to her. Suppose she shouted it across the prairie, spoke of it to the neighbors, to Anne? What response would there be? Was she to be cooped up forever with these people? Would she never have any other associates? She looked about her. The prairie, the dead unending plain, stretched away on all sides into the blue distance. Yes, she was shut in here, and it forced her to look back, to remember. And what did she see then? The well-known rooms, the people at Dyrendal, the fiord, the hills, her father. Oh, Father, Father!

Fate. What *was* fate?

"I'm glad you've come," said Anne. "Per has gone out; I think he's gone to see Morten."

Anne's baby was lying on the bed. The flies bothered him so, poor little thing! The door stood wide open, letting a little more light into the dark hut. The two young women in their neat Sunday clothes seated themselves one on each side of the little table that Per had knocked together. Milkcans stood round the walls, a saucepan of porridge was warming on the stove, various sorts of food were arranged on shelves, and a smoked ham hung from the roof. This was the kind of house that Anne Ramsöy had to live in now.

"You've made it very cozy here," said Else, looking round.

"Yes, I suppose it quite reminds you of Dyrendal!" Anne answered, raising her eyebrows.

They smiled at each other. Both of them were tanned by the sun and wind, and their hands were roughened by hard work. Both had dark hair, but Anne's oval face was still full of the joy of life, and her large, expressive eyes looked as if she could see visions which were best kept to herself. Else's face had a more veiled expression, and she had a trick of bending her head for a moment before she spoke. Anybody could see that she kept most of her thoughts to herself; and in her brown eyes were depths which could hide much.

Else walked across to the bed, to look at the little boy. He was called Isak, after his grandfather. Of course. And folk said old Isak was as hale and hearty as ever; she wondered if he still went on dancing. This little man on the bed looked as though he'd take after his grandparents. Anne listened with a smile and gazed at the wall. Presently, with downcast eyes, Else asked whether it was difficult to look after a baby.

A gleam of mischief crept into Anne's eyes. "Well it's not so bad looking after one, but getting one safely and well into the world is worse."

Else forgot herself and looked up at the other with horror in her eyes. "What! Was it really so awful, Anne?"

Anne thought she would frighten her a little more, just as a punishment for thinking she could hide her condition.

"Ugh, yes! I can't even think of it without feeling it all again. But luckily I had both a doctor and a midwife."

Was Else proof against that? No, she was not; and out it all came, though not without a good deal of beating about the bush. What would it be like, Else wondered, to have a baby out here in the wilds, where they hadn't a doctor or even a midwife?

Anne pretended to be surprised. "Why, you don't mean to say— Are *you* expecting one?" And again there was a twinkle in the corner of her eye. Aha! she had forced this fine lady to drop her pride and show how helpless she was. "But Karen will manage that all right, you know," she added consolingly.

"Karen! But she's had no training!"

"She'll manage, though. Women of our class often do without a midwife."

That might satisfy Anne, but it was cold comfort to Else. "Yes, but when she's had no training? You know how easy it is to get that dangerous fever. And if one had to call in a doctor, it would take weeks for him to travel here and back." She sighed, and bent her head for a moment. "Well, God's will be done. I must manage as best I can."

Never before had she opened her heart so freely to any of the others. Was it class feeling, because she was a colonel's daughter, that had kept her from doing so? It was one thing to make friends with these people, to dress like them, to do the same work as they did. But it was quite another matter to sit here confessing her secret fears to this peasant girl.

And Anne understood this very well. Why shouldn't she make the most of her triumph? The distance between the two girls had been very great; she'd always had to look up to the young lady at Dyrendal. If she went to the colonel's house, it was an understood thing that she had to go to the kitchen entrance. Often she had looked at the lights in that long row of windows, and heard the sound of music in the rooms behind the drawn curtains, but never once had she been inside. She thought of this now. What did she know about the gentry, once they had gone in and closed the doors behind them? What did they talk about at home, what did they read, what did they play, what had they seen on their travels, and what did they think of one another?

Anne had no notion, nor had any peasant in the parish. They saw the colonel out of doors, where he never forgot to tip the little boys who opened the gates for him, talked affably to the poor, and shook hands with her father, Farmer Ramsöy, always keeping his gloves on. But what could Anne know about his relations with his children? Supposing Else were to tell her that he had quarreled with both his sons because they held radical opinions and had married beneath them, that she herself had sided with her brothers in her heart, though she had never dared to show it, and that she had gone on year after year nursing a spirit of revolt: would Anne understand a word of it? Else had grown up in the country, played with the peasant children, milked the cows for the fun of the thing, and gone at will into the servants' quarters. But what did she really know about the peasants?

To-day she sat there talking longer than usual. An anxious dread forced her to open her heart to the other; for, after all, Anne was a woman, a companion in her loneliness. Fate had thrown them together, regardless of class distinctions, so they ought to help and befriend each other.

She bent her head for a moment, and then unburdened herself of the confession which her friend was waiting: when the time came in the autumn, she knew she wouldn't live through it.

"Nonsense!" said Anne.

"Ah, you'll see that I'm right." And all at once she

felt again that strange sensation of looking into the past.
How delighted her father and mother must have been when
a daughter was born at last! What would they have said if
any one had told them that it would end like this?

She went on telling Anne about her girlhood; it was a
relief to talk about it now. She spoke of how beautiful her
mother had looked on that last evening, when Else had
climbed up into her bed to say good night. Anne listened
with growing interest. Well she knew that warm devotion
to one's mother and father, yet for the life of her she could
never have put it into words. Else went on to speak of her
brothers; one of them was a captain in the army and the
other a lawyer. Although they held radical opinions, she
supposed they considered her a fallen woman now, for they
never wrote her a line, though they could easily find out
her address. Well, she wasn't going to ask them, if they
preferred not to. She could not help confiding all this to
Anne. . . . Had she quite forgotten that this young woman
was not her sister?

And other things, which one would not tell to everybody,
came out in spite of herself—about her life in the convent
school in Germany, about the German officer who was always writing love-letters to her, and more besides. It made
Anne laugh, and she herself smiled at the recollection of it.
She even spoke of her father: didn't Anne think him a very
distinguished-looking man, and had she ever seen any one
with a better seat on horseback? "You can't think how
splendid he was to us children." (That was all Anne need
know about it, anyway.) And then she passed on to other
reminiscences, of the dances at home, of her father's young
adjutants, of the students and young engineers who visited
them in summer, of picnics in the woods, of sailing expeditions among the islands on beautiful light nights. How
much of all this could Anne grasp? Well, she had always
known that the gentry knew how to enjoy themselves. So

Else could live her girlhood over again and go on telling
as much as she pleased, provided that she did not overstep
the proper limits. It was an outlet for her homesickness.

At last she rose to go. Her tall, slender figure passed
out of the hut, and wandered off toward another in the
far distance. She had not gone many steps before the little
house behind her was already as if sunk in the ground; nor
could she see her own yet, but only some long patches of
green corn-field. Nobody could see her here, yet she leaned
forward a little as she walked, to conceal the fact that she
was no longer so slim-waisted.

A gray cloud hung overhead: was the rain coming at last?
How she wished it would, for Ola's sake! The cloud had
thrown a whole landscape of dark shadow across the plain;
it looked as if the heavens meant to frighten her, as if her
memories of home were gathering thick and dark above her
head out here in the wild prairie. "Yes, this is where you
will die, with no one to help you, when your time comes to
bear the child whose father is an incendiary,"—that was
what she heard her father saying when he came to her in
dreams. Now the shadow-realm was lying just in front of
her, and right in the middle of it stood their hut, with Ola
still asleep indoors, perhaps. She would have to enter that
menacing shadow. Sunday . . . Sunday . . . What a long,
melancholy day it was, out here in the wilds!

Another person who was out walking to-day was Anton
Noreng. He had got into such a habit of depending on his
mother's advice and help that now he had to resort to some
other woman instead of her. Karen Skaret's broad pale
face, with its far-seeing eyes, was very much like his mother's,
and it always gave him a feeling of security when she was
near. He had some stockings which needed mending and
a pair of trousers with a great rent in the knee. "Can you
do anything to them, Karen?" As for his shirts, he could
never wash them white, however much soap he used. "What

shall I do, Karen?" He put on a helpless, boyish face, and looked at her with pleading eyes. It was never difficult to get round Karen. None of the women had so many to darn and wash and mend for as she had, but Paulina could help her, and besides, she had n't the heart to say no to the boy.

"Well, what's the matter now?" she said. "D' you think I 've nothing better to do than to look after you?" But her voice was as mild as that of a mother remonstrating with her own son. "All right, you can ask Paulina," but all the time she knew that she would have to do it herself. Anton felt almost bashful when he turned to Paulina: the lass was over twelve now, quite a little woman—rather freckled about the nose, certainly, but when her fair hair was nicely combed and plaited on Sundays one almost felt tempted to write her a little love-letter! Paulina giggled, gave him a sidelong look, and said she 'd see what she could do. "You can put them there, and I 'll try and get them done before bedtime," she added, quite in her mother's manner.

"How's things going, over in your hut?" inquired Kal, who was lying on the bed.

"Oh, pretty much as usual." Anton gave a little sigh.

"Have you any coffee left?" Karen asked.

"Very little. Jo's always making himself coffee when I 'm out."

"Well, if you 'll sit down and wait a few minutes, I 'm just going to make a cup for ourselves."

It was like being home on a visit for Anton to sit there looking at a whole family, father, mother, and children, all together. He stayed on and on, and forgot all about the time, until it was so late that they simply had to turn him out.

Morten Kvidal was lying on the bed in his hut, smoking a pipe and reading. His mother had packed a Bible and a hymn-book in his chest, and he himself had added "Synnöve Solbakken," "Asbjörnsen's Fairy-Tales," and "Snorre." At

present he was reading the fairy-tales. It was easy enough
to fly home and drink in the air of the old country when
one had a book like that in one's hands. These supernatural
and subterranean beings seemed to be forces rising out of
himself. If he shut his eyes, he could see the whole thing
before him. The wood-nymph, now—what was the wood-
nymph? The head-master of the county school had said:
"The wood-nymph is a birch-clad hillside which opens its
eyes and comes to life. But the hillside is part and parcel
of our own nature." Never before had he understood it so
well as he did now, looking at it from so far away. And
yet he had left it? But not for good—oh no! He could
feel the old country inside him all the time. Why couldn't
he write poetry nowadays? He would write about the valleys,
the waterfalls, the crags, the forests, and the clear nights
in a human soul. Yes, but he was thousands of miles away
from all that now.

He was having his Sunday rest, so he could lie here dreaming to his heart's content and allow his thoughts to roam
where they would. Last winter he had had one or two
letters from Helena; she wrote so nicely, and said she longed
and sighed for him; fancy that! Then why couldn't she
come out here and join him? Because he wasn't good
enough for her, of course. She thought him good enough
to flirt with and write to, but catch her stooping so
low as to marry him! No, he wasn't good enough for her.
But although he was so far from any town or post-office,
he wrote her a letter every Sunday; they could not be sent off
till sometime in the autumn, but by then there would be
a whole cart-load of letters; he shouldn't wonder if he had
to pay half his crop in postage. And the letters she
wrote to him—perhaps they were lying there in the town,
waiting and waiting like his own?

All the week he toiled and moiled, slaving away with
grim determination. At last he had room to turn round.

A hundred and sixty acres to-day, and double as much to-morrow; the sooner he could cultivate them, build farm-houses, and sell the whole lot for thousands of dollars, the sooner he could hurry home, and throw himself into the work awaiting him there. But Sunday was Sunday. He was taking a rest to-day; to-morrow he would make a fresh spurt.

Steps outside, the door opened, and Per Föll entered, bending his tall form in order to pass through the low doorway. He had on his Sunday best—white shirt sleeves and an open waistcoat—and his hair and beard were newly combed. "Having a laze?" he asked.

"Yes. Creep in."

The seat creaked as he sat down heavily upon it. He leaned forward, and rested his chin on his hands. "Sunday goes precious slowly," he remarked with a forced laugh.

"What! When you 've got a wife and child?"

"H'm." He mused with shut eyes.

Morten watched his clear-cut face, framed by his fair curly hair and big silky beard. Per did not seem to be happy lately; what could be the matter?

"Queer thing," said Per, presently. "I 've been looking for something all day."

"And have you found it yet?"

"Ha, ha! You don't even ask what it is!"

"Well, what is it then?"

"The Sabbath—Sunday." Per opened his eyes and fixed them mildly and seriously upon his friend.

"And you can't find it?"

"No; can you?"

Morten preferred not to answer the question. But Per went on: "You know what I 've always thought of the church and the clergy."

"Yes, you 've made no secret of it."

"But are we any better off now? We've nothing at all here."

"H'm." Morten looked up at the ceiling. He could feel that something was rankling in the depths of Per's soul. A cry for help, a confession to a sympathetic ear was trying to break through. All the week he toiled there in solitude, alone with the sky, the prairie, and himself. A coyote howled in the distance at sundown, then all was still and deserted again. It made a man feel so depressed to be always alone with his evil thoughts. Yes; Morten knew that, too. . . . Per closed his eyes again. "I've been doing a lot of thinking lately, trying to figure out what this spiritual life is. Seems to me it's being discontented with what you have."

"There's something in that."

Taking out his pipe, Per filled and lit it. Morten, stretched at full length on the bed, followed his example. Then Per began to talk about women. There was no denying that they formed a sect of their own, he said. Who could ever tell how much a girl had had to do with other men before she married?

Morten dared not look at him, but he thought: "Mercy on us! Per's begun to worry about all the boys Anne used to gad about with before she took him at last for reasons of her own. And maybe he's wondering why a little chap with black hair and brown eyes was in such a very uncommon hurry to come into the world! Well, he'll have his work cut out."

He tried to change the subject. What an age it was since they had seen a paper; all they had to live on now was the news folks were talking about when they left home. He started on the franchise, and Per really warmed up once more about his favorite themes at the county school—the liberties of the people, Sverdrup, Björnson the worker, and progress. The same old story! Per could not help laughing at the thought of serving up all this again; he might as well save himself the trouble of changing the words and forcing them into new phrases—it was n't a scrap of use. The earth was thirsty in this hot weather, and so were their minds; they were drying up for lack of something fresh to feed on. Why, anything might be happening in the world now! And almost before he knew it Per let fall the remark that he supposed some day the settlement would be big enough to build a church.

Morten pondered. It was the loneliness and the prairie again: they had made Per so dizzy that they had forced this little cry for help out of him. God help us all! Ah, Morten could feel it, too, could sympathize with him! He said he did not think they would have to wait very long, provided that enough folks came and joined the settlement.

They went on chatting about this for some time; then suddenly a sort of groan escaped Per's lips: "Forgiveness —ah, that 's the trouble!"

Morten looked askance at him. Forgiveness? Was he thinking of Anne again? Had this big, strong man been going about alone on the prairie, finding out more and more of her sins, until it all grew so terrible that he saw no remedy but God's forgiveness? Those bloodshot, worried eyes— Morten did not like the look of them.

At length Per got up, murmuring that it was time to go home. Bidding the other good night, he squeezed through the little door, put on his hat, and set off across the plain toward another hut in the far distance.

He walked on slowly. Nothing here but the sky, the prairie, and himself! The sun, sinking down toward the ocean of earth, looked strangely wan. The prairie was reddish and dark, as if plunged in a weird gloom that was closing in on the whole world. Per seated himself on a tussock, and watched the dusk creep nearer and nearer.

Now there was only half of the sun's disk showing above the darkness. Farewell to the day. And now he was all alone again with the night.

The coyotes began to howl their chorus far away to the west. The prairie itself seemed to be lifting up its voice, frenzied and fiery, as if a demon had opened his gaping jaws. At home in his hut they had used up the last candle-end, and there was no lamp; they had to go to bed with the dark and rise with the dawn. It was dark now. Stars were springing out in the sky. Per recognized the Pleiads as old acquaintances. What! had they, too, come all this way? He thought of the knoll with a clump of firs on it, above Föll, which was such a faithful friend. No doubt it was waiting for him to return. He remembered how often he had felt depressed when he was indoors; but when he had gone out-side, and looked about him for a while, he had felt so much better—as if he had been able to store up within him-self the strength of the mountains, the woods, and the lake.

How clearly he could see it all now! Down with the church and the clergy . . . liberty of thought and belief . . . How easy it had been to talk like that in those days! But what about now? There were none of those things in his way here. Neither reaction nor the rich peasants nor the church —nothing. Well, what then? What did he believe in now? What did he think, now that he had gained his liberty? What did he see? This plain . . . receding, always reced-ing from him. There was not a single obstacle here, noth-ing one could shoulder aside, nothing of any kind. He could never climb up anywhere to get a wider view, or go down into the shade to give his eyes a chance of looking upward. He merely became dizzy, because the world around him was so vast, and he himself so small.

There was something uncanny about the relation between the plain and Per. It was making game of him. It was making him wicked and suspicious. He was all alone here with a host of devilish thoughts. Who could this be, tempt-ting him to rush into the hut, to snatch up the child and throw him out, to shower abusive names upon Anne, and drive her away? Had she really run riot with the doctor's son—with this one and that, and many, many more? *His* child with black hair, and those brown eyes? "Ah! you b——! Look out, I'm coming!"

But he stayed where he was, still straining his eyes to catch a gleam of hope. Even if God were not up there among the stars, He must be somewhere. If only he could have strength to forgive her, he would find Him. Then he would be saved by Him, and would not go stark, staring mad. Forgive—that was true Christianity. Now he was sure of it, and he raised his head and looked straight in front of him. But there was the prairie again, receding from him, away and away, mocking and malicious. It did not care two straws what he did. Revenge yourself or for-give . . . Kill your wife . . . Smother your baby! Or else forgive. The prairie and the coyotes were howling it at him together.

His head felt so bad to-night. If only he could get some sleep! Presently he began to sing a hymn; but it sounded like the whimpering of a child who cannot find his mother. And no one heard him but the prairie, the stars, and the darkness.

V

Then the heat came in earnest. The men went about in only a shirt and trousers and the women in a shift and skirt, but even so they could not move without perspiring. The doors of the huts stood open, gasping for air; and who could hope to rest at night when the room felt like an oven and the air was thick with mosquitos? The men cursed and struck out in their sleep. Anne's baby was bitten all over, and cried incessantly.

Kal would often run out in his shirt in the middle of the night; that darned coyote was prowling round the huts again after the pigs and fowls. "Be off, or I'll send a bullet through you!" And if he came outside at sunrise he was sure to see the little beggar making off at full speed across the plain, leaving the hens in a fluster behind their netting, and the cock too frightened even to crow. Then there were some little devils called gophers, no bigger than squirrels. They tried to curry favor with folks, turning and twisting about, and sitting up with their paws in the air, for all the world like a parson in church. But Kal only threw a slipper at them; *he* had n't any use for egg-stealers.

It was an event for the youngsters when their gray Spanish hen hatched out ten chicks. She was teaching them to wipe their mouths after meals, and the tiny balls of yellow fluff wiped their little beaks so nicely, as if they wanted to show that *they* knew how to behave, too. Did you ever! It was just like in the old days at Skaret.

But it was going to be a bad year, after all. The drought was torturing the life out of the yellow prairie, and heaven and earth seemed to be utterly forsaken, except by the pitiless sun. Karen Skaret hung an old skirt on the wall of the

121

hut: if that did n't help, nothing would! She let it hang there, but she did not tell anybody why. It was really an old petticoat, once red, now gray with age, and covered with patches and darns. There it remained, defying the sun. And she herself went about near it, washing clothes, making butter and cheese, cooking, milking the cows morning and evening, never idle for a moment. Her broad face was like tanned leather now, and her eyes large and wistful. The petticoat hung there day after day, and the sun blazed as before. Only wait till to-morrow, Karen thought; something was sure to turn up.

Sunday once more. Men and women came wandering out of their huts and gazed despondently at the blazing sun.

Meanwhile the Skaret children were busy celebrating a quiet little wedding on the plain. The bride was the red cow Kranslin, named after the one Ebbe had taken from them, and in a few weeks' time she was going to have a calf. Her husband was Erik's bull, but they had n't had a church wedding, and in little Siri's eyes this was very wrong. Of course the elder children were anxious to aid her in putting the matter right. Just now the two fair-haired boys were sauntering along the plain, bareheaded and in their shirt sleeves, Anders stout and wide-mouthed, Oluf freckled and jolly—but ready with his fist if any one teased him. He was always the one to give his mother a helping hand—perhaps in the hope of a taste of her cream.

"Have you got the hammer?" he asked.

"Yes," and Anders pointed to the handle sticking out of his pocket. There was something special about that old hammer from Skaret; they always had it with them when they were playing at anything exciting, and to-day it was going to be the church bell.

Behind them tripped Paulina and Siri, with their hair in plaits and wearing the blue dresses in which they had left Skaret. Siri was carrying a little doll made of a knotted handkerchief, and also a bridal-wreath of prairie flowers. What the elder children enjoyed most of all was the absolute seriousness with which she treated the whole affair. She had even wanted to bring a hymn-book. Paulina, who was twice Siri's age, watched her with a motherly air. Poor little mite, she knew no better!

The oxen and cows from the five farms, which always herded together when they had a day off, were grazing in the dry grass. There stood the bride with her fat red sides, whisking away the mosquitos with her tail. She looked thirstier than the others did. "Won't you run and fetch a pail of water for her, Anders?" asked Paulina. "No." he answered. "She can't have the wedding-breakfast till she's been to church."

Oluf led up the bridegroom by his halter. The cow and the bull sniffed at each other. "That's right," said Oluf; "try not to quarrel about the housekeeping." But first they must publish the banns, or the marriage would be illegal! So Siri did her best to look as if she were standing in a pulpit, and shouted over the plain: "I publish the banns of marriage between Tom Tomsen Foss, bachelor, and Kranslin Krandsdatter Skaret, spinster. This is for the first time of asking."

After that she put the wreath on the bride's head. Then followed the marriage, the sermon, and a little singing. By now bride and bridegroom were frothing at the mouth with thirst, so the girls led them forward a little way, while Anders and Oluf scampered off to fetch two buckets of water. Then they had the wedding-breakfast.

"What the blazes are you kids up to now?" cried a voice, and there was Kal coming toward them.

"You go and tell him," said Anders to Siri, who always knew how to get round her father. Siri put on her most innocent expression and ran to meet him. "We're giving the cattle some water, Father."

"What? All the lot of you?" Kal frowned, still looking suspicious.

"You always say we must try and be helpful," said Paulina, as innocently as her sister.

But when Kal caught sight of the bridal-wreath on Kranslin's head, he turned on his heel and began to stare at the sky again. Youngsters must have their fun; they'd no other children to play with out here in the wilds, and besides, it was Sunday. He sauntered back toward his corn-fields.

This was an anxious time for Erik Foss. If the crops failed in the first year, he would be the scapegoat and the others would lose heart or even want to leave the settlement. All his fine plans would fall to the ground. The rumor would get about at home that he had only brought them to ruin and misery. That would put an end to all hopes of ever going back, to stand outside the church and be the chief person present! It didn't take much of this sort of thing to give a man sleepless nights.

And now the schoolmaster had found something new to complain of; not a civil authority or a tyrant this time, but a petty pope. For even Erik was better than no grievance at all. Jo had become quite another person; his face positively beamed with appreciation of his own wit. It was all very fine, he said, to have a Moses to lead them out into the wilderness, but what about the fleshpots of Egypt? If they took his advice they would pack up and leave the place at once.

And he did not stop at that. Why, he asked, had Erik been so anxious to lend all of them money? Had anybody thought of asking what the rate of interest was? The whole thing would turn out to be a subtle form of profiteering; just see if it didn't!

Now, whether it was due to Karen's old petticoat or not, at any rate the sky turned gray one morning, and later on in the day it began to rain. The women let the rain pour down on their bare heads, the animals could feed on wet grass again, the earth drank, and the wells began to fill.

This was not a bumper year, though. The flax had been spoiled; the very crop they had hoped to sell in town and make money on had failed altogether. The wheat was poor, and the oats only just ripened in the ear. When the corn had all been reaped and the sheaves were standing in shocks, the men began to wonder what to do next. They had no barn. There was not so much as a threshing-machine. It ended by their following the example of the ancient Israelites and letting the oxen tread out the sheaves, while a man walked behind with a pail, to see that they did not foul the corn.

Well, so much for the first year! The straw would have to be stacked, and the corn must lie in a heap in the open. Erik did his best to encourage everybody. It would all be much easier next year, he told them. He had brought a hand-mill with him, and they could grind some of the corn with that. Sometime in the autumn they would have to make a trip to town to buy food for the winter, and then they could take a load of oats with them and exchange it for flour.

But Karen was already grinding wheat in her coffee-mill. In an hour or two she would have enough flour for a bowl of porridge.

Then the men set to work to plow again, and Kal was up every morning before either the cock or the sun. All this fine earth was making him feel so greedy: a hundred and sixty acres would soon be too little. The ground was easier to work after the rain, and one could plow it without help. That dolt of a schoolmaster wanted them all to leave. Hadn't he ever heard of a drought, with all his learning?

Morten was plowing, too, fiercely impatient to finish his first quarter. More and more land under corn meant wealth

. . . a big crop to sell . . . money . . . riches. At last
he had elbow-room to work! Nor were the others going to
be left behind. Ola plowed on grimly, stripped to the
waist; let them say what they liked, he'd keep up with the
best of them. Per did not spare himself, either; it did him
good to tire himself out—he could sleep so much better then.
Folks might go about saying that Anne had thrown herself
away on him; but let them wait and one fine day they
would see her living on a big farm. Even Mother's Darling
was working away like a man now; *he* wasn't going to let
little Paulina laugh at him! As for oxen, he could always
borrow Erik's. But Jo Berg was disappointed; they would
not take his advice and leave.

One sweltering afternoon Kal was walking behind his
plow and telling the oxen that they were damned rascals,
when suddenly he stopped dead, and began to stare.

Flock after flock of birds were flying past him—ducks,
geese, and big dark cranes screaming harshly. The prairie,
too, had become alive. Hares and rabbits were scurrying
by in the same direction as the birds; why hadn't he his
gun with him? There went a coyote; why, there were
scores of coyotes, tearing along as though the devil were at
their heels! And what the dickens was *that?* Rattlesnakes,
gliding along the ground, hissing with fear! And *that?* A
great gray wolf. In the distance he could see herds of long-
legged antelopes galloping along with their heads thrown
back.

What the devil could it mean? The cows were coming
in from the plain; they were running home as if they were
scared and wanted to get back to the houses. The wild
animals seemed suddenly to have lost their dread of man,
for a fox came and leaped right over Kal's plow, and then
dashed on. Did you ever! Here were all the living creatures on the Western prairie stampeding past as if they were
out of their wits. What in the world could be the matter?

Was rain coming? A cloud was rising into the air far away in the west. Well, a shower would do no harm. But this cloud had something bright red inside it. . . . How fast it was spreading! . . . The sky was turning red, too. . . . There must be a strong wind to blow it along like that. It looked as if the plain were on fire beneath the surface; little tongues of flame burst out here and there, then a huge sheet of flame leaped high into the air. . . . Yes! it was a prairie fire, and the wind was blowing it straight in his direction.

Erik Foss came rushing up. "Plow, Kal! Plow round your quarter. As quick as ever you can! The prairie fire's coming! Burn away the grass round the house."

He spun round and dashed off to the next man: "Plow! Plow round your lot! A couple of furrows will do. Burn away the grass round the house. Look sharp!" He ran on again, shouting the same thing to each of them. Lucky that the cows had all come in, and that the oxen were yoked to the plows already, except on Berg's lot. "Plow! Plow round your ground. Two furrows are enough! Burn away the grass round the house."

He had told them before that if a prairie fire broke out, the best thing to do was to kindle a counter-fire, burning the grass for some distance around; then the great sea of flame would not be able to get a hold on anything, but would have to pass by at the sides. Already men and women could be seen setting light to the grass round their huts, and round the stacks of hay and straw.

"You must see to the rest, Karen," said Kal.

He drove the oxen down to one end of his quarter, turning up a furrow at right angles to the long strip he had just been plowing; then he swung round and plowed a second furrow. Good! That would keep the fire from jumping across. Without wasting a moment he drove the animals at a trot to the other end of his land, and began plowing two similar furrows there.

When first he noticed the fire it had been miles away; but the wind was driving it forward faster than a bird could fly. It took some time to plow those two furrows; every minute the fire was coming nearer, and of course the danger was worst for Kal, who was nearest to it. He urged the oxen forward and plowed with despair in his heart: what if it should be too late? He glanced toward the west, and saw it advancing—a sea of fire with a wedge of flame in front. Higher and higher, nearer and nearer. Already he could smell the smoke, a smell of scorched grass. If only he could plow faster still, and get it done in time to save his little home!

Meanwhile Karen had risen to the occasion. The grass had all been burned away round the huts. She had shut up the cows and had covered the heap of grain with a tarpaulin and hurled several bucketfuls of water over it. But—where were the children? They had n't come home yet! She could n't see them anywhere. What had become of them? Could they be with any of the neighbors? Where were they? She ran toward Kal, shouting: "Kal! Kal! Where are the children?"

But Kal was deaf to her cries; his one thought now was to finish the furrows before it was too late. The fire had come very near, the smoke was drifting on ahead, and red sparks were showering down on the plain close by. Plow faster! Then a terror-stricken voice behind him cried: "Kal! The children! Where are they?"

"The children? Don't *you* know?"

"No! do you?"

"No. Are n't they at home?" And still he went on plowing.

Suddenly Karen remembered. "They went off to fish!" she cried in terror. "And little Siri 's with them."

That made Kal stop. He had not finished the furrow, but he let go the plow and sprang toward her. "What d' you say, woman? Quick! Are the children out on the prairie?"

"Yes! Yes! Over there by the river!"

Kal looked in the direction of the river; it was a long way off, and soon there would be a sea of flame between, but the children were there. "Look after the oxen," he cried, and throwing down his cap, he set off at a run.

Karen had no time to feel faint, for the furrow had still to be finished; she knew very little about plowing, but plow she must now, and she urged the oxen forward again. The earth turned over in a fashion—not much of a furrow, but still it would do. The fire cast a red glow upon the oxen and the plow, the air was suffocatingly hot, and she had to drive the terrified animals straight toward the flames and smoke. But she went on plowing bravely, and at last completed the furrow. Turning the oxen, she let them loose, and they galloped off, with their tails in the air, toward the huts.

It was late in the afternoon and the westering sun looked as if it were sinking down into the flames to be roasted. As far as the eye could see westward, the plain was nothing but fire and drifting smoke. Kal had the fire on his flank now, and it was drawing rapidly nearer; but he swerved and ran on, still heading toward the river. The heavy, smoke-laden air was hard to breathe, but he struggled on. Were the children making for home, or had they had the sense to stay near the water? He was running in heavy boots, gasping for breath, perspiring and ready to drop. But he mustn't give in, he must try to run faster still.

Sometimes the wedge of flame leaped up into the sky, sometimes it sank lower again, but all the time it was coming nearer and nearer, drawing a vast sheet of fire behind it. Kal swerved again and ran on. His children! The fire had cut him off, so that he could not get back to Karen now even if he tried, but all he thought of was to reach the river and the children. He could taste blood in his mouth, but still he ran on. He stumbled, was caught in a whirl of smoke, struggled up again. Now the grass was burning underfoot and he was running through fire . . . the soles of his boots were glowing hot . . . as if he were trampling the flames with naked feet. But he ran on. The river—he must reach the river! Ah, there it was at last!

On over the smoking, burning earth. The legs of his trousers were scorched, he could feel that his hair was singed, he could only see the red of the flames, but now he was almost there. The wide gray bed of the river lay waiting to receive him; the stream had almost dried up, leaving a bare stretch of sand and stones on each side. Kal stumbled on until he stood with his feet in the stream. His trousers were on fire, and he sat down in the water, splashing it over his hands, face, and hair. The bed of the river offered no sustenance to the fire, and soon it formed a broad path, dividing the sea of flames which was devastating the land on each side.

But what about the children? Kal started wading up the stream, calling: "Anders! Oluf! Paulina! Siri! Siri!"

At last he heard an answering shout. The very sound of it made him stumble and fall. Alive! The children were alive! He picked himself up again. Yes, the children were alive; they had noticed the fire only after it had cut them off, and then Anders had exercised an elder brother's authority and had made them stay where they were. Now they were in the middle of the river-bed, and they all shouted at the top of their voices when they caught sight of their father. The little girls were crying and clinging to their brothers. Kal staggered on till he reached them. They were shut in now by a wall of fire and smoke on each side, and the heat was almost intolerable, even when he and the children lay down in the stream with only their heads above the water. As for all those whom he had left behind, he was sure that they, the cattle, and the huts, were lost forever in this sea of fire.

Meanwhile the little group of settlers saw that the large piece of new ground Kal had plowed up to the west of his huts had checked the fire on that side. The wind drove the flames a few paces across the furrows, but here they could find nothing to feed on; the smoke and the sparks drifted over, but the fire could not follow. Not even the sparks could fly far enough across the rows of furrows to do any harm, but there was still all the dry prairie-grass on each side, and here the wind drove the flames farther and farther.

When the fire tried to turn in toward the huts, the wind no longer aided it; there were two furrows plowed right across, so it could not make any headway. Gaily, as if this had been a merry dance, it flew on again before the wind. The untilled quarters between the neighbors caught fire at the edges, but the wind did not help, and in any case the next lot was plowland, which would not burn. At last the little colony saw the whole prairie in a blaze, while they themselves stood on a sort of island in the midst of the sea of fire. Then they began to run to and fro, wild-eyed, and uttering little moans. They went and shut up the cattle in their huts. Saved—everything had been saved! And now? Now they only wanted to be near one another.

They gathered round Erik Foss. He was pale, but tried to speak calmly. "The danger's over now," he said. "And when it's all cultivated round here, there'll be no more fires." His words came in gasps and he could hardly stand still, but no one was listening. They only gaped and moved restlessly to and fro. It was getting dark, and this made the fire seem all the more alive and powerful.

Jo Berg joined the group; he had managed to yoke his oxen in the nick of time and had plowed his two furrows, and now he came wandering along, bareheaded, utterly be-

wildered, and staring about him with dazed eyes. Where
was he? Was this the day of judgment? "Come!" he cried
suddenly, trying to assemble the others. "Come here, all
of you: let us kneel and pray!"

What had happened to him? Perhaps there was a spark
of the old-fashioned fear of God still left in him. Had his
terror awakened it, and driven out all that free-thinking
nonsense? "On your knees, all of you!" he cried again,
kneeling down, himself. "We must pray." And there he
knelt in the dusk with the red glow from the fire on his face,
his folded hands raised toward heaven.

The women, infected by his example, knelt also. Anne
was kneeling, with her baby on her arm, and his little arms
were clasped round her neck. Per was on his knees, so
were Erik and Else; only Ola and Morten remained standing,
with the same fixed look in their eyes. Nothing could throw
Ola off his balance, and he was busy with his own thoughts.
Jo began to pray: "O God in heaven! O God in heaven!"

But just then Karen came running toward them. "Kal
and the children!" she cried. "Kal and the children!
They're not here!"

The others rose hastily from their knees and gathered
round her. What did she mean? Again she sobbed out
that Kal and the children were *there, there!* Pointing, she
staggered and almost fell. They gazed at the burning plain,
but no one had a word of comfort for her. They merely
stood huddled together, gazing silently. It ought to have
been pitch-dark now, but the whole world was on fire; the
earth had turned into fire and smoke, and the sky was lit
up by the blaze. Karen went on moaning: "Kal! . . .
Kal! . . . And the children!"

She sank down on the ground and rocked herself to and
fro. She could not weep, or bewail her loss, she could only
sob and moan the same words again and again: "Kal! . . .
Kal! . . . And the children!"

Night fell, but still they did not separate; they wanted to keep together. Else held Ola's hand all the time, but otherwise was strangely calm. Ola was gazing at the prairie; there was something, he felt, that he wanted to do, but what it was he did not know.

Erik went up to Karen and tried to comfort her. "At any rate, you may be sure you 'll never be in want as long as I 've a crust of bread," he told her. She looked at him with wide-open eyes, and suddenly he felt ashamed. He might have known better than to begin talking to her about food!

When morning dawned in the east, the prairie was still smoking, but the wind only whirled up occasional showers of sparks. The air was thick and heavy with the smell of burned earth, hay, and moss—scorched, dry air, which it was difficult to breathe.

And now Karen said that she must go and search the prairie.

"Impossible," objected Erik. "Why, it 's nothing but a mass of glowing ashes, as far as you can see!"

It was no use; Karen had made up her mind to go and look for the children and Kal.

"Which way did he go?" asked Ola, who seemed suddenly to have found out what he wanted to do.

"Over there," she said, pointing.

Ola looked at his thick leather boots and then at Else. She was still holding his hand; he gave hers a squeeze and set off at a run.

"Stop, Ola!" shouted Jo.

But there was no stopping Ola now. It was years since he had had a bear-hunt, or a run on skis through rough country, or a dance, or a fight, and here was something really tempting at last. The others watched him running, bare-headed and in his shirt sleeves, first to a well, into which he put both feet, and then on across the smoking country.

Sparks flew up at every step, and he ran more and more lightly, as though something were pricking the soles of his feet. Now they could not see him any longer; the smoke had swallowed him up, he was gone.

They looked at Else. She was pale, but—what did it mean?—she was gazing after him with large, shining eyes and a smile on her lips.

They waited and waited. Some of them wended their way homeward. And now, strange to say, it began to rain.

No one could keep Karen back now. Morten offered to accompany her, but she refused, and told him to remember that he had a mother in the old country. Morten looked down, uncertain what he ought to do. He did not like to stay behind, but still he did so; he kept on wanting to run after her, but the thought of his mother held him back. Karen set off in the direction of the river, and very soon was out in the smoke. Holding up her skirts, she waded through the hot ashes; they burned her dreadfully, but all she thought of was Kal and the children. What did her feet matter, if only she could find the children and Kal?

Where was the river? She had never been there; all she knew was the direction in which it lay. She stumbled over the charred bodies of some animals that the fire had overtaken—wolves or coyotes, it seemed. "Kal! Kal!" She hurried on, calling his name.

Was that some one answering? She heard a distant shout. And suddenly she saw them emerge from the smoke ahead of her. There they were—Kal with Siri on his shoulder, Ola with Paulina on his back, and the boys walking beside them. They were coming toward her, wading through smoke and sparks. Karen clasped her hands. Did she fall headlong? No, for the fearful burning in her feet drove her on. "Siri!" she cried, with a break in her voice. "Kal! Anders! Paulina! Oluf!" . . .

On the following Sunday Erik Foss sent word to the neighbors that he wanted them to come round and see him. They all assembled outside his house. Karen, Kal, and Ola had their feet bandaged in wet cloths.

Erik asked them to sit in a circle, and he himself stood in the middle. He had called them together, he said, because he wanted them to make up their minds—were they going to stay here over the winter, or not? He was pale, and his voice trembled. What if they were all so unnerved that they wanted to leave? He studied their faces. As no one answered, he went on to say that he felt himself to blame for not having told them to plow round their land before. He ought to have seen that they did it at the outset. But none of them were likely to forget to do so in future, if they decided to stay here.

Still nobody said a word. Erik began again. Winter was drawing near now, he said, and as none of them had enough food to last till the spring they must soon take a trip to the town, before the snow came. But first of all he wanted to know whether they really meant to stay on. For his own part, he had no doubt that the whole Dakota prairie would some day be one of the richest corn-growing lands in the world. But of course it was hardest for the pioneers, and the question was: could they hold out?

At last Kal asked, "Does that mean that I've got to give up my hundred and sixty acres?" And Karen added: "We —we'd begun to feel quite at home here. Besides, everything will be all right."

At that the others smiled. Else looked at Ola. Move to the town with him? Never! She knew only too well what that would mean. The others exchanged glances. Even the schoolmaster did not stand up and say that he was going to leave. Not a bit of it; he only sat there hanging his head. How had he behaved on the day of the fire? Like any lay-preacher! Whatever had made him do it? Could he ever look folks in the face again after that? At

any rate, he could n't jeer at everything and every one as
he 'd done before. He could only sit there hanging his head.
If anything, he ought to tell *himself* a few home truths.
Suddenly he stood up and said:

"I think that what we 've gone through has made us all
want to stick together. None of us will ever forget it.
We feel pretty much like brothers and sisters now. And I
think a word of praise is due to Ola: he behaved like a
man."

Whatever was he talking about? Ola could not make head
or tail of it. If he had n't acted like a woman, was that
any reason to make such a fuss? "Yes! And I 've never
even thanked you," beamed Karen, giving him her hand.
"Nor I," said Kal, and held out his hand, too. Else only
sat smiling.

As for provisions for the winter, Erik continued, he had
still a little money left, and they could pay him back when
they made their fortunes. They looked up at him; he had
lent them such a lot of money already! But Erik was delighted at the way things were going. He wound up by
saying that he had one or two cakes of chocolate and several
cans and pails of milk indoors, so if the women-folks would
give him a hand with the cooking he would ask them all in
for a cup of hot chocolate.

A couple of days after this Kal was hard at work again,
plowing. The prairie lay black all around; and every now
and then a gust of wind swept along dark clouds of ashes.

VI

Two of Erik's oxen had strayed away, and he was scouring
the plain with Morten, in search of them. They had brought
their guns with them, but there was precious little to shoot,
after the great fire. Of the oxen they could see no sign.
As they walked along the bank of the river they suddenly
stopped dead and stared. In front of them they saw a
mound, out of which protruded a number of human skulls,
arranged in a semicircle. Exposure and wild animals had
stripped off the flesh, and the hollow eye-sockets seemed to
glare at them ferociously. Rooted to the spot, the two men
gazed at this strange sight.

At length Erik said, "Now I know!"

"What do you know?"

"It's the Indians. They bury their chiefs like that.
We've stumbled upon one of their burying-places."

"You don't say!"

"Looks as if it's an old one, though."

"Yes, but good Heavens! . . ."

Erik became thoughtful. After the close of the Indian
wars the redskins had retired from Dakota to the part of
the country allotted to them by the Government, but every
now and then they made expeditions to the graves of their
forefathers, and nobody could trust them. Such neighbors
were the last to be desired. No doubt it was the Indians
who had stolen his two oxen. If only they'd stop at that!

"Listen," he said. "Can you keep this to yourself?"

"Yes. But why?"

"You know what women-folks are like. It's no use scar-
ing them out of their wits again."

137

At last the time had come for the journey to town. Four wagons were enough to carry as much of the year's crops as they could sell, but the women had saved up some butter and eggs, which would also fetch a little money. Ola had promised his wife not to go, but the nearer the day came, the worse he began to feel. He went about swearing to himself that he would not go; he plowed, and toiled, and swore again: "No. I won't!" But here was this strange urge inside him, mounting up and demanding an outlet. "You must!" it said. "I won't," muttered Ola, urging his oxen forward. "You must," said the voice inside him; "you can't go on forever rubbing shoulders with the selfsame folks, and staring at the same black waste of prairie. You must!" "I'll be hanged if I do!" "You'll be hanged if you *don't!*"

On the morning when the others were to leave, he jumped out of bed while it was still dark, and began to look for his best clothes. "Where are you going?" Else asked. "I must go to town, after all." She said nothing. "I must see if I can exchange one of the oxen, and maybe I can make a few dollars on the bargain. Every little helps."

Still she said nothing. She would not try to dissuade him, but she knew what would happen.

There were endless commissions for the men to remember —window-glass for the huts, flour, provisions, needles and cotton, and all sorts of odds and ends for the women-folks. Whatever they did, they must not forget to buy lamps and oil for the long winter. Lucky that Erik was going too, for he, at any rate, would have a few cents left to spend.

They assembled in the gray dawn, outside Erik's hut. "Good-by, and good luck!" The women accompanied them a little way, then stood watching the wagons disappear slowly in the somber desert, under the purple sky. At the last moment Kal's boys had to run and overtake them; there was yet one more thing to buy in town.

Morten sat in the front of his wagon, singing. At last he was off to the post-office. What would he find there, after waiting all these months? Ola sang louder still; in his secret heart he felt a bit ashamed, but there was nothing like singing to drown the voice of conscience. Even on the day he came out of prison he had hardly felt more light-hearted than now. What fun it would be to see a lot of people, to hear the noise of traffic in the streets, to see the lights in the shop windows, and to hear rollicking laughter again! And what was he going to do? Only watch and listen, of course; he would n't touch a drop. What about Else? She'd be a bit lonely without him, but the little girls at Skaret had promised to look her up now and then. So that was all right; and he went on singing.

Per was walking moodily beside his wagon. He did not like leaving Anne behind; but he would buy her a little present in town and forgive everything. How sweet she had looked when she said good-by!

Erik brought up the rear. He was feeling the weight of the responsibility that rested upon his shoulders; for the winter was long, and he had to think of everything that they might need. The journey to town would take a whole fort-night, and the six huts were left unprotected in the middle of the prairie. What if the Indians should come while they were away?

Else had accompanied the wagons for a short distance. She looked very pale, but she waved again and again, for no one must think that there was anything amiss between Ola and herself. When she parted from the other women, she walked back slowly to her hut. For the first time she was going to be altogether alone. She might have asked Karen to let one of the little girls stay with her while Ola was away, but why should she let the others know that she was afraid? Ola knew well enough that her baby might come any day; yet stronger forces had drawn him away from her, and he had gone. She must face the facts. This was the man to whom she was married.

The day dragged slowly on. Should she cry or laugh? She began to feel more and more inclined to do something rash. She knew that every one else had been storing up cow-dung as fuel for the winter, but Ola had not had time; so now she took a spade and wheelbarrow, and set to work, herself. It had to be heaped up against the wall of the cow-house to dry; even she had enough sense to know that, whether she was a colonel's daughter or not. The wheelbarrow was very heavy when it was full, and it made her back ache; perhaps it was dangerous for her to do this now? Never mind, though; if Ola came back to find her and the child both dead, it would serve him right! Ola —who was this Ola, after all? Surely it must be a joke! She couldn't really be married to a fellow like that!

In the evening, when she had driven in the cows and was milking them, she began to talk to them. To press one's forehead into the warm sides of these big, gentle animals was as good as a tonic. She had not named them yet, but now she christened one of them Barbro, after the old cook at home, and the other Josefine, after her own mother. No one could say that she was alone now!

Afterward she stood in the doorway of the hut, gazing out into the dusk. A limitless dome of sky, flecked with gray, looked down on the charred prairie; every moment the darkness was closing in, as if the night were stealing unperceived across the desert plain, and she alone could see it coming. Well, let it come. It could not make things worse than they were.

It was easy enough to lock the door, but it was harder when the time came to go to bed. The only light she had to undress by was a rag in a little saucer of oil. Still, that was better than nothing. What would happen to-night?

The baby was very restless; it was kicking and seemed in a bad temper; so she talked to it soothingly and begged it to give her a little peace. O God, how tired she felt! At last she lay in bed, staring at the darkness, her hands folded. Was she praying? No; she was seeing visions.

She could see her mother and father together in the big house at home. They had only one daughter, but that daughter had gone to the bad; she had eloped with a jailbird. She saw herself creeping slowly toward them on her knees. It was hard to humiliate oneself so, but what she had left behind was worse. Now they were stretching out their hands to her. Mother and Father were saying, "Come, come, lost child." And what more were they saying? That they would pardon her if she would give up Ola. The price was high. Was she willing to pay it? Could she give up Ola?

She sat up in bed, awoke. Outside was the prairie wind, and the night. By now the travelers would have gone to bed, too, lying under their wagons on the bare earth. How cold for poor Ola!

As she stood washing up in the hut next day, she suddenly felt that some one was near. She looked round quickly. There was no one there.

But hardly had she turned to go on with her work again when the door opened almost noiselessly, and there entered an unknown man, tall, bronzed, and beardless. That lank black hair hanging on each side of his face, those high cheek-bones, the knife in his belt, the moccasins—yes, this must be an Indian.

She did not faint. She looked him straight in the eyes and asked him in English what he wanted. A smile flitted across his face, and he answered in the same language: "Red man very tired. Red man very hungry."

She thought a moment. All she had was some cold porridge and a jug of milk. She put these on the table

before him, and invited him to eat. But the Indian would
not sit at the table. He poured some milk over the porridge, moved back to the door as if to keep open his line
of retreat, and, squatting there, began to eat. She felt inclined to ask him whether there were many redskins with
him, but she did not dare.

When the man had emptied the porridge-bowl, and put
it down on the floor with the spoon in it, he caught sight
of something bright on a shelf. He stole across the room,
took it down, and began to finger it. The object of his
curiosity was a brass tobacco-box with a runic-staff engraved
on the lid; he looked at her inquiringly: was this some
sort of magic? Then the box disappeared somewhere or
other on his person, and, walking backward to the door, he
passed out.

She stood still, listening for more steps, but there was
not a sound. She ventured out and looked about her. There
he was, with a fishing-rod in his hand, making off at a jog-
trot in the direction of the river. Apparently he was alone.
Should she hurry off and tell her neighbors? No. She was
afraid, but she was not going to let them see it.

Next day Kal's two boys came tearing home from a fishing expedition and panted out, "We—we've seen the redskins!" There had been a whole camp of them near the
river—horses, wagons, men, and women. They had tried to
creep nearer and have a look, but a great big fellow had
risen to his feet and come toward them, shaking his fist and
making signs to them to go away. "Be off! Don't come
here!" he had called out, and the boys had taken to their
heels. Later on they had turned round, and then they had
seen the Indians breaking up their camp, and moving off
with their wagons toward the northwest. One or two of
them had been on horseback. And now they had all gone
away.

Kal scratched his bristly beard and looked up at the rifle

which hung over the door. Karen looked at him, then at the children, and said, "For goodness' sake, don't tell Else; remember she's all alone."

The little girls were bursting to tell this great piece of news when they went round to Else's next day, but they did their best to chat away as usual. By and by they went home; they had kept the secret—but only just.

Later on in the day Else was standing in the hut when she heard the sound of hoofs outside. The door opened, the same Indian glided in with a string of fish in his hand, smiled as before, threw the fish down on the bench, and glided out backward again. Going outside a little while afterward, she saw a horseman galloping over the prairie in the northwest.

Hardly had she put away the fish when Anne entered. Her face was pale with anxiety, but she forced herself to talk of the men and their journey to town.

"Don't you think you and I ought to keep each other company at night?" she said. "There aren't many men here now, you know."

Else shook her head. A minute or two later Anton and Jo appeared, and offered to fetch water for her. Else accepted gratefully. They gave Anne a meaning look, but it wouldn't do to tell Else anything, in her condition. They suggested, however, that the two women should share the bed, while they themselves brought their rifles and slept on the floor; it mightn't be so safe hereabouts as some people thought.

But Else was in her desperate mood again. "Not for worlds!" she said. "I'm a soldier's daughter, and besides, don't you see I've got a rifle on the shelf over there?"

Seeing that they could do nothing, the three neighbors presently left. She was alone again. Afraid? No, she couldn't be worse off than she was already.

When eight days had gone by since the men left for town,

she began to watch the distant plain; she knew very well that it was too soon, and yet it made her feel less lonely to stand there watching for their return. But one morning, while she was in the byre, she suddenly felt an icy shivering down her back, a sensation of anxious dread, and an inward writhing that she had never experienced before. A voice said, "It's beginning now."

In a paroxysm of pain, she had to hold on to one of the cows. When it was over she pulled herself together sufficiently to let out Barbro—but then it started again. Her first thought was to go round to Anne, who was her nearest neighbor, but after taking a few steps she sank down on the grass. She screamed, dug her fingers into the ground, and rolled over on her back. No, she could not get so far, she must creep inside again; and next time she had a moment's respite she staggered, not into her own hut, but back to the other cow in the byre. It was something to be near a living creature; at any rate, she was not quite alone then.

The big, clumsy animal turned its head to look at its mistress, wondering why she did not let it out. Else lay down in the stall beside it, moaning. She crept nearer, put her arms round the cow's neck, and held on for dear life— Oh, oh! there it was again!

How long would this go on? She could feel that her dress was soiled by the filth of the stall, that her face must look as if she had smeared it with dirt, that her hands were black with mud. Then she had a paroxysm even more agonizing than the others, and this time she lost consciousness. When she came to it was because a voice was calling her—a new, feeble voice; the whimpering of a little child. She sat up, and took the baby in her arms, weeping, laughing, overjoyed. Ola! Ola!

As the day wore on, Karen Skaret began to feel strangely uneasy. The little girls had not been over to see Else yet.

Why she should take it into her head to go herself just to-day, she couldn't tell; perhaps the brownie had given her a pull. Anyhow, she tidied herself up and hurried off.

When she arrived she found the hut empty. But why was the cow making such a noise in the byre? And why had nobody turned it loose? She looked in.

There was Else, lying in one of the stalls, deathly pale, her eyes closed, but holding in her hands a tiny whimpering creature; and the first thing Karen saw was that she must go and fetch a pair of scissors.

"Save the child," moaned the mother in a feeble voice. "Never mind about me."

"Mercy on us! You have been bad!" said Karen, when she began to attend to her.

Presently the young woman was lying in bed, washed and made as comfortable as possible. Karen emptied a tool-box, and quickly converted it into a cot for the baby. He looked as cozy as anything, lying there asleep. And now Kal and the youngsters would have to fend for themselves, for she must live here for the present and look after Else.

The days passed, and Else began to recover. When at length the travelers came back and Ola entered the hut, with a strangely shamefaced look in his eyes, she sat up in bed and joyfully held out the baby toward him. "Ola, Ola, it's a boy!"

During the days that followed, the neighbors never tired of dropping in on one another to talk about the news from home. The letters which the men had found awaiting them in town were read, discussed, and read again. Fancy! So-and-so was dead. He and she had got married. Quite for-getting that they lived on the prairie now, they went wandering about the old parish, with its well-known hills and mountains, visiting all the farms and talking to their kith and kin. Ah, those letters, those letters!

On Sunday morning Erik Foss came to visit Ola and

Else. He blessed the house, and congratulated them on their son and heir. Refusing a cup of coffee, he asked whether Ola had time to go for a stroll. Ola got up and went out with him. As they crossed the strip of short grass around the hut, Ola looked at the other. "Well?" he said. They walked on and on, not to one of the neighbors', however, but out on the prairie. "Well?" said Ola, again.

At last, when they could barely see Ola's hut in the distance, Erik stopped short. The two men looked at each other. Erik stepped up to Ola and seized him with a thin but powerful hand.

"Look here: did you know that that might happen to your wife while you were away?"

Ola was secretly ashamed of himself, but this question put his back up. "What the deuce!" he burst out. "Hands off, man!" But Erik did not loose his hold.

"I ought to have given you a licking while we were in town, but it's poor sport knocking a drunken man about. And you were drunk all the time. You gambled away all the money you got, and your bullock too; if I hadn't paid up for you, and helped you once again, you'd have come home a beggar. But all that was nothing, compared with your leaving your plucky young wife in the lurch. And just remember this: we've no use for wastrels in this settlement. No! If we treated you as you deserve, we should kick you out like a mangy dog! But there's Else. I suppose you don't know I've had two letters from the colonel?"

"You! Had two . . . !" Ola opened his eyes wide in amazement.

"He offers me a big sum of money to take her to New York and sent her home. What d' you say to that?" Ola hung his head. Not that he was afraid of the other—not a bit of it. He could double him up, long as he was, and put him in his pocket. But what if . . . what if Else left him? That was the thought that made him hang his head.

"For her sake you can stay on a bit longer," Erik continued, "if you'll try and behave yourself. But one thing you'll not escape, and that's a hiding. *I'm* responsible for law and order here. And now I'm going to see that you get a licking."

Ola laughed; but a stinging blow on the ear made him stagger back and see red. He had been willing enough to take his punishment, if that would put everything right once more, but now he rushed involuntarily at the other. Very well, Erik was all for a fair stand-up fight. They closed. And now Ola had forgotten everything; he countered Erik's blows, danced round him, knocked his fists aside, and landed a punch above his eye that made him see stars. Erik reeled, but kept his feet. Why did not Ola take the chance to knock him down and throw himself on top of him? No, no; he wouldn't do that; he didn't mind being punished, but first they must give a little exhibition.

Erik was a devil to fight; how had Scraggy Olina's boy learned to box? If only he could get time to laugh, or applaud! But this was hot work. Take care, don't knock him out . . . keep it going, let him tire himself out. There was plenty of bone in that fist of his—ow! Erik's fist caught him just above the ear, and for a moment the world swam before Ola's eyes. Now to return the compliment. Ha! had he hit too hard? Erik was staggering again. This was something like! For the second time Ola could have knocked him down, but he didn't want to; he'd take his punishment presently, but not quite yet. Another minute and he had tripped Erik up, and the tall man was lying full length on the ground.

At last there was time to laugh! But he was up and coming on again. By gad! he looked as if he meant business! This time Ola let himself be knocked down. Erik knelt on him and seized him by the throat. Ola could easily have thrown him off and knocked all the wind out of his body, but he'd had enough fun now. He cried for mercy. "Ow!" he gasped, "let go. Ow! let go, I say!"

And the best part of it was that Erik really thought he had won! He let go the other and got to his feet, breathing hard and wiping the sweat off his face. "Well, now you can stay here a bit longer, on trial," he said. He strode away—tall, smooth-shaven but for the brown mustaches sticking out at the sides. A moment later he turned again and added, "If you can keep your mouth shut, I sha'n't say anything about this either."

Ola stood looking after him, uncertain whether to be ashamed or amused at what had happened. But on the way home he thought of Erik's threat to turn him out of the settlement. Then it all came back to him—the fire, the prison, and all the other stains which he could never wash off. He hung his head. Could he ever show his face again to Else and the baby?

But now that inner urge and restlessness had worked itself off, and for the present he could labor day and night at breaking up new land. Hard work was a wonderful cure for a man when he felt ashamed; he could take it out of himself as much as he liked in that way. It even established a kind of personal bond between the earth and himself, for every time he fell it helped him up again, if only he worked hard enough. Until he fell again. Ah, but there'd not be another chance to slip away to town for many a long day now!

VII

This was winter, and no mistake—a fortnight's blizzard,
burying the huts so deep that the settlers had to dig their
way out every morning! The hut for the cattle was not
far away, but it was easy enough to mistake the direction
when the snow was falling so thickly; and once you had gone
astray, if only a few yards, there was no finding the huts
again. They had vanished; and what could you do then,
in weather like this? At last the men had to stretch a rope
between the two huts, so that they could feel their way there
and back.

To be shut up indoors day after day was not exactly
pleasant, either. Even in summer and autumn it had been
a tight fit, although they could be out of doors most of the
time. But now men and women had to do all their work
cooped up together in this one tiny room. At Skaret there
were six—and Kal's hut was no bigger than the others.

Then the cold came in earnest. The dry prairie-grass
in the stove soon burned away. Dried cow-dung was better,
but you had to be making up the fire all the time if you
wanted to keep the hut warm. The question was, had they
collected enough of it, if the winter should prove a long
one? What if they discovered one fine day that they had
no more fuel left? They were snowed in, and no road led
through this deep sea of snow to wood or peat. At night,
when the full force of the prairie frost got in and the stove
was cold, the milk and the water would turn into ice, and
sometimes the vessels would burst with a loud report. The
settlers slept with their caps pulled down over their ears,
and wearing thick woolen gloves on their hands. And Per

149

would wake in the morning to find his flowing beard like a little frozen waterfall.

The men-folks were at their wits' end to find something to do. They had undertaken to feed and milk the animals in the cattle-hut, but when that had been done, what else was there? They were prisoners indoors, condemned to a life of idleness. Kal was as cross as a bear. Weeks would pass without their being able so much as to visit a neighbor.

Morten had his carpentry to fall back upon. He had bought some planks and a few tools in town, and even some wood to make into skis; at any rate, he had something to do, and perhaps he could sell a few chairs and cupboards when spring came round. The letters from Helena which he had found in town had cheered him up wonderfully. Strange how even the handwriting on an envelop could warm one's heart! His mother wrote, thanking him for the few dollars he had sent her before he moved out here. But she did not say whether they had repaired the mill or broken up the new land as he had asked them to do. Had they let the whole thing slide? Well, he couldn't be in both places at once.

He worked on steadily with his little outfit—a plane and a knife, an ax and a saw. But now and then he gave a sigh. Even here he was shut in. However hard he worked, it did not seem to come to anything. All the energy he had stored up at home, to be let loose upon the earth of the prairie, had been dammed up again; he would not see the spring or the bare earth for many a long day. He grumbled at the delay, and saw visions. What a lot of plans he had! When he peered out at the little window, he did not see the seething ocean of snow outside, but a mirage of the old country: the snow-clouds were mountains and hills, and the well-known farms stood out clearly on the green slopes. A road was needed here, and another there. There was only a little mill now on the Kvidal waterfall, but some day he would hear the hum of a large sawmill there.

He could see the new Kvidal farm. It was a manor-farm, and that was where he lived. He would make his mark in the parish and in the country; only wait, he would come into his own by and by. But first he must make good out here on the prairie. When spring came he must have another yoke of oxen, even if he had to beg, borrow, or steal. Land, land! He must plow up land, break up land, sow more corn-fields, grow larger and larger crops to sell, make money, pile up the dollars quickly, make his fortune in a few years—and then he could start in earnest, for the real work was to be at home at Kvidal, not here.

"Only wait, Helena! You'll see by and by, Mother."

Before the snow became too impassable the boys from Skaret often dropped in to see him. They would never say exactly why they came, but they always ended by standing there reading the newspapers with which he had covered the earthen walls. It was like a school for them. The papers were chiefly back numbers of "The Emigrant," one of the first Norwegian newspapers published in the country. So this was what they were reading! Well, they wouldn't have many books with them from home—a hymn-book, perhaps, and a book of family sermons. Their mother would read it aloud to them on Sundays; then they would sing a hymn; and that was all.

Was it the journey, or the winter they had spent in the little lumber-town in the East, or the life on the prairie, that had made them so wide awake? Maybe it was due most of all to their memories of the old country, contrasted with the life out here—the mountains and the fiord which were still fresh in their minds, and now this desolate prairie. It gave them so much to wonder at, to compare and to think out for themselves.

Just now they were reading a letter to the paper, from

San Francisco. They turned to Morten. "Where is that?" It was fine to learn all about that, and the Pacific Ocean, and the gold-mines. And Morten enjoyed explaining to them. They went on reading. "Madison"—what was that? A big meeting there, a "synod"—what was that? Morten needed all his schooling now. Oluf even wanted to know how the clergy came to be at loggerheads over God's Word. Surely they must know all about Him, if anybody did! Anders laughed at him, but Morten explained that the Norwegian clergy in the East were carrying on a religious controversy. "Yes, but what are they fighting about?" Oluf was not easily satisfied, and his shrewd eyes shone with eagerness for information. Well, here was an article about Norway: a composer was dead—what did that mean? And something about a political controversy, a state trial—what was that? He must ask Morten. But the distances between all these things were so immense that they had almost to shut their eyes in order to grasp them.

One day they came to Morten and asked him shyly whether he could help them with a letter. Yes, he supposed he could manage that. Whom were they going to write to? Oh, to a friend at home, Severin Rönningen, son of their next-door neighbor at Skaret. All right, here were pen and ink; how would they begin? First he must say that they were all well, then that Father had a hundred and sixty acres of land, and lastly that over here in America a rail-splitter like Abraham Lincoln could become President of the whole country, which meant that he was a sort of king. So they thought that Severin Rönningen in the old country ought to hear that, did they? Well, the letter couldn't be posted till some time late in the spring, and it wasn't Christmas yet, but anyhow it was written.

When they had gone, Morten sat wondering what a letter like that would mean to a friend in the old country. A rail-splitter could become a sort of king, eh? They thought that Severin ought to know that. And some day Severin would grow up, and have a vote in his own country; would he remember it then? What if the emigrants sent home ideas, as well as money, from America? The thought took his fancy.

Between Jo and Anton, relations were again a little strained. They spent the time playing cards, but one accused the other of cheating, and they hurled the cards at each other's heads. It was not so easy as it looked to live cheek by jowl with another man day and night, month after month, and at last they were so tired of it that the very sight of each other made them sick. They had their fixed days for milking and feeding the animals and for cooking, but no arrangement had been made about helping each other to keep open the path to the animal's hut. "You can go to hell if you won't do it yourself!" the schoolmaster said.

Anton accused him of not knowing how to milk. He could not empty the udder, which made the cows give less milk; and, not content with that, he drank up half of it—the pig! Jo laughed at the boy. "If you don't like it, you can just clear out. Go to that palace of yours on your own quarter." "No! This palace is just as much mine as yours, and so are the cows and the oxen and all the rest of it."

"Not at all! It's my hut, and the cows and oxen are mine too. You're only a lodger, and if you don't take care I'll chuck you out!"

This was more than flesh and blood could bear, and Anton was on the point of flying at him. But he clenched his fists and told him some home truths instead:

"You've swindled every one right and left—me, whose money you've used to buy everything here, and the people who guaranteed your loan when you wanted to go to a training college. Cheat! That's what you are!"

"Say it again!"

"Cheat! I'll put it in writing if you like. Cheat, I say!"

Jo laughed contemptuously. Seizing the boy, he pitched him out into the snow and banged the door. All right. Anton had had enough of this; never again would he set foot in the house of such a damned scoundrel. He would go and complain to Erik Foss at once.

He began wading and plunging through the sea of snow. It was just clear enough to-day for him to see where he was going. The other huts would be snowed under like their own, but he hoped that the smoke would show him where they were. Soon he could see nothing but the lowering, woolly sky, and snow, snow wherever he turned his eyes. Often he waded up to his chest in the deep drifts. He became so exhausted that he stopped again and again, thinking: "I shall die. They 'll find my corpse here when the spring comes." But go back to Jo? Never!

If a snow-storm came on he would miss the huts altogether. Good-by, Mother and Father! The tears were very near; he was not much over twenty yet. He thought of how he had never done a stroke of honest work in Norway, but had always stayed at home and let his mother spoil him. He had come to America to escape work and school; besides, he 'd had a notion that folks could get rich here in no time without either. And now he was here. Oh, how he wished he never had come!

Smoke at last against the background of frost-mist! He staggered in. Erik sat there mending a boot.

"Hullo, Anton, have you come for the midwife? Brush off the snow, my lad. It 's cold enough here already."

He listened to the boy's complaint against his mate. Anton swore that as soon as the snow thawed he would go to the town and have Jo summonsed. There must be law and order even in this country. Hammering a peg into the boot, Erik listened composedly to this and a good deal more in the same strain. But when the boy asked leave to come and live with him, he frowned angrily. No, not for a day!

Not for an hour! The provisions for the winter had been distributed, Anton's share was in Jo's hut, and there was no local store just round the corner.

"If you want any food you must go shares with Jo."

"But I told him I'd never set foot again in the house of such a cheat."

"Then you'll starve," said Erik, and went on mending his boot. Anton waited. Erik must be joking. But he took his time over that boot of his. At length Erik looked up, and saw to his surprise that the boy was still there. "Want your mother, do you? Well, if you would be such a fool as to take up with a mate like that, you must take the consequences."

"But—but what shall I do?"

"I can lend you a rope if you want to hang yourself."

Anton stumbled out. Must he return all the way across this sea of snow? What if a snow-storm came on? But there was one thing worse still, and that was to go back to Jo.

He heard a shout behind him. Erik had come out of his hut. "Hullo, you! If you go whining to anybody else and get taken in there, I'll come and chuck you out. You've made your bed, and you've got to lie on it."

Anton plunged on again through the snow-drifts. But he wanted to live now, in order to take vengeance upon the whole colony, and especially upon Jo Berg and Erik Foss.

He remembered that day all his life.

Toward nightfall Jo heard some one approaching the hut. And when Anton put his head in, shamefaced and humiliated, he had not the heart to make the lad beg for admittance. "You'd best come in and thaw," he said.

But now it appeared that one of Anton's feet was frostbitten, so Jo had to fetch some snow and rub it for him.

One day it occurred to the schoolmaster that, as one form of boredom was as good as another, he might as well give lessons for a couple of hours daily to the children at Skaret.

Having made himself a pair of snow-shoes, he set off through the deep snow, with two or three books under his arm. Well, he was a free man now; no one could prevent him from teaching whatever he liked. That was a novelty. But now he would have to show what he 'd had up his sleeve all the time in the old country, in the days when he used to complain of being thwarted and unfairly treated. Now was the time to bring it out. Yes—but what, exactly, was it? Liberty? Should he teach them about liberty? Of course —liberty to believe what they liked. But what should his pupils believe? Had n't he a word to say on that point? Strange how it made one feel to live in the midst of this desert of snow with nothing but the sky overhead! There was nothing to abuse. There was no one to thwart him. The question was: what was he, himself? And it was so insistent that he stopped, and very nearly went home. What was he? What did he believe in? Liberty? Cant. Might as well show a number of hungry children an empty table and tell them they were at liberty to eat their fill! Liberty—ha, ha, ha!

The schoolmaster entered Kal's hut quite unostentatiously. Oh, this *was* good of him! But where were they going to sit? There was n't much room, as he could see. Karen tried to tidy up a bit. Not that it helped much; the only way to fit in would be for the teacher to sit on one of the beds, while the children sat in a row on the edge of another. Kal sat down by the little table, which was always crowded with pots and pans, and went on cutting up tobacco for his pipe.

It was like one of the first elementary schools in the old country. They went back half a century. And the children as well as the teacher wore thick woolen gloves. Karen threw out a suggestion that it would be a good thing if he would examine his pupils in God's Word. So Jo started upon Old-Testament history. Not in the old-fashioned way,

though, for of course he had to give a rational explanation
of the creation.

Karen glanced across at Kal, who blew a cloud of smoke
out of his pipe. The schoolmaster tried to define the difference between that which was myth or legend in the Bible,
and that which was really God's Word. Karen looked at
Kal again. His pipe had gone out. At last he cleared his
throat and interrupted the teaching by a question: was not
the *whole* Bible God's Word? The children eyed their
parents and the teacher. Jo enjoyed watching Karen's face.
"We'll talk about it during the recess," he said to Kal.

The children were allowed to run outside and roll one
another in the snow. In the meantime Jo said to their
parents that if they would rather do the religious teaching
themselves he would confine himself to the other subjects.
Oh, no, not at all, they said; it stood to reason that he, a
schoolmaster, understood these things better than they did.

Next they turned their attention to vikings, wars, pagan-
ism, and the conversion of the North to Christianity. Jo
tried to say something different from the old-fashioned teaching, but he could feel that the result would be exactly the
same as when he talked about the myths in the Bible. He
would only succeed in destroying their faith. Who could
deny that the vikings were pirates, that Christianity was
beaten, hacked, and branded into people, that those missionary
kings were simply butchers and knaves? But say so, and
they lost their "faith" at once.

Moreover, the children would not listen. They wanted
St. Olav to be a real saint. The look in Paulina's blue eyes
told him that he must not speak slightingly of these things.
O Pilate, what was truth? Jo washed his hands of the
whole matter and allowed the age of the vikings to remain
golden, so that the children might have something thrilling
to dream about. Kal had relighted his pipe and was enjoying himself. These stories reminded him of the fights

among the fishermen in the Lofotens. They were n't much
better in the old days, it seemed. Karen took care not to
make a clatter with the pots and pans. Presently she made
up the fire in the stove, and then sat down to mend a pair of
Oluf's trousers. Kal and Karen were going to school with
their children.

And now the boys wanted to know what it was like, in
the old days, in America. "There you are!" said Jo to himself. "These youngsters have changed their country already. All the old man came here for was bread and land,
but the boys are n't content with that, and they are turning
into Americans." So before he left them he told them how
a Norwegian, Leif Ericson, had discovered America; and
then he gave them an outline of the history of the country
in later times. The shrewd eyes of his scholars shone with
eager interest. Kal had never heard so much at a sitting
before. But little Siri fidgeted; she was cross because she
could not understand what it was all about.

As he walked homeward Jo felt uneasy in his mind. What
should he do when he had finished with the myths and got
on to Christianity? To attack other people's beliefs was
one thing; to be sure of one's own ground was quite
another. And if he tried to deceive the children in this
matter they would see through him at once. What did he
believe? He was all alone now with the snow-covered plain
and the boundless vault above. "Remember how you fell
on your knees when the fire had frightened all the sneers out
of you!" What if his father and mother were right?—if all
his fine notions were nonsense after all? The thought hurt
his pride. Were the old folks going to be in the right again?
And were they still waiting for him to write to them in spite
of everything?

But a new idea was beginning to dawn upon him. That
far-away, over-idealized age of the vikings had always dis-
gusted him; but now he was beginning to glimpse another

kind of history—that of the settlers, a saga of the heroes
of labor battling with the virgin soil. Some day there would
be a big school here, in the midst of a rich and prosperous
district, and this saga would be the chief subject taught.
Who knows?—perhaps he himself would be the head-master.
It warmed his heart to think of it. Here was something to
concentrate his powers upon at last!

Christmas was at hand, and the unmarried men were
dreading it. This was as bad as living in a fisherman's
hovel. Erik was alone. Morten was alone. Were they going to sit there on Christmas Eve eating the same old porridge and milk, or fried pork and potatoes? If only they
had some bannocks! Morten had tried making bread and
cake, but without success; the stove was of no use for baking.
If only they had a herring or a bit of salt cod! They went
about with glum looks. Memories of home made them
mournful. Sledging to church on Christmas Day . . . parties . . . above all, the bells ringing on Christmas Eve . . .
their mothers and brothers and sisters sitting round the
dinner table! Well, all that was thousands of miles away
now.

But on Christmas Day the boys from Skaret came plunging along through the snow and invited all the neighbors to
a party. A party! At Skaret? It almost made them
laugh. Ought they to accept? What could Karen find to
treat them to in that little hut where there were so many
mouths to fill already?

But Karen was in high feather. The pig had been killed
for Christmas, and though it was not very old, perhaps, still
it was nice and fat. On Christmas Eve she had given the
oxen and cows an extra-good feed; and she had not forgotten
to put a bowl of milk in the byre, for the brownie. Without
saying a word to anybody she had kept a bag of rice and
a can of syrup ever since they first arrived here. And now

Kal was standing outside to receive the Christmas guests.

Ola, who had the longest distance to go, came walking in front of his team, picking the best way between the snow-drifts; but even then the snow reached up to the bellies of the oxen. Else was muffled up in all the wraps they possessed, with her baby snugly hidden inside everything.

"Evening, Kal! Happy Christmas! Have you room for the oxen?"

"I think so. Glad to see you."

Morten surprised them by coming on a pair of skis that he had made. Per trudged along in front of Anne, carrying the little boy in a warm sheepskin rug. It took some time to brush off all the snow. And when all the guests had arrived the hut was packed as full as it would hold. The childen had to be banished to one of the beds, where they sat demurely in their best clothes, with a plate of titbits to keep them quiet.

A big iron pot was simmering on the stove, and the women could see at a glance what it contained. Rice and milk—a real Christmas soup. Just what they used to have in the old country. And on the little table there was actually a black pudding with lard in it, and brawn, and bannocks with syrup!

"Karen! Karen! Why . . . Karen!" cried all the guests at once.

"Now, then, help yourselves," beamed Karen. But of course they could not all sit at table together, so half of them had to look on until the other half had finished. Well, well, this was Christmas, after all! "Come, help yourselves, now," Karen repeated, as she stood by the stove, watching them. And Kal, who was sitting on his bed, added that they must be sure to eat well: one needed something to keep one warm in cold weather like this.

They talked of their friends in the parish at home. To-day they would be going to church. And when church was mentioned, there was a silence, as if they were listening for something. But no sound of bells came to them from the wilderness of snow outside.

After they had had their coffee, the schoolmaster stood up and recited "Terje Viken" and "Dyre Vaa." These were poems that old and young alike could enjoy. Then Morten thought that it was his turn, so he recited the passage from Björnson about the trees that wanted to clothe the mountain, which he knew by heart. After that there was another silence. They looked at one another. This picture of love for one's country had moved them strangely. Ah, *they* had left their native land! Presently they began to sing the national anthem: "We love this land." Jo led, and Ola sang the bass. The little hut was full of song.

But Karen did not feel that Christmas was complete even now. Presently she screwed up her courage to ask the schoolmaster to read a little out of her book of family sermons. Here it was. . . . But no, Jo would rather not. The rest declared that Karen herself ought to read. Was not she like a mother to all of them?

"You can do it all right if you try, old woman," said Kal, looking down quickly and staring at his hands. He never liked to meet other people's eyes when God's Word was mentioned.

"Very well." Karen put on her spectacles,—she could n't read without them now,—seated herself with her back to the candle stuck in a bottle, which did duty as a lamp, and held up the book. She read rather hesitatingly, but in a conscientious, old-fashioned style, and took care not to omit any of the Bible references: John XV: 20; Mark III: 7. The rest sat close together, listening intently. Somehow she seemed to fill the little hut with the good old-fashioned spirit of Christmas. A book of family sermons and a housewife went so well together.

After the reading they thought they would sing a hymn. Anton's voice had a queer tremor in it; on this day two years ago he had been at home with his mother. How smart Paulina looked this evening with that blue bow in her fair hair! He thought he had never seen anything so pretty.

It was moonlight when at last the guests left. But Jo and Anton lit the lantern they had brought with them and led the way through the snow, followed by the others in single file. They could see Ola groping his way homeward with his sledge and oxen, by the same winding path through the snow that he had plowed up when he came.

"Good night, good night!" they shouted to one another.

Jo Berg was feeling very uncomfortable. Ola had asked him whether he would come and baptize the baby. Should he scoff at the idea? No, he couldn't refuse on an evening like this. And yet . . .

One by one they turned aside to their huts. When Morten reached his own he remained standing outside for a little while. On a brilliant moonlight night like this he could see so far on all sides. But the other huts had vanished again in the ocean of snow; there was not a light to be seen anywhere. Ice-crystals were glittering all over the vast plain, which seemed to roll on and on in waves of snow and moonlight. No, he could not hear the church bells; but a coyote was singing its lonely dirge to the moon.

VIII

Anders came bursting into Morten's hut and panted out, "You must come along to Erik—quick!"

"Why, what's up?"

"He's awful bad."

While he made his way through the snow-drifts he learned from the boy that both of Erik's feet were frost-bitten. He had let loose his oxen one day; they had gone astray in a snow-storm and he had had to go out and search for them. He had waded about in the snow for a whole day, and on coming home with them at night he had been so tired and cold that he had gone to bed just as he was. He had slept for hours without noticing the cold, but had awakened to find that he could not stand. Crawling out, he had fetched some snow with which to rub his feet. He had rubbed and rubbed, but in vain; they would not come to life. At length, being too tired to do any more, he had gone back to bed, and had fallen asleep again.

Three days later Kal had dropped in to ask him something. By that time Erik had become delirious, but he had just managed to say that the animals had not been fed or milked for several days.

On entering, Morten found Jo, Kal, and Per sitting inside, watching the patient. They looked round, but said nothing. Erik was lying with his eyes shut and a deep flush on his face; his head was thrown back stiffly, and his breathing was fast and labored. What could they do with a sick man, out here in the wilds? Karen and Else had been there to look at his feet, and had bathed them with soft-soap, but

there was no vinegar in the place, and already his legs were
very purple and swollen. A doctor? The nearest town was
a hundred miles away.

But could they let him lie here and die like this? They
were at their wits' end. Never before had they realized how
much he had done for them or how helpless they would be
without him. Must they lose him now?

Erik half opened his eyes and began talking thickly and
incoherently. It was evident that he was delirious again,
and seeing visions. He was talking about Nidaros County
and the railway and a new town. "You had better call the
town Nidaros," he muttered. Then followed something
about a church, a cathedral,—"Nidaros cathedral in this big
prairie city,"—about a university, a theater, and libraries
and hospitals. Things which had slumbered in the depths
of his mind came tumbling out pellmell into the light of
day in grand, lifelike, delirious visions. He had no idea
that he was ill; no idea that any one was present.

He closed his eyes again. The three men exchanged
glances. "The doctor," said Kal. "Yes, the doctor," murmured the others. But to take Erik all the way to town in
this deep snow was impossible. To get any doctor to come
here in such weather was out of the question.

"Anyway, a doctor could tell us what to do," Kal suggested.

They sat a while gazing at the bed.

"If I had a pair of skis . . ." said Per, getting to his feet.

What! Go a hundred miles all alone across the snow,
without a single house to take shelter in for the first three
days? Was he really in earnest? Run the risk of losing
his way in a snow-storm, of getting frost-bitten at night, of
being attacked by one of the flocks of starving prairie-wolves
which howled so hungrily at this time of year? Did he
really mean it?

Erik opened his eyes and stared at them. "It's all up
with me," he said. "There's nothing to be done."

"Never say die," said Kal. "You'll pull round all right, Erik. We're going for the doctor."

"You can't." Erik smiled faintly. "Don't do anything foolish."

Kal screwed up his face and scratched the little tuft of beard under his chin. Then he stood up and looked at Morten. "Will you lend me your skis, lad?"

Kal had a wife and family, but still he was ready to set off and risk his life for a pal. And Per was ready to go too. But Morten answered, "I want the skis, myself."

An hour later he put them on. A couple of Karen's loaves in his knapsack, a coffee-kettle fastened to his belt, a gun slung over his shoulder—and he was ready to start.

He knew that he would have to sleep two or three nights in the open, but he could dig a hole for himself in the snow. Suddenly he bethought him of the little compass on his watch-chain; it reminded him of the evening at Whitsuntide when he was walking home to Kvidal and his brothers and sisters had come running helter-skelter down the hills to meet him. How eagerly they had looked at that little compass! "What did you pay for it, Morten? Where did you get it, Morten?" What ages ago that seemed! Now he was here. If a blizzard came on he would never reach any human habitation. If one of his feet got frost-bitten to-night, the compass would be useless. If . . . if . . . ! Suppose he had not started, Kal Skaret would have gone instead; that daredevil old Lofoten sailor was not the sort to go saying, "If, if, if"!

He did not hurry, but went at a steady pace. His earlier experience of ski-races told him that the only way to win was to husband your strength from the outset. One must keep on steadily, steadily all the time. The sun had come out, the sky was very blue, and the prairie rolled on into the distance like an immense carpet of white silk. The glare blinded him—but what a glorious day! He could not see the huts now, nor the smoke, nor anything; there was only this blinding ocean of snow, and the sky, and himself. Now he must try to find his way. He looked at his watch, at the sun, at his compass. Morten was an old sailor; he knew that the town lay to the southeast, and took his bearings accordingly.

If an eagle hovering high up in the blue sky had looked down upon the vast white sheet below, he would have seen a tiny speck moving on slowly but surely, steadily, and always in the same direction. In due course it would reach its goal.

The sun sank down toward the snowy desert, the day was waning, but still he glided steadily on. Down on the horizon the sun became a flame which set the western sky on fire; and now the prairie sea was rippling with waves of white and blue and gold. He was gliding on into fairy-land, and his shadow had turned into a gigantic blue landscape, shaped like a man, which glided on untiringly beside him. At last the sun was gone; the prairie was all blue; then came the night, the stars, and the biting frost. Still he glided on. He knew the danger of sailing too far to the left in the dark or in a fog, and his instinct made him bear to the right. On and on. No moon—only the night and himself. He must not think of sleep yet. He was a messenger, and a life was at stake.

By and by he stopped on a rise where the wind had swept away the snow. Here he could gather some dry prairie-grass, and there was even a little heather. He held the kettle on his ski-stick till it boiled. Then he sat warming his icy feet at the fire while he sipped hot coffee out of an old tin. And did n't Karen's bread taste good!

It was rather slow work to make a snow hut with his hands, feet, and ski-stick, but at last it was large enough for him to creep inside. He took his gun in with him, and drew over his boots a pair of thick snow-socks that his mother had knitted for his last trip to the Lofotens; there was nothing like these to keep the frost out. Then he put on a heavy Iceland jersey over his coat, pulled his cap well down over his ears, took a small blanket out of his knapsack, and put the empty knapsack under his head. Not a bad bed, this! He closed his eyes and was soon fast asleep.

Next day he plodded on in cloudy weather, steering southeast by the compass. Not that he trusted the compass altogether; he relied more upon his sailor's instinct. Gliding on and on . . . not too fast, but steadily. Was that the howl of a wolf? Turning round, he saw something following him. Pooh! it was only a coyote! At midday he stopped for a few hasty mouthfuls; then on again. Far back in the snowy waste behind him lay a comrade, waiting.

It began to snow. Softly, gently at first; then the snowflakes fell faster, the wind began to rise, and soon it increased to a blizzard. He could see nothing now but a seething, whirling Armageddon of snow; and often it felt as if the wind lifted him up and hurled him bodily into another land. But still he struggled on. Now and then he turned his back to the storm and peered at his compass, then, bending forward, he groped his way on—whither? Instinct again. He was out sailing in a sea-mist. He must take care not to go too far to the left. He could not light a fire to-night, and must be content to munch his bread and pork without anything to drink.

Another snow hut. This time he did not dare to sleep, but lay all night wriggling his toes in his boots, for fear that they should freeze. Next morning the air was clearer, and the weather brightened up as the day wore on. Suddenly the sun came out again. On and on. His right heel was raw, but that would have to wait till he had time to see to it. He began to feel tired, there was a slight singing in his ears, and the snow danced queerly before his eyes. But he must go on and on. Helena, Mother, Kvidal, everything had vanished in the mist now; his whole being was concentrated in one supreme effort—to reach the goal, to plod on, and on, and on.

In Erik's hut the men took turns watching. Now and then one of the women would bring some dainty or other to tempt him. Even at night a man always sat by his bed and saw that the fire in the stove did not go out.

The inflammation had reached his thighs now; they were shockingly red and swollen. At times the pain was so awful that he shrieked and whimpered like a child.

Sometimes he lay unconscious for hours; but now and then he would revive, look at his friends, and try to smile.

One day Kal and Per were sitting by his bedside when suddenly he opened his eyes and looked at them. "I've pretty near plowed my furrow now," he said with a smile. "Ah, well! Give my love to Mother. And forgive me for bringing you here."

"Rubbish!" said Kal. "Before you know where you are Morten will be back with the doctor."

"There's a little book in the chest over there," Erik continued; "bring it here."

Per went and hunted out the little note-book which he knew only too well. It was the book in which Erik had written down all that they owed him.

"Put it in the stove," said Erik.

Per and Kal gazed at him open-mouthed. Was he delirious again? But Erik repeated: "I mean what I say. Put it in the stove. I sha'n't want it where I'm going."

Per put it in the stove to humor him. But his eyes met Kal's when the book caught fire. It made them feel that Erik was saying good-by in earnest now.

Erik went on: "You need a better harrow and wagon, Per. You can have mine. And you, Kal, can have my cows and oxen; they'll come in handy, with your big crew!

There's another little book at the bottom of my chest. Send that to Mother."

They pressed his hand and thanked him for his gifts. There was no sense in it, though, they said, for he'd need them himself as soon as he got well. His mother—yes, he could trust them to see to that.

They relapsed into helpless silence again. After a while Erik said: "You must try and help that boy Anton. There's good stuff in him, after all." And presently: "Well, well, it's little enough I've done . . . and yet I meant to do such great things." . . .

Morten had been away for six days, and when at last he staggered, pale and hollow-eyed, into Erik's hut, he found no one there but Jo.

"You've come too late," said Jo; "he left us yesterday."

Erik Foss lay stretched out on the bed as if asleep.

A day or two after this the little colony had its first funeral. They chose a spot on the outskirts of Erik's land; and decided then and there that if they ever got so far as to have a church and churchyard, this should be the site.

IX

At length spring came round once more, and the melting of the snows was so tremendous that huge lakes formed on the plain. Water glittered on all sides, flowing, sinking, steaming, but by and by the land was dry again and began to turn green. The women came out of the dingy sod huts where they had grown so pale during the long winter. Their eyes were unaccustomed to so much light, but they longed to warm up their faces and hands. What a blessing it was to feel the sun again, and how hot it was already! Larks were rising high above the plain, flies were buzzing, a flower had opened its eyes close to the wall of the hut. Spring again! spring! How far had it got in the old country?

The time had come for the men to begin working on the land, but there was no Erik Foss now to tell them what to do. The women, too, could do their work out of doors, where there were air and light and room to move about. Anne felt as if she had grown so old this winter; but no one could mope now, with the sun shining so brightly. She had a little mirror—oh, dear! how gray her face had become!—and she stood in the full sunshine, almost praying that she might recover her former sunburnt glow. How strangely one's memories changed color, she thought. In the winter they had been nothing but sin and shame, whereas now they made her sing as she went about her work.

For better or worse they were her girlhood; they dwelt among the birch woods and mountains and shining lakes, and placed her in the company of merry boys and girls playing in the green meadows. Ah, the dancing, the singing, the gay strains of the accordion! No visitors ever came on

Sunday nowadays; still, it was a holiday; why should n't she tidy herself up a bit now that she could be out in the daylight again and see what she was doing? Oh, dear! how her hair was coming out! Just look at the comb!

While Per was having his afternoon nap she would sometimes go for a little walk by herself, taking her accordion with her. Then she would sit down somewhere and play it. There was no one to dance to the music, but she had her memories, and could play to them. At other times she would go and see the bachelors, Morten and Anton and Jo. "I just thought I 'd look in and see what it 's like here," she would say. "I suppose it 's a regular pigsty." It made the men open their eyes to see how she had changed in a few days; her step was so springy now, her eyes so bright, and the least thing made her laugh.

"How do you manage about the washing?" she asked, and offered to take their dirty clothes home with her; she was going to have a big wash to-morrow, and a few extra things would make no difference. It gave her a certain odd pleasure to rub and rinse those bachelor clothes, and still more to watch them kicking about on the clothes-line; no doubt she was sinning again, but most things were sin, if you went by that stupid old book of sermons.

Besides, how else could she ever have stood the winter, the sod hut, the prairie, and Per? These frivolous sins which kept springing up in her heart were a sort of tonic when she felt too homesick, and Per looked too gloomy and haggard.

The little colony felt strangely lost without Erik. One after another came to Morten to ask for his advice. They needed seed and provisions for the summer, but nobody had any money now. Who should go to town and try to find some way out of the difficulty? If they had a decent crop when the next harvest came round, they could not possibly thresh with oxen as they had done last year; they must have a proper threshing-machine, but where should they get the money? "What shall we do, Morten? Couldn't you go to town for us? We'll see to the work on your land while you're away, you know."

At first he refused. He was the youngest but one, he said, and he never could take the place of Erik Foss. And yet he wanted to go. The responsibility was great, no doubt, but all the more tempting. In the end he gave way and prepared to set out.

Just as he had yoked his oxen, Else came running up and handed him a small gold watch.

"See whether you can't get some money for this," she said, "and send it to Ola's father and mother. You mustn't tell him, though. He's been worrying all the winter because he hasn't sent them anything yet, though *I* think he's got a good excuse, don't you? But you know how fond he is of the poor old things; he thinks of them day and night." Morten took the watch. He had done much the same thing himself on his hurried visit to town that winter. It was so difficult for folks at home in the old country to understand that one didn't grow rich in a day out here.

He never forgot that journey to town. Hitherto he had always been taken up with his own business, but now he was a trusted agent. In the wilderness behind him was a little colony of his countrymen, living in sod huts, whose one dream was to make themselves a home there. What would happen to them if he failed in his trust? Credit? Who would sell goods on credit to an utter stranger? He had a letter in his pocket containing a pass-book worth six hundred dollars, but that was Erik's, and he had promised to send it home to his mother. Whatever happened, he would go straight to the post-office with that!

But how strange it was that Erik had not left more money! He must simply have robbed himself to help all the others. And why had he done it? For the sake of an idea, a far-away vision of the future, a longing to do something great. Could he Morten, emulate him in that?

The little town was transformed. Now that spring had come, it was packed with people who had arrived by train, and were buying their outfits before they continued their long journey over the mysterious prairie. The streets were a slough, churned up by horses' hoofs and the wheels of wagons. The shops and saloons were a babel of many tongues—men and women drinking, quarreling, screaming, fighting in the streets; wives trying to find their husbands; the whole town in a commotion. A constant procession of caravans kept moving off toward the west, as the great wave of humanity rolled in from the east; but the prairie was wide, and they would all disappear out there.

Morten talked with several of his countrymen, and picked up a good deal of news. Farmers from the Eastern States had sold out and were moving westward, drawn by the lure of the prairie. For a long time the settlers had mistrusted the open country, where they could get neither timber nor fire-wood; but now they had changed their minds. After all, it was tempting to go where there were no stones or tree stumps to clear away, and you could put in the plow at once.

On the outskirts of the town Morten watched a caravan of fifty wagons drive away; there were men, women, and children, cattle and furniture; and a clerical-looking man rode at their head. It looked as if a whole community were migrating. Morten learned that this was a congregation of the Norwegian sect of Haugians, which had quarreled with another sect in a settlement in the East, and was now migrating to a new home under the leadership of its pastor. The prairie was wide, and there was room on it to worship God in many ways. The prairie could swallow all of them.

But no one would give Morten credit; and he could not buy seed until he had got the money to pay for it.

Two days had gone by, he had finished the food he had brought with him, the journey home would take several days, and although his oxen could live on prairie-grass, Morten could not. His purse was empty. He had pawned Else's watch and had posted the money and Erik's pass-book. Perhaps there was still time to get the pass-book back? Involuntarily his feet moved in the direction of the post-office. If only he could get a square meal! And the seed! he could never show his face at the settlement without the seed. He must find some way out. But what if there were none? The post-office was right in front of him now. He hesitated outside the door. What ought he to do? A hard test, this; would he be able to stand it? Well, he would wait till to-morrow, anyway. He turned away, but his feet moved very reluctantly.

Were there no other shops that he could try? After being refused in one of them yesterday he had been followed out by a pale young man with spectacles who had been standing next to him at the counter.

"Are you a stranger here?" he had asked in Norwegian. Morten had answered that he was; then they had entered into conversation, and had walked down the street together. The man in spectacles said that he was a Methodist minister. He was trying to find land for his congregation in Iowa, for the settlement had become overcrowded, and a good many had decided to leave it and move farther west. Morten told him a little about his colony in the wilds, and the minister was evidently interested. "Is the soil good?" he asked.

A thought flashed upon Morten. . . . "No, no," he said to himself; "we won't have one of these sects!"

"We've plenty of money," added the minister, "and, like the Roman Catholics, we make a point of supporting our own people."

This was tempting, and again Morten felt that he was being sounded. . . . No, it was too risky; they might pay too dearly

for their seed. So he ended by saying that their land had
been a great disappointment to them; in fact, he could not
honestly advise any one else to come and settle there.

Well, that had been yesterday; but to-day he was utterly
helpless. Maybe he had been too high and mighty in his
treatment of the Methodist? He walked slowly along the
street, with downcast eyes, feeling very small. But what if
the little settlement became a large district some day, with
its own church and clergyman? Surely they must be allowed
to hear the Word in their own way, just as they had always
heard it at home in the church where he had been christened
and confirmed! If he let in an unknown sect with money,
they would soon take the lead. Had he any right to deliver
his friends into their power? No. But he must find a way
out of this. If only he knew how!

Later in the day he ran across one of his former mates
from the lumber-town in the East, and while they were
having a cup of coffee together he told his friend how things
stood. "Have you been to Bö the shoemaker?" the other
asked.

"Bö the shoemaker?"

"Yes. Folks always go to him when they're hard up.
He's a regular Jew, of course, but if you've got a voucher
from the land office showing that you've got land somewhere
or other, there's a chance. He lives in the cellar just opposite the hotel."

When Morten stepped down into the little underground
shop, a stuffy odor of leather, dubbing, and food assailed his
nostrils. A little bald man with a black beard, spectacles,
and a greasy-looking complexion put down the boot he was
making and stood up. "How-dee-do, countryman," he said
in a singsong tone, when Morten had introduced himself.

Money? A loan? The shoemaker heaved a sigh and shook
his head. Morten could feel, however, that he was being
weighed in the balance. The jaundiced eyes behind the spec-

tacles were looking him through and through. What did they see? An honest face: this one did not drink. Bö looked at the voucher from the land office, and asked a number of questions. How much land had they? How much of it had they plowed up? But so far away! Why, it was n't worth a shoe-peg then.

While the spectacles gazed out at the little window on the street-level, through which one could see the feet continually passing and repassing, Morten noticed that there were texts hung all over the walls: "Seek ye first the Kingdom of God." . . . "Pray without ceasing."

"How much do you want?" Morten suggested two hundred dollars. "That 's a lot of money." The shoemaker scratched his beard. Morten mentioned a threshing-machine, and at once the little man brightened up. "I 've got a second-hand one which is as good as new. It 's not been redeemed; you can have it dirt-cheap."

The upshot was that the young man had to sign a document mortgaging his crops for that year, while in the event of their failing he pledged himself to hand over his wagon and oxen in the autumn. Ten per cent interest per month. All right. And then he had to put his hand on the Bible and swear to pay everything, to the last cent.

But on counting the greasy notes he discovered that there were only a hundred and forty.

"Yes; why not?"

"But I 've signed a receipt for two hundred," said Morten.

"Of course. Twenty deducted as a bonus, and forty for the threshing-machine."

"Oh, I see." Morten grinned and hurriedly pocketed the money lest the God-fearing shoemaker should deduct more.

Now he was driving over the wide prairie again, and besides the flour and seed and the threshing-machine he was taking home coffee and sugar, and three young pigs in a crate, for the women-folks. They had not expressly asked him to do this, but he felt sure that they would be pleased. It was a new experience to have so many dependent on him. He hoped that the milk he had brought would last, though, so that the pigs would be alive when he reached the end of his journey.

There had been no letter from Helena this time. Nor had he become a millionaire exactly. On the contrary, he was like a pawned chicken: if the crops failed he would be plucked of everything that he possessed. But the crops would not fail. He was the new Erik Foss now; he must look on the bright side of things and encourage the others, and then they would pull through all right. The sun was shining, the prairie was all abloom with grass and flowers, and how could he help singing as he sat in the front of his wagon? But now and then he put up his hand to his chin, as if he felt that a man in his responsible position ought at least to have a flowing beard.

In this way the little colony tided over the summer. The corn-fields were twice as large this year; and if, as seemed likely, it turned out to be a bumper crop, they might be able to sell wheat in the autumn to the value of several hundred dollars. The first thing they did each morning was to look anxiously at the weather. A drought might still scorch up the corn, there was always the danger of locusts, and a hail-storm might come on at any time. Even Kal almost breathed a prayer to Providence to be a little merciful just for this once.

Providence? Yes; if this turned out to be a decent year, they would certainly have to subscribe for a parson to come out here in the autumn, so that young and old might go to communion. But he thought it best to let Karen talk to the others about that sort of thing.

Morten had never been so anxious in his life. He still felt as if the destinies of all the others depended on himself, and he had quite given up thinking, morning, noon, and night, about all the grand things he would do at Kvidal. Instead of that he paid constant visits to his neighbors, to show what an interest he took in their welfare. And they, in turn, relied upon him as if he had been Erik Foss himself. Well, well; they certainly respected him more since those two journeys to town.

One day Ola came sauntering up to him and remarked with a grin: "I suppose you think I don't know what's happened to Else's gold watch? Now you can see what it's like to be married to a woman like that; it makes a man sort of ashamed all the time." And then it all came out. He had made up his mind that when the autumn came he wouldn't go to town himself with his wheat, for he knew what would happen if he did so, and he wasn't going to give her *that* sorrow again. He would pay Mother's Darling to do the job for him.

This was Ola's way of chastising himself; and yet the old longing was growing more and more intense—the craving to see new faces, to plunge headlong into the rapids again. But he'd see himself hanged before he gave in this time.

When Morten went round his fields by himself he felt something which he never mentioned to any one. He thought of the great human wave that he had seen rolling westward from the town, and it seemed to be carrying him along too. As he gazed out over the prairie he no longer saw a desert, but wealth . . . wealth . . . Only wait! Very soon he would claim his share. It seemed as if this endless expanse of untilled soil were singing a deep-toned song of the future: only wait! Very soon he would join in too. Standing there bareheaded and in his shirt sleeves, so sunburnt and young, he could feel an impulse from the mighty plain flowing in upon him: "Press on, press on, the whole world is open to you." The soft summer breeze, wafting seed and fertility across this vast land, fanned his face, and bore his soul along with it; he felt as if he were drinking in the great times which were to come.

Very different was the effect of the plain upon Per. He had made a mound of earth at a little distance from his hut, but if anybody asked him what it was for, he always changed the subject. For when his fits of depression came on, when the prairie overwhelmed him with its muggy, stifling gloom and he hated the very sight of Anne and the child, he found relief in looking at this mound. At such times he would go and throw one or two more spadefuls of earth on it, and somehow that did him good. It was not his old friend the fir-clad knoll at home, of course, but still it stuck up a little above the ground; he must throw on a spadeful or two more.

One man takes to drink, another yields to the evil intoxication with which this desolate land drenches his head. Sometimes Per yielded, and then he would walk far out into the plain in the dusk. His thoughts would become more and more gloomy, but the prairie kept receding farther, ever farther away from him. . . . What was Anne to do when at length he came reeling back to the hut? His eyes had such a wild look in them; she must n't let him go near the child. If she could get him to go quietly to bed, he would sleep and sleep, and that would make him better. Next day he would be as gentle as a lamb, and ready to do anything to please her.

One day Anne was sitting indoors in the hut when two men entered; they were dusty and perspiring, and their boots were worn to rags. Addressing her in Norwegian, they asked for something to eat, as they had been out in the prairie for days, and had finished up their last bit of food two days before. They were land-hunters. Thank Heaven they had found somebody at last! Anne fetched some milk and porridge, and the men ate ravenously. She looked at one of them; he was beardless and young.

They told her that they had come from Illinois. There
had been a thriving Norwegian colony there, but it had been
hemmed in by Polish settlers, bolstered up by the Roman
Catholic Church. At last the Norwegians could not stand
these neighbors any longer. Six farmers had sold out, and
these two had been sent out to look for land elsewhere.
Might they sleep the night here?

Per was not the one to deny such a request. Yes, they
could sleep on the floor. But next morning, while they still
lay sound asleep and snoring, Morten took counsel with his
mates. They agreed that they had no objection to having
decent folks as neighbours, but they did not want to have them
too near. Those who had come here first must have room for
expansion.

"Right. You go and tell them, Morten," said Ola. He
did so. Fortunately, he had little difficulty in coming to
terms with the two strangers, and he even went a good distance with them, and helped them to choose their land.

He was chiefly anxious about the quarter which had once
belonged to Erik. It was unoccupied land now, for Erik
had not lived on it long enough to secure a title-deed. But
Morten had made up his mind that Kal's eldest son should
have it as soon as he was old enough to obtain a claim; and
Kal himself could cultivate it in the meantime, so long as
no outsiders came and interfered.

Not a soul knew that Kal had gone off quietly one morning
and put his name on the next section-mark to the west. It
was illegal, no doubt, but he would like to see any one try
to take it away from him.

For several days after this Anne went about singing again,
though she noticed Per watching her rather suspiciously.
She could not help thinking of the land-hunter who had
looked so young.

It was almost reaping-time when Karen was awakened
one Sunday morning by the tinkle of a cow-bell outside.

She rubbed her eyes. Was she dreaming? None of their cows had a bell. But it sounded very homelike, reminding her of old times at Skaret. On going outside into the sunshine she saw a whole herd of red-and-white cows grazing on the plain. Were they bewitched cattle? No, she could see smoke beyond them. Surely not Indians? Not a bit of it. In an hour or two a company of men, women, and children came over and said good morning like Christians. The little colony from Illinois had arrived.

It was a real adventure for the women, who had not been away from the settlement since the day they came, to see so many new faces. But how should she entertain these new-comers when she had nothing in the hut but milk and porridge? Coffee? Perhaps she had a few beans left still. Would they have a cup of coffee?

No, thank you. They had made ready a bean-feast in their own camp, and now they wanted the old settlers to go back with them. It was quite like going to a wedding. Even the schoolmaster shaved for once, and put on a flannel collar. Else, sunburnt and graceful, came walking beside her Ola. Anne was feeling like a young girl; what a lark it was to see so many people again! Over in the strangers' camp there were horses, and wagons filled with planks; evidently they were going to begin in style; perhaps they even meant to build themselves frame houses.

"What part of the world do you come from?" asked Kal.

"Oh, most of us are from the Trondhjem district. The one with a red beard is an Irishman, and can only talk English."

First they were regaled with hot chocolate and bread from the town, then with roast meat and a nip of spirits. The talk was very lively, with a cross-fire of questions about the settlement in Illinois and the life out here on the prairie. Was the winter very severe?

The children from Skaret had found some friends to play

with. The Irishman had a pale-faced daughter with red hair; she could only talk English, but they could play together, for all that. And now they were racing and romping all over the plain.

Afterward the camp broke up and moved toward the northwest, the heavy prairie-schooners dispersing one by one to the different quarters. On the following days the smoke of the distant camp-fires could be seen rising into the air; and if the day was very still, they could hear the builders chopping and hammering. Well, they had some neighbors now.

This was a bumper year, and no mistake. When Kal thought of his fields in the old country, they seemed no bigger than postage-stamps compared with the land he had plowed up last year and this, which was rippling all around him like a golden sea. What corn! What splendid wheat! And he had Erik's quarter, too, unless somebody came and claimed it. The thought almost made him tear his hair.

The neighbors joined forces and reaped the lots in turn, the men walking in line mowing, while the women and children ran about binding sheaves and piling them in shocks. The sun blazed down, the sky was very large and blue. Else's baby lay crying in a cradle of sheaves, but she could not go to him now; bareheaded and perspiring, she toiled on like the rest. How handsome Ola was to-day, swinging his scythe, his shirt open at the throat, his golden hair like a halo!—so manly-looking!

Nobody dreamed of going home before the evening; they had brought their food out with them, and once or twice in the day they seated themselves round one of the shocks, ate their cold porridge, and drank long drafts of milk from the can, then lay back among the sheaves and closed their eyes for a few minutes' rest. But bachelors will be bachelors and young women will be young, even if they are married; so Jo would sometimes lay his head on Anne's lap, and Morten would venture to put his arm around Else's waist for a

moment. The husbands would laugh and Kal would chuckle:
"Well, well, well! Nice goings-on, I'm sure!"

But soon they had to buckle to again; they had to hurry
on the work, first here, and then on their neighbors' land.
There might be a hail-storm; you never knew. Up with the
lark, and late to bed at night.

When the reaping was finished the threshing-machine went
the rounds of the neighbors. This was wheat, if you like!
Heaped up in huge piles, great mounds of food, it had to
lie on the ground in rain or shine until they could cart it
to town. It was worst on Kal's quarter, for he had twice
as much as any of the others. As he wandered round his
fields, looking at these mountains of wheat and immense
stacks of straw, it seemed too good to be true; and yet it was
his own, all of it!

One day he was put to a hard test. One of Ola's oxen
had strayed away, and now he had only one left, whereas Kal
had four. This news was a bitter pill, for Kal had meant to
stay at home and plow with two, while the boy Anders drove
to town with the other men to sell the wheat. He tore his
hair. But needs must when the devil drives. Besides, if
he knew Ola rightly he'd never come and ask; he'd simply
sit there twiddling his thumbs. A rum dog! Kal had a
long struggle with himself before at length he could bring
himself to say, "Well, Anders, I guess you'll have to take
Tom along to him." But all the rest of that day he did little
else but tear his hair.

Then came the journey to town. At daybreak the five
wagon-loads of corn rolled heavily off into the plain. Why
should the wagons follow one another in line? There was
no road here. The oxen could lumber along at their own
sweet will, while the men lay on the top of the corn. Far
away in the east the first reddish streak of dawn was showing.
Ola was not with them this time, and Anton was seated on
his wagon-load of corn. The boy still went shares with Jo,

but they were going to dissolve the partnership this year, for Anton would be able to buy a yoke of oxen with the money he got for his corn, and as soon as he came back from town he was going to build himself a hut.

The day was hot; they halted for a meal, and allowed the oxen a few hours' rest. After that they drove on again at the same sluggish pace across the endless plain. In the evening they made a fire, cooked their usual meal of porridge, and then lay down to sleep under their wagons. The darkness and the starry vault were all about them.

On the third day they caught sight of something in the far distance moving in the same direction as themselves; it turned out to be a train of corn-wagons coming from another far-away settlement. Toward evening they struck the military road, which made it easier for the oxen; but from time to time they had to get out of the way to let other wagons, drawn by four light-stepping horses, pass by them. Fresh trains of wagons kept converging upon the road from both sides, until there was one continuous line of wagons stretching on and on toward the town. They began to meet trains which had already been there; the drivers were flushed with drink, singing, yelling, and cracking their whips with a noise like a pistol-shot.

Nearer the town the wagons stood close together. Impossible to go farther to-day. In the streets it was just the same, wagon after wagon in a dense block. They had no choice but to wait for their turn, for each wagon-load had to be weighed separately and emptied at the elevator. Morten and his mates had to stop a good way outside the town. The men jumped down and stood in a group, staring at one another and laughing.

"Well, what d' you think of this?"

"We 've just got to grin and bear it."

Now and then a corn-speculator would come strolling down

the row of waiting wagons. He chose his men carefully, and poured out glasses of spirits.

"Look here, boys, why should you stand waiting here till doomsday? You won't reach the weighing-machine for another three days! Prices are falling every day; we get regular wires from the Chicago exchange. Better sell to us. We can pay eighty cents a bushel to-day, but I swear it'll only be sixty to-morrow."

Taking out a pocket-book, he flourished a handful of notes in the faces of these prairie folks who had not seen any money for a year. Many accepted the offer. But Morten went from wagon to wagon, warning his mates: "No damn nonsense, now. We'll wait."

They did wait. They could not unyoke the oxen. For when the wagon in front crawled on a bit, they had to move forward too. The oxen and their drivers had to eat their meals on the spot, and stay there night and day until their turn came.

This year they had so much wheat to sell, that they had to make four trips to town. They had not made their fortunes yet, but the little shoemaker Bö had been repaid, and on each trip they took back something with them: two more oxen for each of them, a new plow, a reaping-machine, a couple of sacks of coal,—enough to burn at Christmas, at any rate, when the prairie frost set in,—and, last but not least, provisions for the long winter. Per bought a brooch for Anne, and Anders invested in fishing-lines for Oluf and himself, and a new coffee-mill for his mother.

When it came to the fourth trip, Ola could not resist the temptation to go too.

All the way to town he sat singing. The very thought of seeing something new—a lot of houses, lights in the windows, shops, people from all sorts of places, a little noise and confusion, a church spire, horses and smart carriages, women in hats and finery—oh, how could any one help singing? The only drawback was that meddling little tyrant Morten, who must needs keep an eye on him from the very moment they got to town. It was "Ola" all day long: "Ola! Come along now, Ola." What, must n't he even talk to folks now? "Don't you hear, man? Great news from the old country. They 've made Sverdrup prime minister."

Something like news, that! And of course they must discuss it. Wherever Ola went he met cheery souls. "Where do you hail from? Biri? No! You don't say!" Then Ola would have to give some account of himself; and it was n't always easy to tear himself away at once. If you refused a drink, it gave offense; and if you did n't stand a drink in return, you were a mean skunk. Wonderful what a lot of cheery souls he came across this time!

On the morning that the five wagons rolled off over the prairie again, Ola lay insensible in one of them.

It was still early. Kal was grimacing at the rising sun. Morten looked pale. The two men had had to fight a whole gang in order to get Ola away.

When they halted for a meal later in the day, they let loose Ola's oxen as well as their own; but Ola himself lay snoring. It was just the same in the evening. But next morning he was up before the others. With his hair full of chaff, he stood gaping and blinking at the sun, and it stared back at him from thousands of miles away in infinity. "Is that you, Ola?" "Yes, I 'm afraid so. It 's me, right enough."

He thrust his hand into his breast pocket. His pocket-book was gone. Had he dreamed all that about the little red shoes for the baby, which had smelt so good? He felt in the outside pocket of his coat. Yes, there was one. What a cunning little shoe! But where was the other? He hunted and hunted, in all his pockets, in the wagon, in the boxes. But there was only one. That was all that he had to bring

home with him! He had not even a rifle, or he might have
put an end to his troubles there and then.

The others were getting up now, so he hastily lay down
again. He pulled a sack over his face and pretended to
snore. He could hear them putting in his oxen again, and
presently they were rolling on over the plain.

When the evening came he was so hungry that the smell
of fried bacon from the camp-fire made him sit up and give
a cough. The other men were seated round the fire, eating;
they could hear him, right enough, but they would not turn
their heads. At last it was night once more; he fished out
what little food he had left; then he lay down again to sleep.

The days passed, and at length they came within sight of
the smoke from their huts. The women and children were
coming to meet them. Else was carrying the baby on her
arm. "Welcome home!" she cried from afar.

When he was seated in the hut, and she was getting his
supper for him, he suddenly burst out: "Else, you made
a bad bargain when you married me. You'd best go home to
your father. He's still alive, I guess."

She stopped dead, staring at him. "Ola! What *are* you
talking about?"

"I've chucked away everything." He was not going to
tell her any lies. But he could not bring himself to grovel,
either. He flung it at her brutally, so that she might not
even think of forgiving him. "Take the child and go home,
Else. That'll put a stop to all this!"

There was a pause. Then she bowed her head and said:
"You're tired out, Ola. Go to bed and have a good sleep."

As he was removing the tarpaulin from his wagon he saw
something which made him stop and stare. Two flattened
sacks of flour, on which he had been lying all the time without
knowing it. *He* had not bought them. His mates again?
But who? Per? Morten? For a moment he felt a lump in
his throat; then he clenched his fists and swore. None of

their charity for *him!* Why could n't they let a fool like
him go to the devil in his own way? What in hell did folks
mean by interfering?

Here was Else coming out again—and she had n't even
reproached him. That was the worst of all. And now she
said: "At any rate, it's a good thing they did n't do you
an injury, Ola. You must try to take it like a man. After
all, we got the money for the other three loads, so we can
still buy a couple of oxen, and a reaping-machine too."

Oh, could they! He gave her a furious look. He had
never in his life been so near beating her. Comfort? He
would not be comforted. Why, he could lick the whole lot
of them, and yet they must needs come clustering round him
like so many guardian angels! Go to Jericho! If Erik had
still been alive, he'd have gone to him and asked for another
good thrashing. And this time he would n't have moved a
finger to defend himself.

Late in the autumn a solitary ox-wagon approached the
little colony. Morten was seated in front, and inside sat
a red-bearded man in spectacles. He was a clergyman from
Northville.

His home was in the little town, but his parishes were
scattered miles and miles apart over the wide prairie. This
would make the sixth. He had to go the round of all of
them, so he was quite accustomed to traveling and being
jolted about in an ox-wagon. His fee for such a journey,
taking a couple of weeks, was ten dollars in cash, with free
transport, board, and lodging—of a sort.

After a bumper year like this, it was only reasonable for
the old settlers to invest a little money in God's Word.
Presently Kal's children were running round to the neighbors to tell them that the parson had come. Erik's hut had
been tidied up as far as possible, and Else went over to it
with a table-cloth, food, and crockery.

Late that evening the clergyman was seated in the hut, preparing his sermon by the light of a candle-end stuck in a bottle. Footsteps sounded outside. A huge man with a long brown beard opened the door. Per Föll. He did not enter humbly, as poor working-men in the old country had to do when they visited their high and mighty parsons. For this one had not been appointed by the crown to chastise the common herd. No, Per was every bit as good as the parson to-day; so he gave him his hand and bade him welcome.

He sat down and murmured a few disconnected sentences. Was there anything special that he wanted to ask? Yes, there was. One or two important questions on which he would like to hear the clergyman's opinion. He only hoped this man knew a little more about them than he did himself!

An hour passed. Two hours. Little by little Per managed to get the door ajar, and at last out slipped all the things that were seething and working in his brain. In the end he confessed like any child, and showed how utterly helpless he was. Could the parson tell him what to do? The terrors that beset him in his loneliness, the specters that haunted him—all, all had now been confided to the clergyman.

When at length the man in spectacles saw him out, he pressed both Per's hands warmly. "Good night, my dear man. Many of our countrymen feel like this in the prairie. Don't forget that. But it passes over. Try to be very considerate to your wife; and whatever you do, get plenty of sleep."

Sunday was a mild day, with a pale autumnal sky. The sunshine no longer scorched, it merely gave light and warmth. The congregation assembled, dressed in their best and carrying hymn-books. Two crowded wagons drawn by horses came over from the new colony.

It was an open-air service. At last these exiles in the wilds could see a real parson again, with gown and ruff all

complete, just as if it had been in the old country. He spoke
their own tongue. The hymns were the same that they had
sung so often in their church at home. Now they were
singing again, as they did in those days. Some sat on
benches, others on the grass; behind them were the plain and
the sky, and everything was singing. The clergyman stood
on the step of the hut with his hands raised: "The grace of
God be with you, and the peace of God our Father and the
Lord Jesus Christ."

They bowed their heads. Anne was sobbing already. Her
little boy was sitting on her lap, and he stroked her face.
Per stared at the clergyman and fumbled with his beard.
Ola had turned partly round; his bronzed face was a sealed
book. Morten had never been moved like this even in the
church at home. Why was it? Not only because of the
memories which had carried him back, so that he seemed to
see his mother and brothers and sisters before his very eyes.
No, it was more than that. He could feel the emotion of the
others concentrated in himself; not so much because he was
their leader, as it were, but because the bond of sympathy
between them had become so close. He had not spoken to
Ola since their last trip to town. He must shake hands with
him to-day.

When the sermon was ended they sang another hymn; and
all the women were sobbing now. Not that the preacher
had threatened or frightened them, but their memories and
their homesickness had become a sort of ladder to heaven
while they sang.

Afterward there was a communion service inside the hut.
Behind a small table covered with a white cloth stood the
clergyman, who had brought the bread and wine with him.
In front of him knelt the men and women in a semicircle on
the hard turf that had once been Erik Foss's floor. They
bowed their tanned faces and folded their rough, toil-worn
hands. And the little hut became a temple round about them.

When the clergyman laid his hand on Per's head it rested there a little longer than on the others, and it felt to Per like the loving touch of a brother.

At a little distance from the hut stood two men, talking in low tones. They were Jo and Ola.

"You have n't gone to communion, then?" said Ola.

"No; I 'm not quite sure whether I hold with all that. I must think it over a bit more. But what about yourself? And your wife?"

"My wife 's gone home. And I—well, I guess I 'll have to turn over a new leaf before I go in for that sort of thing."

X

Many a home in Norway has on the chest of drawers a photograph of the son in America. Once upon a time he went about the house like the rest of the family, but now he is so far, far away. He must be quite a great man nowadays: he looks so stern with a parting in his hair, and dressed like the quality! His letters are read aloud as reverently as sermons; Mother sheds a tear, Father looks down, the youngsters see new and thrilling visions. Perhaps there are flowers in the window, a print or two on the walls, and a brightly painted cupboard in the corner. But by far the finest thing in the house is the American on the chest of drawers. He is more than an ornament; in course of time he becomes a household god.

Berit Kvidal had one now. The photograph of Morten stood there in all its glory, and when she was alone for a bit she would have a little chat with it: "What d' you think of so-and-so?" She never heard his firm, decided step in the porch now, or his voice laying down the law about all that needed doing; nor could she wash and mend for him as she had done in the old days. But what was the use of fretting? The freckled face beneath the red hair was always warm from hard work, what with cooking and milking, scrubbing and mending, spinning and weaving, the children, the work out of doors in spring and harvest-time, and once in a while a mothers' meeting, with coffee and God's Word.

She had her share of troubles, too, but many a time as she hurried across the yard she would stop to look at the hills, the farmsteads, and the wide fiord in front of the long blue mountains in the west. Steamers and white sails came and went all the time; some were going very, very far, others came from strange, distant lands. Fairy-tales again, but the thought of them refreshed and comforted her.

Morten, too, had gone in one of those big ships. She strained her eyes as if trying to follow him, but the vision disappeared in a white mist which was called America, where it turned into yet another fairy-tale. Of course she still had Simen, who was already twenty, Peter, who was a couple of years younger, Randi aged fifteen, and little Knut and Mette. They all tried to help her, but Morten was the one who had kept everything going.

More than once she had gone with the children on a Sunday evening to look across at the slopes on the other side of the river. There was nothing to see but an alder wood and a lot of tree stumps and stones. But wait till Morten returned; there would be meadows and corn-fields then. It was strange to look at the shabby old houses to-day, and then think what they would turn into when he came back! Berit could see the whole thing, and she got the children to see it too: the large farm-house painted white, the long red outhouse with its two wings. Why, she felt as if she had moved in already, and was the mistress of one of the biggest farms in the country-side!

The children listened eagerly. Randi, the elder girl, took after her mother; a fair, pretty girl. She went about seeing visions everywhere, and when she laughed, it made every one else laugh too. Some day she would be the daughter on a big farm. Ah, there'd be plenty of suitors then!

But the bank kept asking for interest, the sheriff for taxes, the storekeeper for instalments. Berit sighed and racked her brains to find a way out of all her difficulties. Well, well, Morten would be back in a year or two. It was always such a comfort to think of him. Distance was gradually transforming him into a refuge from all anxieties. When she sat by the window in the dusk, gazing at the western sky, she would pick out one of the stars—the brighest—and think more than ever of her boy as she watched it.

Now and then a girl with fair hair and large, wistful eyes, would come to the back door. She always came by way of the wood, and would never go into the living-room. It was Helena. She did not seem to despise Kvidal now. Perhaps it was because Morten was so far away: she could picture him just as she pleased, as a fairy prince performing wonderful feats on skis, or making speeches, or singing with the finest voice in the world. And there was no one to talk to about all this except his mother.

"Have you heard from him?" Berit would chuckle, "Yes, have you?" "Yes, but what does he say in his letter to you?" And the two women would talk about it in whispers.

Then came the long winter with no letters. They knew that he was out on the prairie, but not that he was such an immense distance away from a post-office. Berit thought it hard to bear, herself, but it must be worse for the poor girl. Just before Christmas Helena came round on skis. "Have you heard anything?"

"No, worse luck."

"Do you think . . . that anything's happened to him? That . . . that he's dead?"

"Don't say such things, child! Of course he's not."

Helena sat down on the bench in the kitchen and burst into tears. Presently she sobbed out that she had not treated him as she ought; she could never, never be happy again! If he sent her a ticket now, she would go out to him, even if she had to run away from home like a thief.

Berit mused. . . . If the girl really went out to him, there would be no inducement for Morten to come home. Hard? It was always hard to be a mother. She would have to reconcile herself to playing second fiddle. But Kvidal? What—what if it turned out to be nothing but a dream? "Morten, Morten, you mustn't fail me!"

Night after night she sat up weaving a handsome tapestry in red, white, and blue. It was going to be his bedspread when he came home and married. One day she managed to entice Helena into the living-room when no one was there. "What d' you think this is going to be?" The girl colored. "I don't know." Berit smiled "Nor do I!"

As the spring advanced, however, Helena's visits ceased. Berit met her one day on the highroad and had some difficulty in catching her eye. "Have you had a letter yet?"

"Yes."

"Was there a ticket?" Berit's voice trembled.

"No."

"Have you changed your mind?"

"It—it's all so difficult."

In the middle of the summer the banns were published for Helena and the sheriff's son. Berit was in church, but she did not faint. She dared not write and tell Morten; it might put him off coming home. She was never tired of looking at his photograph on the chest of drawers, and having a chat with it when they were alone together. And she went on weaving the handsome tapestry.

At first fat, fair-haired Simen seemed to be full of Morten's great plans, and he did not spare his younger brothers and sisters now that he was the eldest at home. "Go and chop wood," he would say to Peter. "Come and help plant potatoes," he would command his two sisters. Morten should see that he was able to keep things going just as well as *he* could. But as time went on, Simen began to wonder why the American did not send home a decent sum of money. His mother might call five or six dollars a lot of money, but how far did it go toward paying the bank and the store-keeper and the taxes, let alone hiring labor and farming on a big scale? What was Morten thinking about?

And now it was Simen who had to go out working, as a fisherman in winter, as a day-laborer in the spring and autumn, and wages were no better now than in Morten's time. He could not be away and on the farm, too, earn money and at the same time improve Kvidal for his brother. What ever was Morten thinking about? New orders were always coming: "Start doing so and so. Begin draining the north end of the marsh." All right, if you'll send the money! Surely he must be getting rich now, with a farm of a hundred and sixty acres!

Simen never forgot the look of radiant happiness on his mother's face when she came home one day in that first winter. A letter at last! And money, too. Oh? How many hundred? "Three dollars." His mother felt rich as she flourished the foreign notes. Simen swallowed a laugh. If his mother had got a measly sum like that from a son in the Lofotens, she would only have sighed to think that it was so little; but it when it came from a son in America—the household god—it grew into nearly a million dollars.

Morten did not mention that he had pawned his watch in order to raise this sum; in fact, there was uncommonly little about himself; but of course there were fresh injunctions: "Do so and so in the spring. Tell me the parish news. Is Gunnar Ramsöy still chairman of the council? Are many going to the county school now?"

But Greater Kvidal had caught the fancy of the younger children as well, and one day Simen actually began to clear the ground on the slopes beyond the river. It was easy enough to cut away the juniper bushes and young trees, but when you started on the earth itself, it was another story; stumps and stones, stumps and stones. Lucky he had Peter to help, for it fairly took it out of your back and arms. Peter was just like Father, round-shouldered and quick-tempered. One moment he would be ready for anything, the next he would turn sulky and leave you in the lurch. Every inch of ground had to be turned with a spade; every square foot had to be paid for in sweat. If Kvidal had been

cleared in this way, no wonder the croft was no bigger!
The two brothers kept harping on the thought of Morten
with his hundred and sixty acres of splendid prairie soil.
All *he* had to do was to put in the plow. If it was anything
like the red-and-blue posters that the steamship companies
sent out, the farmers in America did n't even hold the handles
of the plow, but sat there like swells enjoying a sort of
joy-ride while they plowed. That was how Morten did it,
no doubt. And every now and then he would go into his
office and write home: "Do this; do that. Begin clearing
away the tree stumps and stones. Gee-up, gee-up! I 'll
crack my whip over you, if you don't."

Did he think he could save and pile up money out there,
while his brothers spent the best years of their lives slaving
to improve Kvidal? And that when the farm was all in
tip-top condition, he could come along with his fortune in
his pocket and say: "You can clear out now; I 'm the eldest
son, so the farm 's mine"?

The work of clearing made little progress, and both boys
became strangely surly and ill-tempered toward their mother.
If they earned a little money, they no longer gave her the
whole of it. They must try to dress decently, they said, as
she could n't spare them anything. And Peter needed a
watch. Besides, there was the county school: Morten had
gone there, and they wanted to do the same.

Simen had once thought of becoming a blacksmith, and
Peter could make as good cart-wheels as any you could buy
in the town. But the letters from the emigrants opened
their eyes to such wonderful new possibilities that the old
interests lost their attraction. Each of the brothers went
for a winter to the county school, where they learned a great
deal about kings and wars and vikings; and this only made
matters worse. They felt as if they were living in other
times and among other peoples, where only the great deeds
counted, and only the men who rose to the top were worthy

of mention.   Why should they go on slaving here for Morten's
sake?

The letters from the emigrants were all alike in one respect: they told of the wonders of America, but were silent
about the hardships the settlers were suffering.   They started
a kind of "revival" in the parish.   When the congregation
gathered outside the church on Sunday the letters were the
great topic of conversation.   Fancy Kal Skaret with a hundred and sixty acres—quite an estate!   Strange how luck
changed sometimes.   More than one small crofter thought of
Kal.   And Per Föll had written home saying that it was
perfectly true that there were no class distinctions in America; the parson and the doctor took off their hats first, when
they met a laboring man.

There was not much else in Per's letter, except that there
was fodder enough on his quarter for fifty cows.   But even
that gave small folk something to think about.   It haunted
the thoughts of the crofter plodding through the snow-drifts
of a winter morning on his way to the manor-farm, where
he had to do his statutory work for eight cents a day; and of
the fisherman returning home from the Lofotens without a
cent in his pocket.   When lawyers' letters were left at the
door, or Ebbe came to distrain, people always called to mind
those letters from America.   This was the way small folk
had to live here.   That was the way they lived in America.
Look at Kal, for instance!

As time went on, more and more left for America.   If a
crofter's son married nowadays, he thought twice before he
set to work to clear a patch of ground for his little house.
He knew only too well what it meant to start life as a crofter;
most of the year would be spent in working for the farmer
who owned the land, and in the evenings he would have to
wrestle with tree stumps and stones on his own little patch
of ground, in the hope of some day growing enough fodder
to feed a couple of cows.   When he and his wife had toiled

like this for a lifetime, their children would find themselves
homeless; for the landowner would add the croft to his own
farm.   That was the way in which the cultivated land crept
farther and farther up the hills and slopes.   But the letters
from America told them that poor folks might do better.
Cross the Mill-Pond, they said, and you could become a rich
farmer, bigger and prouder than any in the parish at home.

When once they were there, and began writing home, their
letters were just like the other letters from America.   However desperately hard up they might be, they kept it to themselves, and even encouraged their relations and friends to
follow them.   Whatever happened, they must make Father
and Mother think that they had risen in the world; like all the
other emigrants, they wanted to be a household god on the
chest of drawers.

One day Berit was overtaken by the inspector of forests
in his gig.   He stopped and offered her a lift.   This inspector
was regarded as a queer old chap; he went about preaching
to folks that they never ought to buy anything in town, but
ought to make their farm implements themselves as they
had done in the good old days.   As for the schools, they
did more harm than good.   They only made folks more
stupid than they were before.

"Well, Berit, how are you getting on?   I've had three of
your boys with me on my tours of inspection in the woods.
They are bright, clever lads—just the sort of young fellows
we need."

"Yes, sir; but Morten emigrated," and she sighed.

The inspector raised his gray head and threw a glance
round the valley.   Presently he said: "I'm afraid a lot
of our young folks are leaving.   Especially those who've
been to the so-called high schools, I fancy."

"Yes, sir; so they say.   But when you know a little more
than other folks, it isn't easy to go on in the old ways."

"It ought to be easier. Surely the schools exist to educate efficient workers for this country—not emigrants! Why, they're never tired of speechifying about how patriotic they are. And yet the very next day they go and emigrate. I can't make head or tail of it."

Berit thought a moment. She wanted to defend Morten. "But I suppose it comes in useful to have learnt so much," she suggested.

"I dare say. But why should a poor country like Norway spend so much money on schools for the young people who farm and enrich America? Last year I had four boys with me from mountain farms. Their forefathers had toiled there for generations, but when it came to their turn they must needs go to the high school, and then—of course they wanted to emigrate to America. All four of them are going out this year. I shouldn't be surprised if those farms go back to pasture one of these days. That's the way it happens, and it'll go from bad to worse; the schools will see to that!"

A cold shiver ran down Berit's back. What if such a thing happened at Kvidal! "Things may get better again," she ventured.

"How? The question is: are we going to educate the young people to live in Norway, or is the country too poor to provide a living for small folk who have been to the high schools? That's what I'm puzzling my head over. Perhaps the small countries have no future before them. Education and progress will depopulate them. Well, well! it doesn't look very hopeful." He looked round the valley again and began to whistle.

One day an aged couple came slowly up the hills to Kvidal. The white beard of the man straggled over his chest, his eyes were red and watery, and he leaned heavily on his stick. The woman was small and withered. They entered, passed the time of day, and sat down by the door. They had just dropped in, they said, to hear whether Berit had had any news of Morten.

Yes, she'd a letter. And how was their son Jo getting on? Jo? The bloodshot eyes of the old man tried to meet his wife's. They had n't heard a word from Jo. Berit stopped her wheel. Had n't he written home? They shook their heads miserably. It was two years now since he left. The bank had compelled the sureties to repay the money he had borrowed. But the worst thing of all was that he had never sent his parents a line.

Berit got up and put on the coffee-kettle. She felt almost rich when she looked at this poor old couple eating out their hearts for the son who had forgotten father, mother, and home. But luckily she could give them news of Jo. Morten often mentioned him in his letters. Their son owned quite an estate now; he was in a fair way to become a rich farmer.

"And yet he does n't send a cent home," grumbled the old man, looking at his wife again.

After that Berit never met them without their asking her for news of their son. She had not the heart to disappoint them, so she always told them that Morten wrote that Jo was getting on very well.

At the end of two years, Morten sent home fifty dollars. Quite a big sum—if only she had n't owed the storekeeper so much.

After her conversation with the inspector of forests she went about in continual fear lest Simen and Peter should take it into their heads to emigrate. They seemed less and less inclined to do anything on the farm. One day she told Simen that it was time he went to the blacksmith and set to work to learn the trade in earnest. Fancy what a fine thing it would be if he owned a big smithy some day, so that folks need not go to the store or make a trip to town when they

wanted to buy their locks or fittings or horseshoes. But
Simen only laughed. Thank you! A lot of money he'd
make like that! Then she had a serious talk with Peter.
There were plenty of chances for a handy-man like him.
Supposing he set up as a carriage-builder, folks would come
from all the country round to buy his carioles and gigs and
sledges and carts! It might develop into a fine business,
and he might become a rich man, especially if Simen would
join him.

In this way she tried to put it into their heads to stay
at home. And she herself began to see new visions. She
could see all her children prosperous and respected in the
parish, and now and then they would come and stay at their
home, the big Kvidal farm, where she, a gray-haired old
granny, sat enjoying the thought that they had all got on so
well in the world.

Simen and Peter grinned and asked her why Morten had
not started a joiner's shop, instead of leaving the country.
Money—you had to have money. Why didn't she want them
to go out into the world and make their fortunes as he was
doing?

But need they begin on such a grand scale right away?
Couldn't they begin in a small way and work their way up?
Ask Morten, they said. Had *he* begun in a small way?

They read such a lot; they were always coming home with
new books; and tall, fair-haired Randi was just as bad. But
it seemed as if the books only made them long to go out into
the world. They took newspapers and knew all that was going on; but the papers, too, made them long to go abroad.
Fancy how well off the people were there . . . and there
. . . and there! And above all in America.

They were beginning to outgrow the dream of the big farm
at Kvidal, which had kept them round her until now. But
perhaps the hardest blow of all was the discovery that they
were beginning to feel ashamed of their home and parentage.

So they had got it into their heads that folks looked down on them because they came from Kvidal? Well, well! Heaven knew that their father and mother had done all they could.

XI

The settlers had plodded along for five years on the prairie, and new recruits had joined them in ever-increasing numbers. At last the great moment had arrived, and they could begin to build themselves a church. They had long since decided that it should stand on the spot where Erik Foss lay buried. It would not be a cathedral exactly, but a building made of turf, boarded inside and out, and sufficiently large to accommodate a couple of hundred persons.

The little company of emigrants who had come here first were known as the old settlers, and they formed a clique to which the others could not easily gain admittance. First Else and then Anne had a baby, and what could be more natural than for Paulina, who was fifteen now and tall for her age, to go and look after the house while the housewife herself was laid up? As for Karen, she was the only midwife within a hundred miles or more; but it all went swimmingly every time. They were so thick on the ground at Skaret; when they wanted to lend their neighbors a hand they went in a body, but when the others came to them it was only by ones and twos. What of that? Kal was no skinflint.

"Anders," he would say, "take a couple of oxen and go and help Morten; he's pottering about over there all by himself." Payment? No, not when it was one of the old settlers.

On the other hand, Kal was niggardly about time; hadn't he plowed up twice as much land as his neighbors? But pals were pals, and that made all the difference. One day the boys took it into their heads to build another room on to the hut; the old one could be the quarters for Mother and

204

Father, while the four children could camp in the new one. Kal screwed up his face doubtfully and consented; but would n't it look like showing off?

Just as the boys had finished the roof of this annex who should come strolling by but Morten. "By Jove! Look at that!" he exclaimed. He had grown a short, curly beard lately, and his eyes were always looking about in search of fresh expedients. Kal stood by with a somewhat shamefaced air. He had a sort of feeling that he ought to have asked Morten's leave; they had all come to look upon him as their adviser and the boss of the settlement. "The boys wanted to do it," he said apologetically. "About time, too," answered Morten, "and the same thing 'll soon be needed everywhere, if the women-folks are going to be so prolific!"

Kal took this for a hint. A few days afterward, the two boys arrived outside Ola's hut, armed with spades and axes. "What 's all this?" he asked. They explained. Else was delighted. Later in the summer Kal sent the boys to Per on the same errand. Then it occurred to Else that it would all be so much brighter and cleaner if they whitewashed the walls and ceiling. No sooner said than done; and in a few weeks' time all the huts had been brightened up in the same way.

Morten was still living alone, but his corn-fields were steadily increasing in size, and in spring and autumn he often felt as though he were working himself to death. Since the news came that Helena had married the sheriff's son, the old country seemed to be farther away than ever. From that day onward the others noticed that he often looked as though he slept badly; and when he laughed, it sounded strangely mirthless. He still meant to go back to Kvidal some day, but not until he had become a rich man.

He made up his mind that he would not waste another winter looking after two or three oxen and cows, so he left them with Anton, and went off to town to work as a joiner.

It was all grist to his mill.   He was waiting impatiently for
the day when he could buy some horses.   He made good
use of his time in town.   Every evening he attended a free
school, and thus learned to speak English properly, besides
gaining a better acquaintance with American life and institu-
tions.   What a splendid country it was, and what a wonderful
history it had!   What opportunities it presented to a man
who had the will to work and get on in life!   No wonder
he began to see new visions of the future.   If he really meant
to climb the ladder—high, high up—America was the very
place for him.

Must he give up the old country, then?   Certainly not,
and yet . . . ?   Now he would imagine himself as the Governor of North Dakota, now as the uncrowned king of the
parish and a member of parliament in Norway.   It was
lucky that nobody could read one's thoughts!   At any rate,
he clung to his mates on the prairie just as much as he did
to his mother and brothers and sisters in the old country.
His mind was becoming divided into two.   He had countrymen there and countrymen here, but it seemed as if the latter
needed him most, and certainly he could get better results
out of the Kvidal in America.   Always he seemed to hear
the prairie singing of the days to come—of the young men
and women for whom it was waiting, of the big farms, of
the railway, of the towns which would spring up.   "Will you
help?" it sang.   "There is room here, room and to spare for
all who have the will to work."   But was that all?   Had he
no other aim than to rise in the world?

The next summer something happened which set him
thinking furiously.   The wheat was very promising that
year, and the fields were twice as large as before; if they
had bumper crops again, they would be able to afford horses,
and even frame houses, for the whole colony.   But one Sunday, when the clergyman had come, and was holding a
service in the open air, a cloud blew up from nowhere and

a sudden hail-storm scattered the congregation in all directions in search of shelter. When it stopped, they emerged from their huts to find that the plain was white all around them. The hail had stripped off the grain, nothing but bare stalks remained, and the whole wheat crop had been ruined. In an icy wind the settlers waded through the hailstones to their huts, where a night of black despair awaited them.

Morten very nearly gave the schoolmaster a thrashing on this occasion. They were walking home together from the service, and Jo remarked with his jeering laugh, "This is how Providence answers our prayers!"

"Shut up!" said Morten, fiercely.

And yet he lay awake that night repeating Jo's words. They were utterly helpless, and therefore they groveled in the dust before an almighty Being. The answer? They had had it to-day. Was that the long and the short of it? He had never thought much about religion before. But now he lay tossing from side to side. They all looked to him for guidance, and he felt the burden of the responsibility. A church? A parson? Hadn't they enough to do earning their bread by the sweat of their brow, without wasting their time on that sort of humbug?

Two or three days after this, a caravan started eastward. Most of them were Irishmen who had arrived in the previous autumn; their first experience of a prairie winter had been bad enough, but a hail-storm in the middle of the summer was the limit. They fled in dismay, leaving their huts and their newly plowed fields unoccupied.

The Norwegians, who had come to the settlement empty-handed, had no choice but to stay where they were. From their fishing days in the old country they knew only too well what a black year meant, and yet they had never given up in despair on that account; what they had to do now was to hang on as best they could, and then start afresh next year. When winter came the men went off to town and took

the first work that offered; they had to get food somehow
for the wives and children who stayed behind. Kal went,
and so did Anders, although he was barely sixteen. Jo was
the only man left at the settlement. And before long the
workers in the town had earned enough to send load after
load of food out to their families on the prairie.

By and by Morten had a new riddle to puzzle over. The
next year's crops were finer than ever, and what were the
settlers planning now? To buy horses and build frame
houses? Not a bit of it! They wanted to collect money for
a little church. It would take more than the hail-storm to
shake their belief in Providence. The Sunday feeling died
hard; a single bad year would not kill it. They were determined to worship the man in heaven, even if he ruined them
every year. Morten could not make head or tail of it.

A number of new settlers had arrived that spring, and
Morten summoned them to a meeting outside his hut. Most
of them were Norwegians, with a couple of Swedes, an Irishman, and a German. Soon he had them all sitting or standing around him. Ola Lökka, a stocky, red-bearded peasant
from Hallingdal, got to his feet and gave it as his opinion
that they could think of a church when they'd made their
pile. If any one wanted more praying and singing he could
do it at home in his hut.

The German, a broad-shouldered giant with a big gray
beard, addressed the meeting in English. He was in favor
of building the church at once, he said, but the services
ought to be in English. His speech was interpreted for the
benefit of those who could not understand what he was saying. Murmurs of dissent. No, no; they were n't going to
have that.

The Irishman had a light-red beard and a hooked nose.
He, too, spoke English, and he led off by offering to contribute a hundred dollars to the church fund. Moreover, he
was willing to cart the building materials here with his own

horses—always provided that they would agree to hang a picture of Our Lady over the altar, and have a basin of holy water at the door for folks to dip their fingers in when they entered the church. Would they do that? He was even willing to give the picture. Was n't that a fair offer?

But the murmurs were still louder this time. Husbands and wives exchanged horrified glances. "Gosh!" said Kal, and looked down at his fists. The two Swedes swore under their breath. Ola gave Per a kick on the shin. Ho, ho! that chap was trying to convert them to his superstitions. For a hundred dollars? No, not for a million!

Per rose, and everybody stared at the big man. "I reckon we can manage to pay for the parson and the church as well," he said. "Morten, here, has told us how many bushels of wheat each one will have to contribute. We can bring the building materials in our wagons when we drive back from town. We need n't trouble our Catholic friend for his horses. And I move that we elect a building committee right away."

The proposal was adopted. Morten expressed no opinion; he merely presided over the meeting and listened to the views of the others. But he was pleased with the turn things had taken. The committee consisted entirely of old settlers: Per, Else, and Jo, with Morten himself as chairman. Per went home that day in high feather; he was looking forward already to the day when he would sit on the parish council and help to elect the clergyman. The king had no hand in it here, thank goodness. Per was in America now.

A year had passed. Morten was perched high up on the little church tower, hammering and sawing. He was the only skilled carpenter in the place, so he had to do most of the work, while the other settlers farmed his land for him. For the rest, Per and Anton were both clever with their hands, and Anders had grown into a big lad of eighteen who helped him all day long. "I must keep an eye on that young fellow," Morten said to himself. The boy had been in town again this winter, earning money in the daytime and going to school in the evening. He was always studying; Morten would have to look out for his laurels!

"Hullo! Bring me up some more nails." Anders came up with them. The boy showed no signs of giddiness; on the contrary, he stood on the ladder coolly unfolding a sheet of paper. A plan. He had learned to draw at the school in town.

"What's that?" asked Morten. It was the drawing of a weathercock on a spire. "Oluf and I have been working on it for several days. It's made of iron; we've almost finished hammering it out now." "Well, I'm blest!" said Morten. Bright boys, those two.

The spring work was well over for this year, and when Morten looked down from his lofty perch he could see all around him on the sunlit plain little huts and wooden houses with the smoke rising from them, and pale-green fields which contrasted with the grayish yellow of the prairie. Altogether there were about thirty settlers now, and a good many of them had come from the parish at home. They kept writing to him and turning up out here, and many a time he had felt inclined to warn them not to come; but what right had he to do so? After all, he himself had left Kvidal.

Jo shouted up to him, "Aren't you giddy up there, Morten?"

"Come and see for yourself."

"Not I! I'm not going to commit suicide just yet. But tell me: how could a man sitting on Mars with a telescope tell the difference between your tower and a blade of grass?"

"Try and find out the answer yourself; it'll give you something to do."

He took no further notice of the skeptical schoolmaster. A little tune kept running in his head; what a pity he couldn't find the right words for it! It might serve as a hymn when they dedicated the first temple built in these parts. One day the bell would ring out from the tower: Come! Ye people from the land of mountains and woods, come hither! The same God that ye worship there will meet you here. Come, come. O thou that art dead, come in spirit and join thy kinsfolk. O thou that art homesick, come and find thy mother and father in the old, familiar hymns. Come! Come! Come! Outwardly Morten went on whistling and hammering as before, but inwardly he heard nothing but the church bell and the strains of the hymn.

Supposing the god for whom they were making such sacrifices only sent another hail-storm this year, or a plague of locusts: what then? They would humble themselves still more, and go on worshiping him. What a pitiful being was man! What a noble being was man! Morten stopped hammering for a moment and tried to grasp it. Here was a riddle that he would never solve. Jo was right. Seen from infinity, a church tower was no higher than a blade of grass. And yet heaven and earth were in this temple, small as it was. How could *that* be? Well, he must get on with his work.

One day he was inside the church, putting up the altar. Presently Anne and Else entered, dressed in their Sunday best. "Bless the work," they said, and looked about them. My word! how fine it was getting! The windows were in place already, but the floor was still littered with shavings. Bareheaded and perspiring, Morten came toward them and held out his hand.

"Let us know when we can come and wash the floor," said Anne.

"Come in three or four days' time. It ought to be ready then."

How good-looking they were! he thought. Anne's oval face, with its setting of dark hair, had still such a fresh glow, and her eyes were so bright and dancing. Else had regained her slender, lithe figure; her features were so delicate, and her brown eyes so grave and thoughtful. They still kept young, in spite of the hard work and the trying winters.

Else was unpacking something wrapped up in paper. It turned out to be a white cloth embroidered with figures in red. A group. Seemingly it was meant to be the Last Supper. He could not tell whether it was well done or not, but he looked at her and asked, "Is it an altar-cloth?"

"Yes, if you think it will do," she said shyly; "Anne and I made it together."

"*You* did most of it, though," said Anne.

"No, I didn't! Why, you did every bit of the embroidery!"

"But you drew the figures."

Morten thanked them and shook hands with them again. Presently they left. The presentation of this gift to the church was an event in their toilsome existence in the little sod huts. That was why they had put on their Sunday best. Morten went on with his work, thinking that women had a wonderful knack of making it feel like Sunday.

On leaving the church in the evening, to go home, he found a stout, fair-haired young fellow waiting for him outside. Morten started back. "What! You?"

"Good evening," said the other, and held out his hand. It was his brother Simen. For two years the lad had been begging him to send him a ticket. Morten had always refused. And here he was!

XII

They walked along together to Morten's home. When they entered the hut Simen stood looking blankly round the squalid little room. A fisherman's hut. And he had thought that his brother was a millionaire! "Well!" he gasped.

"Yes, this is where I live. Sit down. And now, what on earth brings you here?"

"We're a party of ten or twelve, all from the parish. Half of them stopped in the town, and the rest have come out here to settle on the prairie."

"Ten or twelve more! Why, I believe every young fellow in the parish is emigrating!"

"Of course. What else can they do?"

"Haven't they got land at home? How much of Kvidal have you plowed up?"

Simen grinned. "How much did *you,* when you were at home? You said it needed capital. We say so too; it *does* need capital."

Morten swallowed the taunt. "Well, I've not been able to send much home. But I will, one of these days. You'll find it's not so easy as you think. We've just got our title-deeds, and have bought another quarter by preëmption; very cheap, but it costs money, all the same—several hundred dollars. You see what our houses are like. We've no horses yet; only oxen. And if I can't earn a couple of thousand dollars to build a wooden house, my three hundred and twenty acres won't be worth a straw."

Simen could only grin sheepishly. He had fully intended to tell his brother a few bald truths, and ask him why he had not sent more money home. But the words stuck in his

213

throat. Why, his brother was worse off than any poor devil in the old country! And still they wanted all the young fellows to come out here.

"How 's Mother getting on?"

"Oh, much as usual. They all sent you their love."

The word affected Morten so much that he had to turn away to hide his emotion. He realized now that the life out here held him fast; he was drifting farther and farther away from his mother and his home. He began to get supper ready. Meanwhile Simen unpacked a knapsack, and presently handed his brother a parcel.

"What 's this?" Morten undid the paper. A brightly colored cloth, woven in red, white, and blue. He stood staring at it in astonishment.

"Mother wove it for . . . well, she thought perhaps . . . if you married some day . . . "

Oh. Morten had to turn away again.

Here was something else—a pair of braces that his sisters had worked for him. And a pair of embroidered woolen gloves. Home. Home. At that moment Morten could see everything at Kvidal—the people, the houses, the animals, even the grindstone behind the barn.

They went on talking late into the night. Morten had a hundred questions to ask. Eventually they agreed that Simen should work for wages for a year. Morten could not farm his land now without help, and hired labor was scarce.

Next day Morten was busy in the church as usual when Anton and Per entered, carrying a large box between them. Hullo, what now? "It this any good?" asked Anton, when they had deposited the box on the floor. Morten saw that it was a pulpit, octagonal in shape, with carved figures on three of the panels. One panel represented Moses with the tables of the law; another, Abraham sacrificing Isaac; the third showed the Carpenter's Son before Pilate. You could see with half an eye that the work had been done with a sheath-knife, but Morten was not going to discourage the carver.

"Splendid! Who's the artist?" he asked.

"There he stands," said Per, pointing triumphantly at Anton.

"But . . . but it must have taken a long time. And we never even saw it in your hut."

Anton grinned. "No one ever comes and looks *me* up."

Morten gave him a quick glance. It was quite true. Once a boy was labeled a skunk, it did n't help much if he changed a good deal as the years went by. The others simply forgot to look him up. That was exactly what they had done. But he had got on well this year; had his own hut, oxen and cows, and was doing his best. Strange that he had n't said a word to any one about this work of art! Perhaps the effort of keeping it to himself for a twelvemonth had been good for him.

"You 're a brick!" said Morten and shook his hand warmly.

The time had nearly come for dedicating the church, and the settlers could talk of nothing else, on their visits to one another. One day Morten and Per were together in the church when a wagon drawn by horses drew up outside, and in walked the red-bearded Irishman in his Sunday best. He held his hat in his hand, and began to address Morten in English. It was quite a little speech. Per could not follow, but Morten interpreted for him. It appeared that the Irishman was anxious to present the church with a bell for the tower.

Per looked askance at him. "H'm . . . yes. But is n't he a Roman Catholic?" he remarked.

Morten could not help laughing. "The bell won't ring any the worse for that," he said.

H'm. Per knitted his brows and pondered. At length he shook his head. No, he could n't possibly agree to that. Morten laughed again. Per had always talked so much about liberal views and progress. And narrow-minded ecclesiastical tyranny. But it did n't go very deep, evidently.

The Irishman looked from one to the other, waiting for an answer. He added that the German had sent his respects and asked him to say that he had a harmonium which he would like to give to the church, if they would accept it. Per cleared his throat, but relapsed into thought again. Presently he smoothed his big beard and remarked that this was going to be a *Norwegian* church.

At this point Morten hit upon a way out of the dilemma. "We 'll buy the bell, and the organ too," he said to Per. "They can sell them to us cheap, for a few bushels of wheat." Per cheered up at once. That would be quite another matter. Of course he 'd no objection to that.

Morten clinched the agreement with their red-bearded visitor, and added that of course every one would be welcome to come to the church. The Irishman flourished his hat by way of farewell, and took his departure. No doubt he, too, had been yearning for a place of worship out here in the wilds. Now that one had been built at last, he was doing his best to secure a foothold there, but it almost looked as if his Christian brethren wanted to shut the door in his face.

Immediately before the dedication of the church Morten called another meeting to appoint the various officials, and the building committee were reëlected as a parish council. The old settlers again—always the same story. No wonder that there were one or two murmurs this time.

He told them of the new acquisitions for the interior of the church, and added that at present they had no altar-piece; but his mother had just sent him something which might do instead, if they had no objection. Thereupon he showed them the tapestry which his brother had brought him. The Norwegian colors! It reminded them of the old flag. And it was woven in the style they knew so well; many a woman in the old country had sat at her loom weaving this sort of thing for use or ornament. They passed their hands over it appreciatively.

"But perhaps we ought to ask the parson before we hang it up," said Morten. Per brought his fist down on the table with a bang. The parson? No, no! He 'd be hanged if they did n't decide this for themselves!

The great day arrived, and the sun was shining brightly. Broad-bladed wheat was undulating in ripples on all sides; instead of the first scanty patches of corn-field which had made them think of the poor little farms in the old country, there were wide expanses of cultivated land; very soon they would have to give up lending a hand on their neighbors' farms, and each one would need his own machinery and hired labor.

With such splendid prospects before them, what better day could they have for dedicating the church? The bell began to ring in the little tower. Oluf Skaret had been practising for several days, and now the great moment had come: here he stood ringing and chiming the first notes of the bell over the wide plain. The boy was seventeen now, but never in his life had he been so deeply moved; it seemed to him that the prairie for miles and miles around was stirring, and asking what this strange, unknown sound meant. For thousands of years it had slept, but now it must open its eyes. *Ding, dong!*—what could this be? Even the larks high up in the sky had stopped singing. The corn-fields were listening, the huts, the fleeting clouds. *Ding, dong! ding, dong!* Oluf went on ringing and ringing. Suddenly he felt that this was a call; he knew now what his vocation in life would be.

The clergyman had put up for the night with Jo, who was going to play the organ. Here they came, side by side, the parson in black cassock and ruff, carrying a big book with a gold cross on the cover, and the schoolmaster clean-shaven and in his best. Far, far out on the plain men and women were wending their way toward the church. Now they stopped for a moment to listen to the bell. A great day! At last it was really Sunday out here in the wilds; how loudly the bell was ringing! Heaven knew that they had had their trials—poverty and toil, hard winters, disappointments, and the homesickness which was worst of all. But it was a Christian settlement now, a parish with a church, and a bell which they would all hear ringing on Sundays and holy days.

The strangest-looking vehicles were jolting along over the roadless plain. There were prairie-schooners drawn by oxen, with women and children inside; the oxen refused to trot, but give them time and they would reach the church by and by. A *kubberulle,* too, with wheels like grindstones, and nothing but a couple of planks for the women and children to sit on, while the men walked alongside. The Irishman and the German, and two or three other farmers with money in their pockets, who had moved out here from the East, came driving along in smart high-wheeled buggies drawn by a pair of horses. The old settlers had no great distance to go, so they walked at a leisurely pace, most of them dressed in the Sunday clothes they had worn in the old country.

Look, here was Kal coming with his family. Paulina was almost grown up now. She had on a new dress which Anne had made for her and a white head-kerchief with red spots. How determined she looked, flourishing those big hands of hers; but it was a pity she did n't hold herself better. Had she overworked herself already, helping her father? Kal had left his sheepskin cap at home for once, and was wearing the broad-brimmed felt hat that Morten had bought for him in town. Karen had on the same dress and shawl that she had worn at the auction before leaving Norway; but she had sprinkled a few drops of scent on the point of her kerchief; and now she was actually on the way to church again, with her well-worn hymn-book in her hand. Fair-haired Anders, with a straw hat cocked over one ear, was walking beside his father; but little Siri had remained behind. Her new dress had not been finished in time, and this was such a bitter disappointment that she had stayed at home, crying.

But who was this coming? Why, it was Siri herself, running after them, with a bright new milk-can in her hand. Perhaps they would n't take so much notice of her shabby blue dress if she carried this? The very thing! Look how it shone in the sun! Siri dried her tears; she had made up her mind to come to church after all.

And there were Per and Anne, with their elder boy walking between them and the younger on his father's left arm. The burly giant looked as if he 'might be the father of the whole congregation, and yet he had only a wife and two little boys with him. Anne looked insignificant beside him, in spite of her slim figure and her pretty face.

Next came Ola and Else with their babies, one of whom was big enough to toddle along between them, while Ola carried the other. Ola's face wore a defiant look. The more folks respected his wife, the less they seemed to think of himself. No doubt he let himself go a bit when he was in town, but that was only once in a blue moon. Had n't he cultivated his quarter as quickly as anybody? And yet no one ever voted for *him*.

Anton Noreng, on the other hand, had become quite famous on account of his pulpit; of course they had to make him into something after that, so they appointed him parish clerk. To-day he was going to sit in the choir and lead the singing. There he went in his blue-duffle clothes and straw hat, a handsome young bachelor of twenty-five.

Half a dozen children who had walked over the prairie barefoot were sitting on the ground outside the church, putting on their shoes and stockings. A group of men were standing round a grave with a white-painted wooden cross—

the only grave here at present. They were talking about the man who had been laid to rest there; no one who had known Erik Foss would forget him in a hurry.

The church? It was only the size of a meeting-house, but it had a tower, a spire, and a bell. There was a lot in a name, and everybody preferred to call it a church, even if the outer walls had not been painted yet, and the seats had no backs to them. The harmonium was playing already; Jo was quite an organist. Music had been the only subject he did not quarrel about at the training college. Every time the door opened, the strains of a choral came floating out. The men took off their hats long before they pushed open the door. Even outside they talked in hushed voices, and inside the church every one was silent. Instinctively the women seated themselves on one side, and the men on the other, just as they had done in the church at home.

The German was wearing a shiny top-hat to-day. He would not understand much of the sermon, but a service was a service. Who should come with him but the Irishman, accompanied by his wife and two young red-haired daughters. Well, nobody could object to the Catholics coming. Of course they took the opportunity of crossing themselves on their foreheads and chests when they entered the church, but even Per was willing to put up with that.

The congregation began to sing. How strange it felt! Many of them were so used to seeing old Noreng in the choir at home, and now his son was standing there instead. Was n't it strange? Some of the women had not sung in a church for years; no wonder they had to wipe their eyes and blow their noses now and then. They seemed chiefly to be singing about two things: their homesickness and their anxiety about the corn in the fields. These two things lifted them, as if on wings, high above the earth.

But Morten could not sing to-day. His eyes were ever on his mother's tapestry, which served as the altarpiece.

Once it had been meant to cover his nuptial bed. Now it was hanging here. Oh, Mother, Mother! His thoughts were trying to find their way home. He seemed to have drifted so far away, not only from his mother and his home, but also from that which had once been great and good in himself. Now it was all money, money, and everything had turned into business. Did he ever think of anything else? Wealth, wealth, wealth—did he ever dream of anything but that? What if he had been as humble as his father and had stayed on the little farm at home? Would n't he have been a better man than he was now?

The clergyman walked to the pulpit. What stillness! Everybody was listening, scarcely daring to look up. Even the German. Even the Irishman. God's Word was God's Word, even if you could n't understand the language. A great calm had descended upon them. This year, at any rate, there would be no hail or locusts. Most of them were conscious of a comforting voice, telling them that they would see their old home again one of these days. Henceforth they had only to work, and behave like Christians. What did they care whether the clergyman were preaching this doctrine or that? They were not listening to his words. They were not even thinking. To them religion was the hymn which was still echoing in their souls, and a sense of sanctity within and around them. They were worshiping the unknown, which has no name.

A baptismal service followed, and children of various ages were brought to be baptized. One little girl of five years, whose parents had been living far away from any church until now, became frightened and angry when the water was going to be poured over her head. "I won't!" she screamed, and pushed away the clergyman's hand. Her mother had to come and hold her firmly until it was safely over.

To-morrow there would be confirmation, and no fewer than three of Kal's children were going to be confirmed. To-day all the grown-ups stayed for communion, except the school-master, who had not made up his mind about it yet. Row after row of bronzed men and women came forward and knelt before the altar.

Then the bell began to ring again. Its pealing followed the worshipers as they walked or drove to their distant homes across the level plain, bidding them God-speed, and telling them that they must not forget to come back, now that there was a church here at last.

XIII

Simen had never thought that it would be like this. He was thoroughly unhappy from the first. He had come from a parish where most of the houses were painted yellow, red, or white, and where the landscape was so much alive that it fairly danced with joy. Here there was nothing but a grayish-brown desert, and a few sod huts which in Norway even a beggar would refuse to live in. The wind blew about so much straw and hay from the stacks that you waded in it as you went from one hut to another. Had they forgotten how to sweep a farm-yard? Wagons, plows, and other farm implements lay rusting in the open because there was nowhere to house them. If he dropped in to see Jo or Anton, their huts were worse than a pigsty.

It was enough to make a fellow die with laughing to see Mother's Darling trying to make *mysost* [1] because he could not find any other way of using all the milk he got from his two cows. What was still worse was to see Anne and the young lady from Dyrendal looking so untidy, and slaving like any crofter's wife in the old country. And she the daughter of the old colonel!

Anne often asked him to come to see her; she had always so many questions to ask him, and was never tired of hearing him talk about the parish and her friends there. Even Simen himself seemed to smell of home, of green leaves, and the landscape for which her heart ached. "Come again soon," she begged. "Mind you come again soon." It made her feel cheerful and lively again to have him there. She began to tidy and smarten herself up when she expected his visits, and

[1] A kind of cheese made by boiling cow's or goat's milk.

it dawned upon Simen that, after all, she looked very young still. But Per was not so pleased; he began to look askance at this young visitor.

What Simen hated most was the way they rushed everything here. His brother woke him up at the peep of dawn: "Get up and milk the cows." What? *He* milk the cows? That had been women's work in the old country, and he felt ashamed to take a pail and sit down under a cow. Then there was the food—porridge and milk several times a day, but never a bit of bread or cake or a bannock, and salt pork for dinner, week-days and Sundays alike. How different from living at home with Mother! He thought of her nice cakes and bread, of the fish and salt herring at which he had grumbled so often. How much better off he had been in those days! If he had guessed that it would be like this he would never have come.

This year the settlers could not go round and help their neighbors with the reaping; the fields were so big now that every one had more than enough to do on his own land, let alone helping on somebody else's. It seemed quite strange to part company, but they had no choice, for while they were all at work on one quarter the corn might begin shedding on another. It was all very well for Kal, who had so many hands; but for the others it was nothing less than a crisis. To hire help was out of the question; casual laborers would not come so far out as this at present. There were two people at work on Per's land and two on Ola's, but even if the women stuck to it like men, there was a limit to their strength.

Morten had his brother to help him now, but that was not enough; he had also got hold of a horse-whim; but even then the work was more than he could manage. A dead-lock. It made him furious. The reaping-machine was not one of the kind you could sit on; no, instead of the joy-ride he had looked forward to, Simen had to trudge behind, steering it with his hands. And when it came to his turn to bind sheaves, that was no joke, either, in this broiling sun; it meant taking off his coat and waistcoat, and soon his shirt and hat too, if he was to work as fast as Morten expected him to.

There were no holidays now, as there had been at home; no meetings for young men in the evenings, no county-school debates on newfangled ideas. When evening came at long last, and his limbs were stiff from the day's incessant labor, he had either to do the cooking or else fetch home the cows and milk them. And then? If he wanted his clothes washed he had to do it himself; if he wanted them darned or patched he had to do that too. Mother had n't time to-night! And after that he tumbled into bed to get two or three hours' sleep.

It required four men to do the threshing. But they were only two. So two had to do the work of four. First the wheat had to be driven to the machine. Hurry up and load the wagon! hurry up and pitch out the sheaves! Next day the oxen had to be yoked to the whim, and the threshing-machine started. The one who was feeding the machine had constantly to run backward and forward, fetching fresh sheaves, and the one whose job it was to clear away the straw had frequently to run across to the oxen and urge them forward.

Morten was always telling him to hurry up. But it fairly took it out of a chap to go on like that from morning till night, with just an hour's rest in the middle of the day. Simen felt inclined to go on strike. But would he have an easier time with strangers? Suppose they had slaved away like this at Kvidal, they might have done a good deal, after all.

Once more the grain lay heaped up in huge piles, and the breeze kept whirling clouds of chaff high into the air. The next thing was to stack the straw—or, at any rate, as much of it as the wind had not strewn over the fields. The sooner they could start driving the wheat to town, the better. They would have to make many trips this year; perhaps they would go on right up to Christmas.

"This will never do," said Morten to himself. "We must have a road. We must have horses. Then it will only take half the time. And we must have more machines." He knew that the big farmers in the East had a steam-driven threshing-machine which could vomit hundreds of bushels a day. He must have one here. And horses,—not one or two, or even four, but at least six or eight,—so that they could use a plow with three shares. *That* would make a difference. It was no use going on as things were now. But who should take the lead, if he didn't? Money? They ought to make a good profit on their wheat this year. Moreover, the old settlers had made up their minds that this time they would bring back planks for building frame houses. For five years they had braved the prairie winter in their huts, and now the women said they really must have decent houses to live in. Far be it from him to hang back.

He could not but feel annoyed at the ease with which Kal kept forging ahead. He was leaving them all behind. And Morten himself was obliged to give him a push now and then to make him forge ahead faster still. He had even had to help him at the land office, lest Erik Foss's quarter should be passed on to some one else. As soon as Anders was twenty-one he would get it as homestead land, besides having the right to another quarter as preëmption land. In this way Kal had got his claws into four quarters. And then there was Paulina: as soon as she was twenty-one she, too, would be entitled to a homestead. The same thing again. Kal was living next to the plain, and they could help themselves to as much of it as they pleased. They kept piling up land. They were leaving him behind.

And Kal's one and only ambition in this world was to

plow up new land. His head was haunted by the vision of endless corn-fields; after starving all his life in the old country he wanted to turn the whole world into corn-fields and food. He had known what he was about when he bought two more oxen in the spring; it meant that he could stay at home now, breaking up new land on his second quarter, while Anders drove to town with the other men and sold his wheat.

But something inside Morten seemed to be nerving itself for a spurt. Ahead of *him?* Ahead of Morten Kvidal? Had not Erik Foss dreamed of a town out here? And talked of a pile of gold for the man who owned the site on which the town stood? Where would that be, Morten? Secure that bit of ground, Morten. And then Kal and the rest would see!

Yet, for all these fine plans which kept running in his head, he was terribly homesick. At every meal, and on Sundays, the two brothers talked of the parish at home, of Mother, and Kvidal, and all their friends. Morten questioned and questioned. How was So-and-so getting on? Had they built any new houses in such and such a place? Which of his friends had got married, and to whom? He was beginning to smell the sea, to remember the slopes, and the fiord dotted with white sails. He grew sick with longing to see it all again. Surely there must be some girls left there! What were young women to him, if he couldn't go back and find them in the valley at home? Here? He would never marry here.

Marry? He lay awake at night picturing himself as a lonely old bachelor. Was he going to have no son to inherit a big estate from his father? What was he working for, then? Kvidal in Norway or Kvidal here? He must give up asking Simen about the parish at home. At times, when he saw it all very clearly, he got down to a deeper self, beyond the struggle for money, horses, more land, more power, and position—to something calm and holy. It was as if a church bell kept ringing there, and appealing to the Sunday-powers within him.

Out here he was a slave to the land and the almighty dollar, but at Kvidal he would become his true self again. He must go back. Had he really been seven long years away from home? Perhaps Mother's hair was gray now. He must send her a decent sum this year—say a hundred dollars. Would that be sufficient, though? He sighed. Even that would mean giving up the horses, if he was going to build a house. Simen, too, cost him a good many dollars a month. Why not tear himself away from all this and go home?

But the settlers wanted to have their own clergyman now, and the parish council had put an advertisement in the Norwegian-American papers. Moreover, the settlement had become large enough to be a township; they would soon have to elect a township board, three supervisors, a justice of the peace. Leave all this? Give up, and let the others forge ahead? They were just turning the corner and entering a new era, with a road, perhaps even a railroad, banks, a town, an elevator to which they could drive several loads of wheat a day, and it meant wealth at one blow for every one who owned land here. How could he leave all this? But what about Kvidal in the old country? Who was looking after it now? Hadn't he promised to return soon? to build a big farm there?

The wagon-loads of wheat began to roll townward again. Simen went for Morten, and Ola had hired Oluf Skaret, who was nearly grown up now. By and by the wagons would come back with planks,—planks for all of them,—and then they must work hard if they wanted to have a roof over their heads before winter set in.

Strolling past Kal's huts one day, Morten stopped short and stared. Two horses were grazing there, not full-grown yet, but about two years old; brown, long-necked, and long-legged. Kal was standing by the haystack as if by chance, with a guilty look on his face.

"Yes, it's asking for trouble, I know," he said, scratching his head. "But Karen—no, I mean that young cuss Anders —would have them."

"But you've only got two," said Morten. "Buy four, and then you can plow with them."

Kal had never heard a more blasphemous suggestion! No, no; it was better to begin at the bottom. One foal would have been more than enough. But it was all the fault of that young idiot, Anders! And the Irishman, of course, who would n't give in till he'd palmed off both of them on the boy. Morten congratulated him, and walked on in high spirits.

Kal stood there, thinking. Even Karen was getting quite swelled-headed about her pigs and poultry; new huts kept springing up, and there was a cackling and noise on the farm which was certainly no fault of his. When he thought of the day when these two young horses would be full-grown, the prospect made him feel almost dizzy. He trembled every time they neighed, and had constantly to go and tap their hoofs and stroke their noses. He was going to build a frame stable for them this autumn, and the door would have to be a high one; you never could tell how big a horse might grow in America.

And Karen had got another bee in her bonnet now. She must needs get Anders to bring some young trees from town, —alders and oak-trees,—and now she had stuck them in the ground at a little distance from the huts. Fancy having no more sense than that—an old woman like her, too!

No doubt she wanted them to look like the little thicket of birch-trees on the north side of the byre at Skaret. Well, she'd have to live to a hundred if she wanted to see them as tall as herself.

One day there was a new sensation. A store. You could

buy almost anything there—coal for your stove, oil for your lamp, matches, coffee, tobacco, all sorts of things. The storekeeper, Peter Skaarness, came from somewhere on the west coast of Norway, and evidently he had money—what with his horses and the fine frame houses he'd built for man and beast. He was a man in the forties, tall and gaunt, with black hair and a goatee. His temper was not of the best, and at the parish meetings he always criticized the old settlers. The sort of man to become a lay-preacher and start a sect of his own just to spite them. He had only his wife and his old mother living with him. His mother was too weak to work out of doors, but that was no reason why she should not do something for her bread and butter, so he set her to grind wheat in a coffee-mill.

If you wanted to do business with him you generally had to go and fetch him in from his fields. "Well? What d' you want?" he would say. On coming indoors he would hunt out a bunch of keys from somewhere or other, shake it, and ask you again what you wanted. Boots? H'm. He chewed his quid, spat, and pondered. Boots would be in the back room. He took a look at your feet, thought a moment, spat, and guessed he'd something which might do. Plows? They were over at the branch store. Coffee and 'baccy? Wait a bit—yes, they were up in the loft. Whisky? Well, he should n't wonder if he had a keg down in the cellar.

If you were hard up he never said no, but a loan was a loan, and interest was interest, and he could n't take less than twelve per cent. a month. If a new-comer started off with a bad season, and wanted to tide over the winter, he had to go to Peter Skaarness and mortgage his oxen, his cows, and very likely next year's crops as well. Morten had his eye on him. How much longer could this be allowed to go on?

In the middle of October Simen came back from town one day with a big bundle of letters, which he threw down on the table in front of Morten. Most of them were applications from clergymen. This meant that he had to call a meeting of the parish council on Sunday. Strange to say a good many turned up who were not members of the committee, and of course Peter Skaarness was one of them. But Morten felt that he could not very well eject them, and soon the hut was crowded with weather-beaten men in homespun clothes. Else, who was a properly elected member, was the only woman present.

Morten read out the names of the applicants. All were young men of Norwegian parentage, some from the training college in Madison, others from the German Lutheran college in St. Louis. He gave an account of each of them, and read extracts from the letters. As soon as he had finished, Peter Skaarness got to his feet and spat.

He only wanted to ask one question: were the old settlers going to run the whole district? They seemed to have taken it into their heads now that they had a right to appoint the clergyman. Morten laughed. According to the rules, it was the duty of the parish council to appoint a clergyman. Who else should do it? Skaarness's black beard seemed to grow more pointed than ever; clearing his throat, he inquired whether a man who was not a true believer could be chairman of a Christian parish council.

Morten asked whom he meant.

"You!"

Per began to mutter impatiently. This was a great day for him; he was helping to appoint a clergyman at last. Morten laughed again. They were n't there to discuss his own beliefs, he said. Nor could he remember that he had ever taken any one into his confidence on the subject.

Ola Lökka, the Hallingdal peasant, stood up—red-bearded, freckled, and bent. He had his own characteristic point of view to-day, as he had had when they were talking about building the church. If they must have a parson, he said, they ought to have a *cheap* one.

"Yes, yes; we'll decide on the salary afterward," said Morten. "A young man won't expect much."

"But if we choose one who's small and light, he won't cost so much; he'll be so easy to feed."

At this there was some tittering, but it was plain that more than one wanted to know how much the clergyman would cost them.

"What about a parsonage?" some one asked.

Per stood up. "Erik Foss's hut is unoccupied," he said.

"Oh!" said Else, in a horrified tone.

Per banged the wall with his fist. "Are we in the old country, where the parson's a swell and a pope, or are we in a *free* country? The parson'll have to live as we do. He's our servant. If he's too swell to live in the hut which used to belong to a man like Erik Foss, he can pack up his traps and go back where he came from!"

The other men squirted tobacco-juice. Most of them agreed: Per was right: what was good enough for them was good enough for the parson. But first of all they had to appoint somebody. Morten recommended one named Oppegaard, who wrote very sensibly and had an excellent testimonial from the Lutheran College in Decorah. The letters didn't say whether he was light or heavy, Morten added with a smile, glancing at the man from Hallingdal.

Eventually they appointed Oppegaard, and fixed his salary at five bushels of wheat per annum from each quarter of cultivated land. For marriages, christenings, or burials he was to have a fee of five dollars in cash. And now the question was, could he come here in time for Christmas? Better write and ask him, said Morten.

XIV

The journeys to town continued all through the autumn; by and by the snow came, and they had to drive the wheat on sledges. Once, when they were returning home, a snowstorm came on, and soon obliterated every sign of the trail. They had to struggle on as best they could, in a whirling, blinding blizzard. But were they going in the right direction? Before long the oxen gave out; they could not go a step farther. The men wondered what they should do next, for they were still twenty-four hours away from the settlement. Coyotes were howling all around them. Not that they were afraid, but it sounded so uncanny. And what if there were wolves too?

On this occasion Ola Vatne was with them. It was the last trip of the year, and he thought he deserved *one* jaunt, anyway. He had gone on a spree,—just a little one,—but had slept off the effects in the first twenty-four hours of the homeward journey. This was rather fun, he thought, as he waded along, in snow up to his thighs, feeling inclined to sing. The others did not whine, either; old Lofoten sailors like Per and Simen and Jo had been out on a winter day before now. Whine? Not they! But singing was another matter.

If they remained where they were they would be snowed under. A storm such as this might last for weeks. The oxen had given up altogether and lay motionless in front of the sledges. Simen remembered that folks were sometimes caught like this in the mountains in Norway, but there they could shelter in caves or under trees, and were only a few hours away from human habitations. But it would not do to stand still. They had bought some spades in town; Ola seized one of these, waded along in front of the oxen, and began to shovel away the snow. The other men followed his example. Soon they had cleared a space in front, but it remained to be seen whether they could get the oxen to move. Coaxings and threats had no effect. Beating them with the reins proved equally ineffective.

Then Anders pulled a handful of hay out of a sack of fodder they had brought with them in case of need, and standing in front of the animals, tried to tempt them with that. At length the two oxen in front got to their feet and stretched out their noses. The others followed suit. They moved a step forward. Anders began to walk backward, and the animals followed. Well, they were going on again, anyway. But whither? The men went on shoveling, half blinded by the driving snow, but persevering. They were getting on. If only they had brought a compass!

But how long could they stand working like this? The snow kept falling, falling, falling.

The men took it in turns. So did the boys from Skaret; *they* weren't going to let any one go home and say that they hadn't done their bit like grown men! The hours passed. At all events, they were moving forward and not backward. It was pitch-dark now, but they mustn't give up. Whenever it was Ola's turn to rest, he walked along with his back to the storm, singing—

"Oh, how I wish I'd a wife in town,
Trala-la-la, trala-la-lee."

When morning came they were all utterly worn out—what with the cold, the snow, and the strain. How many yards had they gone? And in which direction?

But they were in luck for once, for it cleared up as the morning advanced, and this put fresh heart into man and beast, though they still had to shovel away the snow for long distances at a time. Luckily they had enough food with them for that day, at any rate. The following night was so cold that they could not remember anything like it, even in their fishing days in the Lofotens. When at last they reached the settlement, they and their oxen were more dead than alive.

Jo had started a regular school now, and had even bought a globe and a map with his own money, on his last visit to town. His hut was crowded with little scholars, for many of the new settlers had children. He was a proud man on the day when the Irishman and the German sent their children to him; the school language was Norwegian, so their children would have to imbibe their wisdom in Norwegian, whether they liked it or no. Not that that was any difficulty, for the children all played together, and the foreigners had learned to understand Norwegian long ago.

Jo was beginning to feel rather pleased with life. There was no one to boss him here, as there would be in the old country. He could teach the children whatever he thought fit. As to Christianity, he had not made up his mind yet, but he could always leave out the doubtful subjects and concentrate on the others.

The subject he laid most stress upon was one which he had invented himself, so to say—namely, the history of the emigrants, and especially the heroes among them. For years he had been writing in all directions for information and reading everything that had been printed about it. And what a wonderful saga it made! Pioneers forcing their way through the virgin forests, fights with wild beasts, Indians, forest fires in the East which stamped out whole settlements, prairie fires out here, the frost, the locust, the long pilgrimages across the country to find gold in California—it was an epic, greater even than Snorre or Homer. Take, for instance, the Norwegian, Snow-shoe Thompson, who for twenty years went backward and forward on skis across the Rocky

Mountains with the mail, in blizzards and bitter frosts, often attacked by Indians or wolves—twenty years, and without receiving a cent for it! The State had cheated him. Vikings? There were plenty of them in this wonderful new country. Jo blossomed out in the midst of his cloud of tobacco-smoke; there was no parson or head-master over him now; he was his own master and his spirit could unfold itself freely. Really, it was rather fun to be a teacher in such circumstances. But the settlement would have to put up for a decent school-house next year.

Now and then there would be an interruption. Enter Per. Might he have a little chat with the children about history? He could still remember all those kings and wars and dates that he had learned at the county school. Certainly he might do so. Per beamed. Afterward he went home and told Anne that he had been giving a little lecture at the school.

The last expedition to town had brought back a letter from Morten's mother, which said that Helena had died in childbirth. Morten sat moping over the letter. Not even the sheriff's son would have any more happiness with that lovely woman now. But the strange thing was that Morten seemed to have got her back. She was no longer to blame for what had happened between them. After this he felt he could not wait any longer; he must tear himself away and hurry home. In the spring, he thought. Yes, in the spring. He would build a decent house to make his land more saleable; then Simen could hire it for a year or two; and after that . . . he would see. In the spring . . . in the spring.

The women-folks had to put up with a sore disappointment. Winter had come so early that the houses could not be finished this year. The men had been so busy with their journeys to town and the autumn plowing that they had not had time even to lay the foundations; and how could they do any building in such weather as this? Another winter in sod huts. The women went about sighing. Luckily they had stoves

now which kept warm all night, and coal instead of cow-
dung and prairie-grass. Kal was the only one who had managed to build a frame house, and that was only a stable for
his two horses.

One day Morten said to Simen: "Don't go and see Anne
so often. Poor old Per does n't like it."

"What!" Simen pretended not to understand.

"Oh, don't play the fool. You know as well as I do that
you 're always there when Per 's out."

"Rot! Anne only wants to hear the news from home."

"Drop it," said Morten.

Another winter. It meant nothing less than imprisonment for folks whose one thought was farming and whose
life was summed up in crops. But all of a sudden the
weather turned mild again and it began to rain. Soon the
snow had all melted, and a slight frost made the air very
crisp, with sunshine in the daytime and moonlight at night.
On a pleasant afternoon like this, a couple of weeks before
Christmas, a prairie-schooner with a pair of horses came jolting into the little settlement. The driver was a young, clean-
shaven man, and inside the wagon sat a woman in furs and
a veil. Beside her shone the brass fittings of a large trunk.

The news flew from farm to farm. The new parson had
arrived. He had come without warning, and, what was
worse, he had brought a wife with him. How should they
house such swell-looking folks? His wife was evidently a
town lady. Nobody had room to put them up. What ever
should they do?

They had not even got ready Erik's hut. In fact, Kal
had been keeping plows and harrows there. Morten was out
somewhere, so they fetched Per instead. Per, being a man
of the world, shook hands with the clergyman and his wife,
and welcomed them to Nidaros Settlement. Their house?
Yes, if they would come along with him—and he led the way
to Erik's hut. Jo followed them with a feeling of embarrass-

ment. Per threw open the door. It was a little untidy at present, but . . . He was enjoying this thoroughly; he was more of a boss to-day than the parson himself. One man was as good as another here, and the house for these two was neither better nor worse than what the others had to live in.

The lady gave a little cry of dismay, and the clergyman looked inquiringly at the two men. "Is—is there no other house?" he asked.

Per and the schoolmaster shook their heads. Else came hurrying up, hardly knowing whether to cry or laugh, and invited them to supper.

"Has no one a frame house yet?" the clergyman asked again.

Per thought a moment. "Yes; the Irishman."

"Oh. But is n't he a Roman Catholic?"

Yes, that was so.

The young man looked despairingly at his better half and sighed. "Then there 's nothing to be done."

"And there 's the German," Jo added.

"Oh? Is the German a Catholic too?" inquired the clergyman, seeing a faint gleam of hope.

Per had it all at his finger's ends. He was not a Catholic exactly; he belonged to a sect called Herrn-huters. H'm. The clergyman looked at his wife and shook his head again.

"Our houses are just like this," Per remarked, with a hint of severity in his tone.

"Oh, well, then, it 's good enough for us, too," said the other, and giving his wife his arm he walked on.

While the new-comers were having supper with Else, Anne and Paulina turned out Erik's hut, washed and dusted it, and lit a fire in the stove. Who could spare some bedclothes? A couple of blankets and a pillow hung there on a line; these must be beaten, and Anne herself undertook to provide sheets.

Per prided himself on his fairness; the parson and his wife could n't do without food, so he turned up at Erik's hut with a bucket of potatoes and a leg of veal. The others must bring their contributions too. Nobody starved here, so the parson must n't starve, either.

Late in the evening Ola and Else accompanied the new-comers home. A lamp was burning, a cozy warmth met them as they entered, and a miscellaneous collection of pots and pans, raked together from the other huts, stood near the stove. The big trunk took up a large part of the floor. But the air smelt musty, and the lady seemed in no hurry to take off her coat. She looked at her husband. When the others had gone, she sank down on the wooden bench and burst into tears.

She had grown up in a well-to-do home in a town in the East, had gone to balls and played at concerts. She had dreamed of a white-painted parsonage with a garden and trees, bright, airy rooms, servants, and neighbors of her own class. Her Jacob had often joked about going out as a missionary into the wilds, but she had never taken him seriously. It was a wonder that she had survived the journey; and then to come to *this!* Think of all the vermin there must be in the walls and bed and blankets. She bit her handkerchief; it was all she could do not to lose her temper altogether.

The clergyman paced up and down the little earthen floor. His fair hair shone gold in the lamplight, his eyes were fine and full of visions, but his voice was rather weak. Well, here they were at last. When he had refused to be a banker like his wealthy father and brother, and decided to go into the church, it was not for the sake of amusement. He had done it with a purpose. Had n't he often dreamed that it would be something like this?

"Mathilde dear," he said, "a missionary among the Zulus has to risk his life, and he runs the risk gladly for the sake of the Gospel. At any rate, we are among Christian friends here. Can't you see already how warm-hearted they are? Look at all that they have given us. . . ."

Presently he adopted a lighter tone, stroking her hair, and telling her that in reality there was plenty of room. The house was twelve feet short and eight feet narrow—why, they could give a ball! Room? There was tons of room.

"Oh, do be quiet! There's *nothing* here. Bedroom, kitchen, study for you . . . and . . . and . . . nursery some day . . . all in one room. And what a room!"

"Well, my dear, just think if we had to live under a bush."

"Oh!" She bit her handkerchief and looked daggers at him.

"There was One greater than I, and He had not where to lay His head."

"But He dwelt in other people's houses."

"So do we. And we've even got a house all to ourselves."

"But how shall we get a servant?"

"We'll have to do without one."

"I'm to do everything alone, am I? And perhaps live here for years and years. Is there such a thing as a baker, or a butcher, or a grocer here?"

"I don't suppose so."

"We're to starve then, too!"

"We'll manage all right, you'll see. Did you notice how touching the church looked? Think of all these good souls living here for years in the wilds before they could build a House of God. Can you think of anything finer than to work here—in this very place?" He spread out his arms, and became lost in his own visions.

This was how the parson and his lady began life in Nidaros Settlement.

XV

Moonlight on the frosty prairie. Heaven knows whether it was early or late, but Per Föll had been walking there for hours. He was drawing a long black furrow across the shimmering white ground. His hands were thrust in his pockets, his hat was on the back of his head, and his big beard pointed straight at the moon as if he were on the way to pay it a visit.

Behind him was the hut, with Anne and the children. He turned. No, there was no light there. He looked east, west, north. Not a light to be seen anywhere. It must be late. It must be a long time since he left home.

But he *would* get to the bottom of this, once for all. He must settle his account with the prairie. Come! Come! It was always luring him on. He would n't yield to the temptation, he knew how dizzy he would get; or at any rate, he would n't go more than a few steps. But he was like a drunkard: first one dram, then all the rest. Farther and farther he went, as if he were letting himself drift out with the tide. On, and on, and on. The farther he walked, the more dizzy he became, and the more powerless to resist that which was burning and torturing him within.

It was Anne again, and this time with Simen. When Per was alone with her he did not believe it, but out here it hurt so; the old wounds opened again and bled, bled. . . . Had n't she run riot in the old days with this one . . . and that one . . . and that one? Nonsense, Per! have n't you forgiven all that? But would it do any good to forgive to-night? No; he was being drawn on and on, and even the moonlit plain seemed to be chanting that there was no hope, no hope left.

Moonlight, distance, and stillness. One could walk on like

this day after day, night after night, and it would always be the same. Yes, he was getting dizzy—so dizzy that he reeled. Was the plain trying to lure him on to madness? No! Look: he could go as straight as an arrow if he liked. "Come on," said the prairie. "Can you stand another dram or are you a greenhorn?" On and on. Anne? Pehaps she was sitting on Simen's knee now. Giggling and making fun of old Per. "His beard is two feet too long," she was saying. "Hairy old bull! he 's only fit to marry a cow." . . . Per clenched his fists, waved his arms about, and strode on. A huge shadow followed him, as if the darkness had assumed a head, hat, arms, and legs. The shadow was like a whole landscape, and this landscape was himself, Per, who was out walking to-night, and forced to go on and on. Anne was expecting another baby now. When did Simen come? Oh! Oh! . . .

He sobbed, stood still, looked round in search of help. He stared at his shadow: "For God's sake, cant *you* tell me what to do?" The shadow shook its head.

On beyond him stretched the plain in the moonlight. The distances made the world seem so fabulously vast that he himself dwindled away into nothing. Look at the sky; not so much as a mountain or a hill cutting a piece out of it, or a lake drawing it down into its mirror. An ocean without coasts, a land without frontiers. Look up or look down, there was no end to it. Walk on—but where would he get to? Shout for help—but who would answer?

As he wandered on he began to reel again, and gesticulate wildly with his arms. The shadow did the same. Little by little he was realizing that nothing could save him. Was the prairie going to win, after all? The thing must be decided now; whatever happened, he must go on and on. Once he had forgiven, and that had saved him. God had given him a finger, as it were. All his troubles had become so small then;

even the prairie had lost its power. But now it was different. Forgive? No fear. God? He could stay where He was. This evening Per was out alone with Evil and the plain.

He was still resisting, as a capsized fisherman struggles frantically to keep his head above water. But he could not last much longer. He could feel the strength ebbing out of his limbs. Very soon he would have to give up. "On, on," said the plain; "Simen will take her for good and all, one of these days. He will move into the hut and turn you out. Ha, ha, ha! Come on, come on," beckoned the plain.

With another sob he stopped again. Oh, this was more than he could bear! He looked round wildly for some means of escape. "Pray, Per. Pray, or you will plunge headlong into the abyss. There's still a chance. Pray! Pray!"

The big man sank to his knees, and folding his hands, raised them above his head. "O Lord God, answer me! Save me! Or I shall go stark mad."

"There is no God," chanted the prairie in the pale moonlight. Everything was receding away and away. . . . Pray, Per. Or strike Anne dead. What did the prairie care? It merely receded away, and away, and away.

On and on. The shadow following him. The big landscape in human shape was dogging his footsteps all the time. Per looked at it. Here was a comrade in misfortune, lured and drawn on like himself, stopping, holding back, and yet forced to go on and on, just as he did. It began to stagger like a drunken man; so did he. Now he understood at last! The long fight with the prairie had been fought to a finish to-night. The prairie had won. Per had lost.

On. On. Since he must pass out into the night, he would go the whole hog. The shadow and he were both going to the bottom, the sooner the better. He tried to catch hold of his shadow and dance with it. "Come along, old pal! Let's see how high you can jump!"

What? Could n't he get hold of it? Would the shadow try to slip away from him, too? Take that, then! Per gave it a kick, rushed at it, tried to seize it by the throat.

Out on the moonlit plain the big man danced about, kicking and hitting out wildly with his long arms. But the shadow on the ground only mimicked him, goading him on, more and more, till at last he began to yell. . . . The night was dead still in the cold moonlight.

XVI

Next morning Anne came bursting into Morten's hut. "Per—have you seen anything of Per?"

The neighbors soon assembled outside her hut. Kal was carrying a rope. The others looked at it. Kal himself did n't quite know why he 'd brought it, except that he always used to take a rope with him if anything was up, in the old country. However, when Morten divided them into three search-parties to go in different directions, they all agreed that a rope might come in useful.

Morten and Simen took some food with them and started toward the west. They had been away for several months, working for wages in the town, while Anton again took charge of their cattle, and made *mysost* out of the milk. It was April now; there were only a few patches of snow left here and there, and very soon the spring work on the land could begin. At present they were busily engaged in building the new house; but of course when a neighbor was in such distress as this, everybody left whatever he had in hand.

They could hear Anne sobbing and calling after them, "You *must* find him!" Morten was pale, and he avoided looking at his brother. They walked on quickly in the sunshine, stopping now and then to stare across the vast level expanse. The pools and patches of melting snow were steaming, and a faint, bluish, transparent haze hung quivering over the limitless plain. When Simen said anything, Morten did not answer; he felt inclined to give him a hiding with the rope he was carrying.

Anne was left alone with the children. They could see that something was amiss, and stood clinging to her skirt and cry-

ing. She tried to comfort them and herself. Was it really
so serious? Very likely he had only got a fit of the sulks
again and wanted to frighten her. After all, he was no better than a child, for all his great hulking body, and if she
made him something nice to eat, he would be good again.
She filled a saucepan with thick cream and put it on the stove;
cream-porridge was his favorite dish. She stood watching
it. The cream came to the boil, and separated into porridge
and a liquid resembling melted butter. She added milk, and
stirred in flour. The porridge was ready now, but where was
Per? What could have become of him?

The day wore on. She went outside and gazed across the
plain, west, north, south and east. The prairie lay there
steaming in the sun. Not a soul in sight. Where could Per
be? When the darkness drew on, she began to fear the worst.
After putting the children to bed she sat down on a chair, and
waited in solitude. By and by she laid her head on the bed
close to the younger child. She began to sob. This was
worse than ever; what *had* she done this time?

Simen? What was the boy from Kvidal to her? Coming,
as he did, straight from the old country, he had seemed to
smell of the birch woods. Her own girlhood revived as she
questioned and questioned. Did they still make bonfires on
spring evenings, and sing? Did they get engaged? She
had wanted to hear more, and more, and more; it helped her
to see her father and mother, her friends, and the valley at
home. And what harm could there be in that? If she sometimes crept away by herself with the accordion, and thrilled
with memories of old days and all the good-looking boys she
had known, was there anything wrong in that? Yes, everything was wrong, according to that old book of sermons.

The thought of those golden days of girlhood had been like
a tonic to her out here in the wilds; if she had taken many
a draft of it to keep her sane, was that wrong? Yes, that
was wrong too. Was everything nice a sin? Of course it

was. Maybe she had romped a little with Simen in the hay,
and put her arms round his neck once in a while, just because
he had come straight from all that she was longing for. Was
that wrong too? Of course it was wrong. Sin? Everything was sin; even to tidy oneself up on Sunday, to turn
one's face to the sun, to play a dance-tune on the accordion.
Everything was a sin. O God, O God, forgive!

Else came in to see her. She tried to comfort her, but that
only made things worse. Karen came too; but she was so
quiet and motherly, she only looked at Anne, and made no
fuss. "We can lend a hand with the milking," she said and
it felt like a caress on her cheek.

The moon had risen again, and the plain was silvered over
with rime. Morten had said that the old settlers would see
to this affair themselves. Better not mix any of the new-
comers up in it. At length Anton and Anders returned.
They'd been walking all day. Had Per come home? Anne
only stared at them dumbly. Karen told them that he had
not. Presently Kal and the younger boy came in, and asked
the same question. They were dead tired, and muddy from
walking all day over the slushy ground. Well, well, they'd
better have a bite now, and after that they could start off
again.

Toward evening Morten and Simen caught sight of Per.
The moment he set eyes on them he began to wave his arms
wildly, shouting and swearing that if they came a step nearer
he would kill them. "Rot! we'll just go for him," said
Morten. Then Per caught sight of Ola and Jo advancing
from another direction, and again he began waving his arms
and shouting threats. But Ola was not so easily frightened
as all that. Finding himself attacked on two sides, Per took
to his heels. He dashed away, lost his hat, but took no notice. Then he floundered into a pool, sank to his waist, fell
forward, and lay full length; but sprang up again just as
his pursuers were upon him. Turning, he confronted them,

glaring, gesticulating wildly, and shouting to them to leave him alone. "Keep off!" His features were contorted. "Keep off, I say! What the devil d' you want to do to me?"

They stopped a few paces away, and Morten tried to reason with him: "Now Per, old man, you come back home to Anne and the kids."

"Hold your jaw!"

"Are you angry, Per? We 've all been that, many a time; but this is going too far, you know. Come, walk home with your old pals, and make friends again."

Suddenly Per caught sight of Simen. "What! Is that young monkey standing there grinning!" Lurching forward, he rushed at Simen, and aimed a furious blow at his head which would have sent him flying if he had not ducked to avoid it. In a moment Ola and Morten were upon him, and Jo grappled with him too. Surely among them they could master one man! But they reckoned without their Per. Regaining his balance, he shook them all off. Ah, would you! Had n't he once cleared a whole tap-room, up in the Lofotens? Morten, who was bleeding at the mouth, shouted to Ola not to strike him. They went on struggling with him, but before they knew it he wrenched himself free and was off again.

Then Morten put on the authoritative voice of the chairman of the parish council, and shouted: "If you don't stop this, Per, and behave yourself, I 'll have you kicked out of the parish council at the next election. And you 'll never have another chance of appointing a parson!" Per turned and stared at him. The shot had gone home. The corners of his mouth widened out into an ironical grin. But for all that he stood still. He allowed them to approach him, and let Morten take hold of his coat. "Come home, Per. Show that you 're a sensible chap."

Per muttered something, but obeyed. He walked slowly; still, that was better than nothing. But his eye fell on

Simen again. Like lightning he hit out, and catching the young fellow full on the jaw, sent him flying. "Ho! that's better! But look here, Morten: you 're a decent lad; you tie my hands. I shall murder that young rip, if you don't take your rope and tie me up. Here you are," and he stretched out his hands.

It seemed best to do as he said, and when they had tied his hands behind him, the big man walked on between his mates across the prairie. It was a long march. Morten got him to eat some of the food he had brought, putting it into his mouth for him; and then they went on again.

When at length they approached the settlement, Per halted, and began to laugh in a shy, inane way. "No, no," he said, "I can't go home like this; it's too bad. Where's Simen? Oh, bolted, has he? Just as well for him. You can untie me now."

But when he got near enough to his own hut to see Anne and the others standing outside in the moonlight, waiting for him, he stopped dead. "The devil! There she is."

"Remember what you promised me," said Morten, trying to get him along.

"Come, now. Are n't you coming in to have your cream-porridge?" Anne coaxed him, trying to pretend that nothing was the matter.

But he only scowled angrily at this cheery speech. "Bring me the boy, Anne—not the eldest, you can keep him, but little Per. I must have him; bring him here at once! And then I 'll go."

"Mercy on us!" gasped Anne, looking blankly from one to another.

"D' you hear, Anne! Bring me the boy. You can give your cream-porridge to Simen."

Per stood waiting in the moonlight, surrounded by his mates, two of whom were holding the rope. They were at a loss what to do next. At length Karen walked up to him slowly. "Per," she said, "listen to me. I think you 'd better come home with me to-night. You can sleep on the floor. And then you can talk it over with Anne in the morning."

"Hullo, Karen, what are *you* doing out so late?" said Per, with a little giggle, beginning to look ashamed of himself again. "Yes, I 'll come. But can't you get her to give me the kid?"

"No. We 'll talk about that to-morrow. Come along, Per."

They all breathed a sigh of relief when they saw the tamed giant walking quietly away beside the little prairie-woman. Anne was crying bitterly, and Else promised to stay with her till the morning.

Morten told Kal that they had better pretend to think that Per was going to sleep quietly; but a couple of men would have to remain on guard somewhere near. Anton and Morten kept watch the rest of the night in Kal's cow-shed. For a long time all was quiet. They had given Per the boys' bed, and for several hours he slept soundly. Toward morning, however, he woke up and wanted to go out to find his little boy. They dared not let him go back to his own hut. Kal tried to coax him to lie down again; but no, Per insisted on going. Karen came and coaxed him, the boys got up from the floor and did their best to dissuade him, but it was all in vain, he pushed them aside and opened the door. The moment he did so, two men emerged from the cow-shed and barred the way.

No one ever forgot that morning. Five men wrestled and fought with the mad giant. When they got him into the house, it was still worse, and Karen and the girls had to escape. A fearful battle ensued; windows, crockery, and saucepans were smashed, benches overturned and trodden to pieces; and the worst of all was to hear Per roaring like a wild beast. At last they got him down. Next they had to bind him securely—this time against his will. For a time he lay there shouting for help, then he flew into a rage and tried to break loose, and finally he burst into tears. After watching him for an hour or two they saw that he had fallen asleep again.

Next day they removed him to Anton Noreng's hut, where there was more room. Anne came to see him, tear-stained and forlorn. Per was sitting on a bench, but the moment he set eyes on her in the doorway, he jumped up in a fury. "Go away! Go away!" he screamed. "Go away before I get my hands free." And he tugged and tore at the ropes.

When Kal came home after keeping watch one night, and Karen asked how Per was now, he did not answer. He sat down and tried to eat his breakfast, but the tears were running down his cheeks. He shook his head. "God save us all from the likes of that," he said.

A couple of days later, a prairie-schooner drove slowly over the plain toward the town. There were four men with it, and Per sat inside, bound hand and foot. Now and then he screamed, and implored them to tie something over his eyes. The plain, the plain, the plain! It was drawing him, drawing him. Everything was spinning round. Hi! Hi! he was on a merry-go-round—hold tight! Perhaps it was all a joke, after all. He sang and laughed; and presently burst into tears again.

"What'll become of poor Anne? Where are you taking me? To an asylum? Am I really as mad as that? What about Anne, though, and . . . and the kid?—little Per. Who'll look after them? And I'd plowed up so much this year. No, no, no, *don't* take me to a mad-house! Think of poor Anne!"

On the succeeding Sunday Anne sat at the back of the little church, hiding her face in her hands. While the others sang, they could hear her sobbing. And during the sermon they could hear her groans, as she sat there with bent head, absorbed in her own grief.

Simen stayed at home. He was building his brother's house, and meant to leave as soon as it was finished.

BOOK III

I

Morten Kvidal was going home at last. It was Sunday, and he was making the round of the old settlers to say good-by. The spring sowing was safely over, and his little frame house had been built, so Simen could take charge of the farm for a year or two. The neighbors were still busily hammering and sawing, but Anne's new house had been finished by the combined efforts of her friends.

He was looking rather pale to-day; there were so many ties to keep him here. Life was just beginning in earnest, with horses, machinery, and a lot more land to cultivate; soon there would be a road; perhaps a railway, too, some day; there might even be a town, with farming on a big scale, and huge profits. And yet he could no longer resist the homesickness which had smoldered within him all these years. It was foolish perhaps, but go he must. He must see Kvidal and his mother again.

"Of all the crazy notions!" said Jo. "Why, you're a sort of little king here already. Fancy leaving now, just as we're beginning to go ahead in style!"

"What message shall I give your father and mother?"

"None."

"Hang it, man! Surely you'll send them a message?"

"No; why should I? Say what you like to the old folks. But don't give them any message from me."

Morten shook his head as he went away. They were all more or less homesick. Jo Berg was the only one who was above such sentimentality. Perhaps the real reason was that he was getting to realize that his martyrdom in the old country had been only bluff. Maybe his father and mother were right in saying that he would never settle down to anything. He could picture them at home, feeling more in the right every day. Why should he send them a message into the bargain?

Anne sat sewing in her new house, and she brightened up when Morten entered. After all that she had gone through lately, it was a comfort to move out of the dark hut into a house like this, with so much light from the tall windows. The floor, ceiling, and walls were of freshly planed wood, which smelt so nice that the air seemed easier to breathe. Her dark hair was streaked with gray, and her face looked worn, but a gleam of youthfulness sprang up in her eyes when he asked whether she had any messages for the old country.

"Oh yes! Give them all my love, Morten. . . ." She gazed in front of her for a moment, then looked up at him with appealing eyes. "But promise me one thing: you won't tell them too much about poor Per, will you?"

They went on talking, and she told him that she had let her farm to Kal in return for half the profits on it. "But I do wish you weren't going away, Morten. We're thinning out; there aren't many of the first lot left now. Mind you come back again."

It was hard to go round like this, saying good-by, and he could see that the others did not find it easy, either. They were losing their mainstay again. Anton confided to him that he was engaged to one of the red-haired daughters of the Irishman. They were soon going to be married. He asked Morten to give his love to the old folks and say that he had grown up at last.

Else and Ola were sitting over a book in their hut. They got up when he entered. "Reading the Bible?" asked Morten. "No; an English grammar," answered Ola. "I'm trying to pick up some of my wife's book-learning."

"Fancy that, now!" Morten said to himself. "This looks promising. Trust a woman to win in the end!"

Else had no one to send her love to. Yes—to the landscape at home. To the mountains and the sea. She sighed,
but tried to smile. Ola asked him to take fifty dollars for
his old father and mother; it was such a business to sit down
and write them a letter. He followed Morten outside and
walked a little way with him. When he held out his hand to
say good-by, he looked rather shyly at Morten and said:
"You won't give me away too much, will you, old man?"
Morten gripped his hand, and walked on quickly. How well
he knew that feeling—the ambition to stand well with one's
friends in the old country!

On reaching Kal's farm, he was surprised to see how much
more prosperous it looked than any of the others. The new
outhouse was twice as large, and there were several inclosures
full of yellow, black, and spotted pigs, besides other inclosures
with fowls, ducks, geese, and turkeys; you never heard such
a chorus of grunting, cackling, quacking and gobbling in
your life!

Kal was sure to be somewhere near the horses. Yes, there
he was, doing his best to break them, behind the stable.
Oluf was riding one, trying to get it to obey a bit and snaffle,
while the animal jibbed, plunged, and endeavored to throw
him. Kal was driving the other in loose traces, but it only
danced about and reared and tried to get away. Karen stood
in the door of the hut screaming, while the two girls shrieked
with excitement, and Anders lounged with his hands in his
pockets, thoroughly enjoying the performance.

"Hullo! Here's Morten!" cried Kal, and the horse became more unruly than ever. Steady there! Steady! No
wonder he couldn't manage, with two of these brutes to
break in at once. "Put them in again," he said to the boys.
"I'm dead beat."

He never told anybody why he so often sat in the stable
looking at the two high-spirited animals in their box-stalls.
It put him in mind of his young days. He'd been just as

wild as that, once. And he thought of all that he'd had to carry and pull for so many weary years. It seemed as if the two horses kept looking round at him and saying, "Never mind, Kal; we'll do the pulling and carrying for you for the rest of your days."

It was a painful leave-taking. Karen made coffee for them, crying quietly all the time. "To think of your leaving us, Morten! Well, remember us kindly to all the folks at home. And you must take a look at Skaret, to see what it's like up there now."

Paulina was very pale, with dark rings round her eyes. Well, it *was* rather hard on her that Anton had taken up with that Irish girl!

The three men walked a little way with Morten. "Remember us to all our pals," said the boys, "especially Severin Rönningen." Little Siri came running after him with a dollar that she had earned by selling the eggs of her three hens; Morten was to give it to lame Anne on the hill, if she were alive still.

But Kal walked on with him after the others had said good-by, and Morten could see that there was something he wanted to say. Finally he stopped, and took out a ten-dollar note. "This'll do to buy a little coffee and sugar for my brother's wife," he said; "and maybe there'll be enough to buy Siver a pipe too. It's not much better up at Skaret than it was in my time, I guess."

After they had said good-by he turned back again, and paced slowly along at Morten's side. Even now he had not said what he wanted to. He screwed up his eyes, and blinked at the sun and the prairie. At last he blurted out a question: did Morten think it cost a lot at those training colleges for clergy? Morten smiled. It wasn't exactly cheap, he thought. No. But it was that young cuss Oluf. That boy had such a head! He couldn't say he'd ever set up for a saint, himself, but Providence had given him his fair share of blessings, and it seemed only right that one of the boys should be a parson.

"Yes, you could pay back a little to Providence in that way," said Morten, repressing a smile. Exactly. Some folks might say that he ought to go on piling up houses and machines and horses, but the wife and he were satisfied with things as they were. "Besides, it's Karen's idea. I—I think it's altogether too swell for a common man like me to be the father of a parson!" Morten smiled. It was the old story. Whenever he wanted anything, it was always Karen's fault.

He never forgot their final parting. For once he saw Kal looking utterly forlorn. Morten turned several times to watch him as he plodded homeward along the level fields, gaunt and crooked from lifting heavy burdens in the old country and here, but invincibly tough in body and mind. Good-by, Kal.

The big emigrant ship was cleaving her way through the ocean again, but this time she was carrying the emigrants home.

The first-class and second-class alike were crowded, but the passengers there were accustomed to traveling. On the third-class were country folks who had been pining for years to get home, not only to their native land, but to one particular farm, far in among the fiords, high up in the valleys, or in more open country with lakes and forests. A huge hawser stretched across the deck confined them within a space so narrow that there was little room to move around when they came out to enjoy the sun and air; but they stood about talking, men and women together, with a sprinkling of Danes and Swedes among them, and all felt like kinsmen, even if they had never set eyes on one another before.

Here and there might be seen casual laborers sporting town clothes, fur collars, and gold watch-chains—weather-beaten looking men who had been working in the forests or on farms in different parts of the country. And here were peasants who had passed through the big cities, merely shaking their heads at all they saw there; once their homes had been in a country parish in Norway, and now they lived in a Norwegian country parish in America; and they still wore homespun clothes and broad-brimmed hats, as they did on the day they left home. They had gone to America only to earn enough money to redeem the family farm, and had toiled away there with scarcely any feeling of being in a foreign country, because they had always seen the farmsteads at home so clearly. They had the same gaily painted emigrant-chests, to-day, that they had brought with them from Norway. Some of the older couples were accompanied by a boy or a girl, born in America, who was being taken home to see what the old country was like.

Such were Morten's companions on board. He chatted with one and another, and some of them were ready to tell him their story at once. They had left Norway for such and such a reason, had gone to this place or that, and had begun by doing so and so. "And where do you hail from?" But Morten had little to tell them. He had meant to go home rolling in riches, to build a big farm; and now he was going—but where were the riches? No, he had nothing to tell them about himself.

At length the day came when they hoped to get the first glimpse of the old country. A strange restlessness pervaded the whole ship, especially the steerage. Would they soon see a haze on the horizon? One or two young fellows climbed up into the shrouds, but the boatswain ordered them down. Men and women crowded to the side of the ship; children got crushed and screamed. The sea was all blue ripples, the sun was sinking in golden clouds in the west—a perfect evening! The gentlemen on the first-class deck were looking through their field-glasses.

Suddenly a thrill ran through the crowd. "Look! *There* it is! Yes, that's it! Can't you see where I'm pointing?" "Let *me* see too, Father!" And fathers lifted up their children. "Look!"

And now it was no longer a faint haze above the sea, but a gray line growing more and more distinct. The swarms of gulls, which had been following the ship of late, began screaming: *ah-oo-ah-oo!* Then they met flocks of guillemots and ducks riding on the water and uttering noisy cries. They seemed to be saying, "Welcome home." Then the band on the upper deck struck up. The fluttering handkerchiefs looked like scores of little flags waving to the gray coast which kept rising higher and higher above the sea. But here and there a woman pressed her handkerchief to her face. Every one stood gazing at the land. They had forgotten their new acquaintances on board. Very soon they would step ashore, and hasten on to their homes.

But, strange to say, Morten's thoughts had flown back to his friends on the prairie, thousands of miles away. If only they could be here now! Just for a little while. Who knew —some of them might never see the old country again.

The big ship steamed in through the skerries in the clear moonlit evening. Fishermen's huts, rocks, a boat with its nets out a little distance from the shore, a smell of tar and sand—oh, how well he knew it all!

Three or four days later a neighbor dropped in to see Berit Kvidal. "Well, Berit, your grand visitor'll soon be here They tell me Morten's been seen in town."

"Who—who, did you say?"

"Why, don't *you* know about it?"

"No, what d' you mean? Was it Morten you said?"

"Yes. He'll be here to-morrow," said her neighbor.

And to think of the state the place was in, both indoors and out! That was a busy day at Kvidal.

Sitting on board the little fiord steamer, Morten thought of the day he left: Helena on the beach, the dog running along the rocks and trying to get on board, Mother and the little mare driving home. He saw the same rocks and beaches gliding past, and the farms that he knew so well by name standing on green slopes between the birch-clad hills and the fiord. Salmon-nets were out in the water a short distance from land, boats drawn up on the shore. Everything just the same.

For eight years he had seen in a golden light the day of his return. And now he was coming home. But how different everything was from what he had planned! He was not coming back as a Crœsus, and Helena would not stand waiting for him on the beach. But one or two friends would be there; perhaps all of them, for they must have heard that he was on his way.

The steamer turned into the bay he knew so well. The crofts belonging to Lindegaard clustered around it; many of the houses had been painted; how it brightened things up! And far in among the well-known hills he could see a green slope; and the little houses on it were as gray as ever. It was Kvidal. He bent his head and pulled his hat over his eyes. He must n't let people see how hard it was to breathe.

Several others besides himself stepped down into the agent's boat. They were country folks with baskets and chests, but, strange to say, he knew none of them. No crowd was waiting on the beach. The triumphal procession of which every emigrant dreams, was a disappointment, now as always. "Bless me, if it is n't Morten!" said Ola the agent, who was rowing the heavy boat. "An' I did n't know you." A few faces turned toward him. Even if any of them recognized him, he only lived up at Kvidal.

A round-shouldered man with a brown mustache and a brisk manner was coming down the beach toward him. Could that be Peter? "Welcome home," said the man, holding out his hand.

"How—how 's Mother?"

"Oh, she 's alive, all right."

And there was the little mare, the same as ever. "Hullo, old girl! . . . Why, I almost think she remembers me! Have they been kind to you, old girl? You 're very thin, are n't you?"

He had the same chest that he had taken to America. And now he was sitting on it, with his brother beside him, driving up the valley once more. The farms, at any rate, were waving to him, and saying welcome home. His soul became merged in the landscape. Here he was. He 'd been away a longish time, but here he was again. He had a thousand things to ask about, but on the way home he could only sit gazing, gazing, and hardly uttered a word.

At length they jumped down at the foot of the slopes up to Kvidal. But the little mare was as game as ever; she took the steepest hills at a gallop, and the men had to give her her head. Rather different from driving oxen over the prairie!

And up there by the gate was a bent, white-haired woman coming toward him; was it . . . Had she changed so much as this? "How do you do, Mother . . ."

III

It was not a dream. He was really here again, going in
and out and to and fro, standing still for a moment to look
at something he remembered, gazing at the distant mountains, or at the wide fiord with white sails passing up and
down it; he felt that he wanted to grasp and drink in the
whole scene at once. The gray house looked no younger, but
it was still like a mother to all of them, and the byre with
its green-turfed roof still had the same air of profound wisdom. Out in the world such things as horses, cows, and farm
implements were necessaries; one reckoned their value in
terms of money and utility. Here they were friends. Every
now and then he went round and had a look at the grindstone behind the barn, or enjoyed a little chat with the old
clock on the wall.

At times he seemed to see his father—bow-legged, round-
shouldered, and as fiery as gunpowder, but contented with his
humble lot. It was his son, the boy Morten, who had pestered him till at last he got him to attempt the leap up to
something bigger. What happened? His poor father had
hanged himself in the barn one day—and whose fault was it?
Well, well, Morten was going to make amends for that, and
handsomely too; no doubt he had come back now with a pot
of money, to turn the old place into a big farm.

But what was the use of brooding over these gloomy
thoughts? That neat little room over the kitchen, with
window-curtains, a chest of drawers, and a bed, was evidently
meant for him. To lay one's head on Mother's pillows
again, to feel oneself at home, to be lulled to sleep by the roar
of Kvidal waterfall—what more could one wish? He slept

soundly and well, with a sense of well-being he had not known for many years. It was late next morning before he opened his eyes, to see his mother standing by the bed with coffee and cake on a tray.

"Slept well?" she asked, looking at him tenderly.

"No, a bad night!" he smiled, stretching himself luxuriously.

She sat on the edge of the bed while he drank his coffee. "I'm afraid we haven't got on much with the farm," she ventured, looking at him a little apprehensively. She knew that he had been round the fields, the day before, with Peter.

What should he say? Certainly *her* hands gave no evidence of idleness. But she had never been one to save and scrape; like him, she had always lived in the hope that she would be better off some day. What matter, then, if she went rather too often to the store, and gave half of what she bought to a neighbor who was down on her luck? And did she think that he had come back now with his pockets full of gold, like the hero in a fairy-tale? Did his brothers and sisters think the same? How wrinkled her face had become! And her hair—how thin and white it was! Her eyes looked so large and far-sighted. Mother, Mother, fancy seeing you once again!

She began to unburden herself of some of her anxieties. Peter was so touchy. He answered her so rudely when he was angry, and sometimes even threatened to leave her. He couldn't have the farm anyhow, he said. Why should he stay here, wearing himself out? The same thing year after year. And Knut had such a head on him! It really was a pity he couldn't afford to become a lawyer or a parson. He didn't care much about farming. She looked at Morten; what did *he* advise?

Morten smiled bitterly, but before he could reply his mother went on to something else. "Poor girl, she didn't get much out of life," she sighed, without daring to look at him. He knew whom she meant, and answered by a light caress on her cheek. Presently she took the tray and went downstairs.

How was it that he, who had once been so lively and talkative, went about so quietly now, hardly saying a word? Did he feel he was not the person they had expected? This visit home was going to be a disappointment to both them and himself. And why did his head feel so queer when he looked at the mountains, or at the valley, or the fiord? This landscape was so unrestful—shooting up and plunging down. It made him so dizzy that he wanted to hold on to something. Was it because he was so used to the prairie now?

The midsummer nights were as light as day; they tempted him to get out of bed a little after midnight and go for long rambles in the woods and fields. How gorgeously the western sky dressed itself in scarlet and gold on such nights as these! The dew fell in showers about his feet; and the foliage brushed his hands and made them wet. Was that a thrush singing already? The Kvidal waterfall was weaving all this into its endless chant. "Home," it sang. "Welcome," it sang. . . . Standing high up on the mountainside, he would watch the sunrise; the farmsteads were still asleep, and the snow-capped mountains in the west were mirrored in the shining fiord. Herring-boats came rowing home over the mirror, after the night's fishing. Presently a breeze from the ocean sprang up, wafting inland the fresh smell of the sea.

Morten stood drinking it in. At last, at last he had all that he had longed and pined for in a strange land! Every day the landscape and its memories seemed to be getting him more and more into its power, drawing him closer and closer to itself. How he wished he could write a song about all this, or play it on a fiddle!

His younger sister, Mette, was thirteen now, and a regular tease. If he stood still for a moment in the farm-yard, looking about him, he was sure to hear some one laughing, and her rosy face and tousled yellow hair would peep round the corner. "Are you laughing at me?" "Yes." "What is there to laugh at?" "You 're so funny." "You dare!" he put on a fierce look and ran after her. Mette screamed and took to her heels, and he chased her all round the meadow.

On Saturday evening his sister Randi came home. She was in service at a farm, but had heard of his return. Randi was a grown woman now, tall and florid, with light brown, curly hair.

"Lord!" she exclaimed, stopping in the doorway and staring at him. "*You* with a beard, Morten! Did you buy it in America?"

He took her by the shoulders and gave her a little shake. "Don't be disrespectful to an old man!" he said. "But how's this? You haven't got a ring on your finger."

"No. That's out of fashion now."

"Aha! then you *have* got a sweetheart?"

"One! D' you think I 'd be contented with *one?*"

"Well, well! Then perhaps you don't want this little thing which I found under a bit of turf in America?" And he held out a little gold ring with a red stone in it.

"Oh, my!" She stared at it, turning it over and over in her fingers.

The others crowded round her and stared too. Yes, the jewel was a real one, right enough. Then they showed her what *they* had got: Mette a dress-length of blue-checked calico, and her mother a shawl with red flowers on it, which she hardly dared even to smooth with her hand; Peter a tie-pin and Knut a watch—an American one too; if you put it to your ear, you could hear it ticking away like blazes. "You shouldn't have spent all that money on us," said Berit, looking concerned. Morten flung out his arm: "Oh, we Americans always have plenty of money."

By and by the young folks suggested having a romp out-

side. Morten gazed at his brothers and sisters; they had been
mere children when he left, and now they were so big that
he hardly knew them. "Tag!" cried Mette, giving him a
dig in the ribs to wake him up. He tried to catch her, and
she dashed off, squealing with delight. Could this be the
chairman of the parish council? In a minute they were all
tearing round the houses, shouting, screaming, and laughing. They were children once more. Berit came out to look
on. It ended in a wrestling-bout between Morten and Peter;
and the younger brother actually won.

Supper. They were all there this evening except Simen.
They talked about him a little; no doubt he'd be busy har-
vesting wheat now. The evening sun stenciled the west
window on the floor, and shed a golden light on their faces.
Morten sat studying his red-headed brother Knut. The boy
was virtually grown up now, but lanky and awkward. His
pale-blue eyes looked very innocent, in spite of the artful
schemes he was always concocting. At present he was telling
a story about a bear up on the slopes, and of course he had
been there and seen it. His mother was quite alarmed.
"But you never said a word about this before!"

"Oh, Knut has so many strange adventures, that he hasn't
time to tell us half of them," said Randi, slyly, and the others
roared with laughter. All right, if they wouldn't believe
him . . .

As they were getting ready for church on Sunday morning Peter said, "I suppose you'll drive, Morten?" But the
American answered that he'd been having a chat with the
little mare, and she thought she'd rather stay at home and
rest to-day.

"Yes, but Mother wants to drive with you."

"Oh; that alters the case. I'll go and ask again."

And now he could hear the familiar church bells ringing
down in the valley.

It was a still, hot summer's day. Haymaking had begun,

and the hay was hanging to dry on long rows of hurdles.
The roads were crowded with people on foot and driving.
The little mare trotted along briskly in front of the cart, in
which Morten was seated with his mother beside him—wearing her new shawl.   They drove past Peter, Knut, and Mette,
who waved their hands and laughed.   One or two men took
off their hats to the American; things would soon be looking
up at Kvidal; he was rolling in riches, they had heard.

For some time Morten sat silently looking in front of him;
then he asked, "Whereabouts is she laid in the churchyard?"

His mother answered in a low voice, "On the north side,
close to the old man's grave."   Presently she looked at him
and said: "They 've just put up a granite gravestone.
You 'll have a look at it, won't you?"

"Perhaps," he said slowly.   "But I 'm not sure I can bear
it to-day."

And now he was standing outside the church, acting the
part of the returned American—the cynosure of every eye,
with a crowd around him.   Once it had been Erik Foss; to
day it was Morten.   School friends came up and shook hands
with him.   "How do you do? Fancy seeing you again!"
And of course he had to answer no end of questions about
the others, who had gone out to America with him.   Well,
poor old Erik had n't lived long.   No; they 'd heard that;
but what about the rest?   Oh, they were getting on all right.
Morten was in his element; he was behaving just like all the
other Americans who came home, saying little and keeping
people rather at a distance.

"And what about Kal Skaret?   They say he 's got a mighty
big farm now."   Morten nodded; yes, Kal owned a lot of
land.   "And the houses?" some one asked.   Was it really
true that they were only sod huts?   Morten answered that
they were the usual houses that settlers built at first; and Kal
seemed to get along all right with them.   How many cows
and horses had he now?   Morten could n't say he 'd counted

them, but there were a good many, and there'd be more before long. And what about Ola Vatne? Was he doing well
too? How did he get on with a colonel's daughter for his
wife? Morten replied that Ola and Else were getting on
well; they seemed to suit each other, and Ola was a hard-
working man. Finally they asked about Per Föll. Well—
Morten hesitated, but ended by saying that Per had been
poorly of late, though they hoped he'd get better. Otherwise they hit it off well, he and Anne.

But what did Morten think about emigration? Would he
advise the young folks to go or not? Morten smiled; he
would neither encourage nor discourage them. There were
ups and downs in America, as elsewhere. They stared at
him. Evidently they wouldn't be much the wiser for talking to *him!* If they wanted to hear gossip about his pals
out there, they must go to some one else.

Here was rich old Ramsöy coming to church—a sturdy
farmer with a black beard, a collar, and gold rings in his
cars. He actually shook hands with Morten to-day, although
he only lived at Kvidal. Welcome home, he said; and what
news could he give of his daughter Anne? The old man did
not seem to care much about his daughter's husband; he did
not even ask after Per. Presently a young woman came up
to Morten. Who should it be but Anne's sister Bergitta?
Fancy her being so young and pretty still!

And then Morten was invited to Ramsöy, so that the old
man might have a regular good talk with him. Bergitta
added that he must be sure to come; when might they expect
him? As she stood there in her gray dust-coat, with a black
kerchief on her head, she was not quite a young lady, and
yet she was a little more than a peasant girl all the same.
Her delicate features and rosy complexion looked as young
as ever. But why hadn't she married?

How strange it felt to enter the old church, where he had
been christened and confirmed, and had sung in the choir

Sunday after Sunday! His mother and sisters were sitting on the women's side. Peter and Knut were near him. During the singing old memories crowded in upon him, and he felt a lump rise in his throat. His mother looked up from her hymn-book and smiled across at him.

It was not till a fortnight later, after he had helped with the haymaking, that he summoned up courage to visit the churchyard. It was Saturday evening, still and cloudy; now that the meadows had been cut, the corn-fields looked all the taller, and a wonderful peace enveloped the mountains and the fiord. Entering the quiet churchyard, he made his way to the grave, with its new polished granite gravestone, and read the gilt-lettered inscription: "Here lieth Helena Larsdatter Linderud, daughter of Lars Noreng." The dates of her birth and death were given below; she had only lived to be twenty-five.

He sat down with his chin on his hands. How often had they met on the hill opposite! He seemed to hear her voice, to see her face, to feel her arms around his neck. She died belonging to another man, and yet she seemed to be his own again now. Ah, well! It had to be so.

Later in the evening he came out through the iron gate and walked slowly homeward. There was no more to be said. It had to be so.

IV

It was a strange time. He felt that he could not go on forever living like a chicken under his mother's wing; in the long run he would have to do something, and what then? Had he come home for good, or had he not? Should he begin to look into things as if he were taking over the management of the place, or should he not? Sometimes his mother would mention the big farm, with the main building here, and the outhouse and its two wings there. Such a thing as doubt never entered her head for a moment. When she looked at him, her eyes were full of the old visions. How could he have the heart to disillusion her so soon?

One day she said that if Knut was going to be a parson, she supposed he'd better begin studying in town; and she fixed her eyes trustfully on Morten's face. Should he laugh or cry? One evening Mette took him by the hand and led him up the field, while she confided to him that she wanted to go to a training college for teachers. The money? She looked at him as if he had been a savings-bank! It made him feel inclined to ask, "Have you gone mad—all the lot of you?"

When the hay had been gathered he took his brothers to the slopes on the other side of the river to begin breaking up new land. This was a great day. He had looked forward to it for many a year; and now he had come back from America at last, and the wonderful work was beginning. Well, it certainly took it out of your arms and back. Stumps and stones, pickax and spade—work away! This was not the fine soil of the prairie, where you could put in your plow and go straight ahead. But had n't he said that Kvidal was going to be a big farm? Work away, Morten!

273

This was the earth with which his forefathers had wrestled of an evening after doing a full day's work on the land-owner's farm. The ground they cleared had been fertilized with sweat. Those were men who had never been to the county school, or to America, but they did their bit, all the same. Now was the time for the young fellows who had been to school to show that they could do still better. A big farm, Morten—don't forget that. Have n't you been eight years in America collecting the money to conjure up a big farm at Kvidal?

His brothers looked at him, and then at each other. *They* had tried this before; how soon would Morten get tired of it? Presently, when he straightened his back for a rest, he began to make a calculation. Suppose he settled down here for good, where did he stand?

The money that he had brought with him might suffice to patch up the houses and make them good enough for a small farmer. He could sell his farm in America for, say, a thousand dollars. But how far would that go? He would have to hire a lot of labor and pay a lot in wages if he wanted to clear an acre and a half of this sort of land in a year. That would mean some thirty acres in twenty years' time, and even then Kvidal would n't be a big farm. By then he would be an old man. And during all those twenty years he would only be a small farmer, looked down upon by the rich and mighty! It would be "only Kvidal" all those years. Well, well! he could throw the old dreams overboard. He could bend his back and be humble. But would he? Was he old and toothless enough to be humble?

Meanwhile the other half of his mind was away in the prairie. He had been a leader there, but here he was nothing. Out there he owned three hundred and twenty acres of splendid earth to-day, and could own as much again to-morrow. The railway, the town, all the visions and ideas that the vast plain called up in his brain when he was there—

had he forgotten these? In a few years' time he might be
a great man, a leader, out there.

What in Heaven's name had made him come home just
as things were getting lively? A horn might sound on the
mountains; a Neckan might sit playing in Kvidal waterfall,
but was that any reason why a man should throw down
whatever he had in his hands, and run toward it? Yet that
was what he had done. Why? Was it homesickness? And
Mother? And Kvidal? Yes, that was why he had done it.
He gazed ahead of him and sighed. Then he seized the
pickax and set to work again. If he went on like this for
a hundred years he might succeed in breaking up as much
new land as he could plow in three or four days on the prairie.

Before long he had to rest again, and stood looking about
him in the warm autumn sunshine. There was such a de-
licious smell here, from the alders, and from the old roots
that he had torn up. Far away on the hillside was a group
of birch-trees which looked like a golden rosette against the
green of the surrounding pines. And white sails on the
fiord. . . . Home, home! This landscape was weaving a
spell about him, but . . . but was he going to sacrifice his
life for it? Or should he tear himself away and escape?
His country was very dear to him, but what about all that he
had on the other side? Did that count for nothing?

His neighbors on the prairie were leaving him far behind.
They would be kings in a small way, one of these days. And
he himself was wasting his time, slaving away here when he
ought to be carrying on Erik's work out there.

How difficult it was to go home to Mother! If he meant
to settle down here for good, he would have to shatter all her
dreams. He would have to confess that he was no Crœsus.
That he couldn't work miracles. What would his brothers
and sisters say? They would jeer. So that was the end of
it! After he had posed as a sort of Providence, too!

He asked Peter one day what he meant to do when he set

up for himself. Peter answered by asking for money. Would Morten help him to start a local store?

Morten stared. "Why, are n't there more than enough stores here already?"

"Yes; but that 's what I 'd like best."

"I see. But why not be a carriage-builder instead, when you 're such a good hand at that sort of thing? Start a workshop."

"All right, if you 'll find me enough capital to start on a decent scale."

"Can't you begin in a small way?" Why, Morten could even tell him of large towns in America which had grown up out of a single blacksmith's shop!

But Peter only laughed. "What about yourself? Why did n't *you* do it?"

What could he answer? He thought of all the lads who had set to work to clear a bit of rough ground for their home. They knew that they had a lifetime of poverty before them, and yet they had had the pluck to go on. That was how the country had been cultivated. But nowadays the lads had been to a high school, and times had changed.

Later on in the autumn he went with his brothers to the young people's club, presided over by the head-master of the county school. The members were just as radical and uncompromising now as in the days when Morten and Per Föll had been the shining lights. But all of them were burning to hear about America, and seemed ready to start off tomorrow. They debated hotly about the newest ideas, and passed resolutions recording their views on the largest questions. They even sent an address to the Government and parliament, declaring that the young people in Norway wanted things done in such and such a way. They had become so wide awake and patriotic of late! But they were ready to embark for America the very next day.

Morten scratched his chin; he did not know what to make

of all this. And on his walks about the parish it surprised him to see that everything was at a standstill. A road decided on ten years before, was still only a plan, something to be discussed. "Wait till *I* get a chance," he said to himself.

Among those who came to the club was Bergitta Ramsöy; and every time she entered, Morten felt that he had been waiting for her. When they sang, he could hear her voice above the others. She had been a close friend of Helena Noreng's; but was that the only reason? Sitting there among the other girls, she looked so young still, and he remembered that, after all, she could not be more than twenty-five. Her refined face beneath its fair hair had become very thoughtful, and those large gray eyes, once so gay, had more depth now. Often she looked down, as if trying to recollect something. And every now and then she would look across at him and smile.

He thought of Kvidal. "Ah, if only I had you out on the prairie!" he said to himself. How was it, though, that she had n't married? One day he learned the reason. She had been engaged for several years to a telegrapher. He had died. After that she had become religious, and used to go and weep at prayer-meetings. She seemed to have got over it now. What a beautiful girl she was! Fancy having her out there on the prairie!

As they went home one evening from the club, she began to question him earnestly about America. Her brother was taking over the farm; very soon she would feel like a lodger in her own home; she felt she must do something, and was wondering whether she should go out and join her sister. What did Morten think? A pang shot through him. "If you advise her to go, you 'll have to go too," he thought. Presently she looked up at him with a little giggle. "What 's the joke?" he inquired. "Is n't it rather funny to live at Kvidal when you 've a big estate out on the prairie?" "You should see how small the houses are." "They may get bigger." "So may Kvidal." He said it to defend his home and his mother.

But she would not discuss that. She looked away for a moment. Then she told him that her sister had written about his long journey on skis to fetch a doctor to Erik Foss. What, had Anne written about that? Yes; and Bergitta thought it much finer than winning any skiing-race. He could feel the warmth in her eyes. And he thought of Helena. She, too, had wanted him to be a hero, but not at Kvidal.

They went for a long walk that day, and talked of old times. They called to mind a spring evening when the two sisters had come rowing over the lake with their accordion, and bonfires were blazing on the hills around. Long ago. Long ago.

During the next few days Morten went about humming absent-mindedly, in an unusually irritable mood. It seemed to him that he had so many minds; and that was anything but pleasant. At one moment he would be thinking of all the clever things he meant to do in the parish—the old dreams of his younger days. A moment later he would be out on his big farm on the prairie, and one of the leading men in that great, free land.

Shortly before Christmas he had rather a shock: he was appointed a poor-law guardian. He must take care; he was beginning to rise.

But at the very first meeting of the guardians he disagreed with the chairman, a schoolmaster. Morten thought that they were spending too much money. Relief for this man and that man, this woman and that woman. . . . Why could n't they earn their own livelihood? That schoolmaster stuck his pen behind his ear and observed that in *this* country they had outgrown the idea that the poor ought to suffer. Morten asked whether the poor were not supposed to work either.

But he was outvoted. He went home swearing under his

breath; they'd all be paupers in this country sooner or later.
On the other hand, he could see the prairie, lying there in
the spring breeze, and calling for young men and women
who were willing to work and trust to the strength of their
own hands. Choose, Morten, choose.

After Christmas he received a letter from Simen which
filled him with excitement. North Dakota had been admitted
to the Union; the road to Nidaros Settlement had been begun; great plans for a railway were in the air. Ah, they
were beginning with a vengeance now! He lay awake all
that night. In reality he had made up his mind already.
He would go back. He must. But he shrank from admit-
ting to himself that it would be for good this time. No! He
clenched his fists and swore that he *would* come home again.
Think of all the improvements that he meant to carry through
in the parish!

As he sped across the hills on skis and looked at the
fairy-land of white woods, he felt that his soul was spellbound
here forever. Even if he journeyed to the end of the world,
he would always yearn and long for this. The hills, the
fiord, the blue mountains lay there chanting night and day:
"You are we. We are you. Wherever else you go, you will
always be an alien." But another wave had caught him and
was carrying him farther and farther away: the more he
loved all this that was his own, the more he longed to leave it.

His two brothers were away fishing. He told his mother
that he had to go back and sell his farm; if he wanted to
get a decent price for it, he must see to the matter himself.
Very well. His mother looked at him with large questioning
eyes. No one, not even his own mother, had really been
admitted to his confidence since he came back. And now he
was going away. . . .

Before long he was standing on the deck of the fiord-
steamer again, looking at his mother and the little mare on
the shore. He watched the well-known landscape vanishing,

hill by hill.   But he could still see the little gray houses on the slopes of Kvidal.   Good-by, Morten; when shall we see you again?   He clenched his teeth.   This was the second time that he had lost his hold on his own native place. Bergitta had left for town the day before.   He felt rather ashamed of not having told his mother how matters stood between them; but she might have asked why they could not have the wedding at Kvidal before they left.

He could not see anything now . . . and his mother and the little mare would be half-way home. . . . When would he come back again?

V

Neither Morten nor Erik Foss had foreseen the manner in which the town of Nidaros was ultimately to develop.

Peter Skaarness was harrowing his land one day in late spring, when he suddenly pulled up his horses and began to stare. The new road went close by, and whom should he see passing along it but Morten. He was driving a pair of horses in a high-wheeled cart, and had two more horses following behind. A young woman was seated beside him. Peter Skaarness stared at them and swore. "Hell! There'll be no more peace here now!"

When the local officials had been elected that winter, Skaarness had been appointed a justice of the peace. And why not? Was he not the storekeeper and money-lender? What could be more natural than for folks to vote for him? It was true that the law had put a limit to the rate of interest, and unfortunately it must not exceed twelve per cent; but he knew a way out of that. Any one who came and asked for a loan had first to buy an old plow or harrow at a price far exceeding its value; or cart a few loads of wheat to town; after that he could talk about a loan.

Hadn't he a right to see that he wasn't ruined? Never mind why so many had voted for him; the fact remained that he was a justice of the peace now. He could marry people, and settle disputes; and if he had a grudge against any fellow, he could lock him up in the potato-cellar that he used as a jail. So powerful had Skaarness become, although the parson was always raging against him. The parson? He didn't care a damn about that. But Morten was more dangerous.

On arriving at Morten's house, the two travelers got out.

Bergitta was sunburnt after the long drive over the plain, and had on a long gray mackintosh and a black head-kerchief. She stood looking about her with large, wondering eyes. Why, there was the sod hut where Morten had lived for years; she must go and have a look at that. What an awful hole! She looked at the small frame houses, the stacks, the black stretches of plowed land, and ended by bursting out laughing. She would never have gone to live at Kvidal with him, but here, so far away from everywhere, with these endless corn-fields and the houses that looked like match-boxes, it was quite another matter; this was an adventure. To think that it was really herself standing here! It seemed so incredible, who could help laughing?

They had been married in a Norwegian church in New York. The journey over the plains had been wonderfully interesting to Morten, for great changes had taken place in one short year. There was this new road; and lodging-houses had sprung up at intervals of a few miles along it, so that travelers no longer had to sleep under their wagons. He saw new settlers everywhere; in time there would be a continuous chain of settlements all the way from Northville to Nidaros.

Simen came out of the stable, stopped short, and opened his eyes in astonishment. "What! Have you been buying horses, Morten?"

"Horses! Never mind them! Look at my wife!"

"Wife!" Simen stood rooted to the spot, with a bucket in his hand, gaping.

"How do you," said Bergitta, stepping forward with a laugh.

As soon as she entered the little house she began laughing again. She stood in the middle of the floor, looking about her. "Goodness, what a mess! It needs a woman here!" Then she went and looked at the kitchen and the bedroom; and they were worse still.

Morten intended to spend the next day visiting the old settlers and showing off his bride; and this time he was going to drive. Luckily no one could see that the horses had been bought on credit. He meant to work on different lines now, even if he had to borrow money from Skaarness himself.

It was a true spring day, with sunshine and showers; the air smelled of damp earth and vegetation, and a huge rainbow quivered above the distant plain.

They could not help laughing at the sensation they created. Anne was standing outside the house washing, with her sleeves turned up. Suddenly she had to hold on as if she were fainting. "Bergitta!" The two sisters threw their arms round each other's necks and cried a little; but Bergitta had not much time to look at the three children, let alone answer questions about everything at home. Morten wanted to drive on; they could have a good talk another time.

Isak, the elder boy, who had black hair and brown eyes, had run off already to tell the neighbors.

Karen and Kal were delighted when Morten produced a small box and said it contained the old clock from Skaret. "Yes, you must hang it on the wall. Good-by. You shall hear the news from home another time. Good-by."

Morten saw three yoke of oxen on Kal's farm, and five horses grazing. The dickens! They were leaving him behind. But wait a bit!

Bergitta had to put up her umbrella. There was no road, and they had to worm their way in and out among the fields. What a sensation the horses created! Presently they arrived at a little frame house with curtained windows. Who lived here? "Ola Vatne and the colonel's daughter," answered Morten. "Those two? You don't say! What a cozy little house!"

Else, the young lady from Dyrendal, sat sewing indoors; a little gray and hollow-cheeked, and with three children around her. Ola was writing at a table; he was an official at last, a member of the township board. "It's quite time I began," said Morten to himself; "they're all leaving me behind."

They had no time to stop and have coffee. Morten could feel that Ola was standing there staring at his horses. Well, let him. He had only oxen still, and this would vex him; see if it did n't!

It was something of a shock to find Mother's Darling married and with a son and heir already. His Irish wife was a big, red-haired woman with a freckled, nutcracker face. They conversed chiefly with signs, for Anton was not much at English, and she had not picked up a great deal of Norwegian yet.

"What is his name?" asked Bergitta, pointing at the baby in the cradle.

"Peter," answered Anton.

"No, no! *Patrick!*" cried the mother, with a furious glance at her husband.

As a matter of fact, the baby had not been christened yet, Anton explained; his wife wanted him to be a Catholic, but Anton did n't, and neither of them would give in.

"What do *you* think about it?" asked the Irishwoman, looking at Morten.

"Say it in Norwegian!" said Anton, who wanted her to speak his language at home.

"Good-by," said Morten, hurriedly. "See you again soon. Good-by, good-by."

Bergitta indulged in another good laugh as they drove on. "I can see that those two fight day and night," she said. "What a comical couple! We must ask them in soon, just for the fun of it."

Next they called on Jo the schoolmaster. They found him breakfasting in the kitchen of his new frame house, unshaved, with milk and bread crumbs on his grizzled mustache. The place was in a fearful mess. He jumped up, wiped his mouth, welcomed them perfunctorily, and imdiately began holding forth about himself. "You'll have to mind your P's and Q's now!" he said. "I'm one of the chief authorities here."

"Indeed! President of the limited States?"

"No; chairman of the township board."

"I take off my hat," said Morten.

Jo began pacing up and down the room, pouring out his woes. It appeared that all schools were under the supervision of the county council, which insisted that all the teaching should be done in English. "In English! Did you ever hear of such a thing? As if I'd do it!"

"But can you refuse?"

"I can close the school."

"That would be a pity."

"Oh, well! I was born under an unlucky star. Whatever I try, is sure to go to the devil. It always does." He stared out at the window and nodded emphatically.

But Morten had shown off his wife here too, and now he wanted to be getting on. "Good-by. No; no coffee, thanks."

Just as they were going to drive away, the schoolmaster came running out of the house. "I say! I forgot to tell you: we've got a justice of the peace now."

He walked along beside them, talking excitedly Think of it! Skaarness had actually been marrying people! There were folks who owed him so much that they didn't dare to be married by any one else. It was said that his words of advice to the bridal pair—well, Mark Twain wasn't in it! And the way he decided cases— Listen to this, for instance: the other day two lawyers from Northville had come to him with a boundary dispute. Skaarness was plowing. "Whoa!" said he to his team; but he wouldn't leave the plow. "Fire away, I'll listen to you here." The two lawyers had no choice, so they set to work to plead, and quote the law, and show him maps. Skaarness looked at his horses and yawned.

Presently a thought struck one of the lawyers. "By the by," he said, taking out a ten-dollar note, "you remember I borrowed this last time we met." Skaarness took the note and put it in his pocket. Then the other lawyer remembered that he had once borrowed twenty dollars; he handed them over, and Skaarness pocketed them. This reminded the first lawyer that of course it was thirty dollars, not ten, that he had borrowed; and so it went on till one of them had no more money left. All he could do when the other pulled out a note again was to go on quoting law. But Skaarness cut him short. "Stop jawing! The other fellow's right," he said, pointing at the lawyer who had paid last. "Gee-up!" And with that the justice of the peace went on with his plowing.

Jo slapped his thigh and guffawed, and the other two roared with laughter.

Presently Morten asked, "Don't you want to hear about your father and mother?" The smile faded from Jo's face. "Yes. Are they still alive?" Bergitta started; he might have been asking about somebody he had never seen. "No," said Morten, "they're gone, both of them." Jo was silent for a moment or two; then, twirling his mustache: "Oh, well, they were old—and worn out." And he turned on his heel. Bergitta and Morten looked at each other and drove on.

On the following day the clergyman invited Morten and his wife to supper. "What! Are we going to *them?*" said Bergitta, much impressed.

"Yes, he's often asked after you," said Simen to his brother. "There's something important he wants to see you about." Morten had been on very good terms with Oppegaard before he went home to Norway; it would be nice to have a chat with him again.

Evidently their parson had money. He had built himself

a fine, white-painted house opposite the church; and he kept forgetting to collect the bushels of wheat that the farmers owed him as his salary.

They entered a comfortable room with rugs on the floor, flowers in the window, and pictures on the walls. The lady of the house was standing there to receive them, tall and stately, her handsome face framed in dark hair. She was ever so much more friendly nowadays than she had been in Erik Foss's hut on the evening of her arrival. "Welcome," she said, shaking hands with them; and she even patted Bergitta's cheek. And there was the parson himself, fair and young-looking, with his light-blue eyes and oval face. "Well, here you are at last—the man we've all been waiting for! And so you've brought a lady back with you!" It gave Bergitta a shock; fancy a fine gentleman like that calling her a lady!

Presently he said to her: "You're looking at the pictures, I see. I suppose you wonder why there are such a lot of portraits of clergymen? I'll tell you the reason. The clergy in America have helped to make the history of the country. The emigrants came out here led by clergymen. They spread over the country, again led by clergymen. Who founded most of the settlements in the forests of the East and out here in the prairie? Who founded the towns and built the hospitals, schools, and universities? The clergy. They always led the way. Besides preaching the Gospel, building churches, and linking up the scattered settlers in organized parishes, they were men of the world and pioneers. . . . Now we must have something to eat, and after that I want to talk business with Morten."

Supper over, the two men retired to the little study, and as soon as they had lighted their pipes the clergyman began: "I suppose you've heard that there's a township board here now. But what I've looked for in vain, though most of the farmers are hard-working, honest fellows, is a leader."

Morten compressed his lips and forgot to smoke.

"The first thing we've got to do is to stop all this borrow-ing from Peter Skaarness. We must have a bank."

Morten nodded. He had come to the same conclusion.

"What we need is working capital. People must be able to get a loan on reasonable terms. But the outside world has n't noticed us yet, in spite of the enormous possibilities here. The railway is sure to come soon; but we must have a bank at once. Will you help me? The farmers trust you. And I know that others can safely trust you, too. You are just the man we want. I think I told you that my brother is the head of one of the biggest banks in Minneapolis; will you come with me and talk it over with him?"

Morten hesitated; what was he letting himself in for? The clergyman went on:

"The rumors about the extension of the railway are bring-ing land-speculators here already. But the railway company won't be put upon. They'll build their lines where they want to have them. And now they require—this is between ourselves, of course—a confidential agent for this district. That's all I can tell you at present."

It seemed too good to be true. Morten sat still, a fixed smile on his lips. At length he ventured: "When the rail-way comes, I suppose a proper town'll be built here. Is any-body thinking of doing it?"

"Doing what? Building a town, do you mean?"

"Yes."

Oppegaard laughed. "No, my friend; those days have gone by. The town-makers belong to the past. Nowadays it's the railway people; they are all-powerful in such matters. I've seen little towns in the East which have had to move their houses to the place where the railway wanted them. But we can talk over all that with my brother. He has something to do with the company which is planning to bring a line out here. When shall we go?"

That night Morten dreamed strange dreams. He had got wings at last; he could rise into the air and fly . . . fly . . . at last!

When the morning of their departure arrived Morten told Bergitta that she had better go and sleep with Anne while he was away. She narrowed her eyes a little and smiled. All right, she supposed she must.

Skaarness was working on his land when the clergyman and Morten drove past, with their trunks tied on at the back of the wagon. What did this mean? He felt instinctively that they were plotting something against himself.

Before long a number of surprising things began to happen. Morten Kvidal bought two quarters of land from a Dutch settler who was leaving. They were not even close to the road, and nowhere near where the railway was expected to go. Where had he got the money from? By and by a number of big cart-loads of bricks arrived on the scene, and a gang of workmen who lived in tents started building a house. Instead of taking years, it was finished in a few weeks—three stories high, with big windows and gables. It bulked strangely large among the little houses of the settlement. Rumor said that this was going to be a bank, where folks who had their title-deeds in order would be able to borrow money at a reasonable rate of interest. The bank-manager was going to live in a flat over the bank, with a doctor above him, and a midwife in the attic. This was something like! And Morten was going to act as surveyor for the bank when the farmers applied for loans.

Had the world discovered the settlement at last? Before Christmas a second building had been run up, next door to the bank; and here there was a real shop, just like those in the big towns, with large plate-glass windows displaying all sorts of tempting things such as furs, silk dresses, accordions, and violins; while behind the counter was everything you could think of, from coffee and calico to harness and kitchen utensils. When all the lamps were lit, the place looked a perfect Paradise; it was worth a long walk across the prairie merely to stand outside and stare.

Did it end here? No; before the winter was over there were rumors of a post-office. Impossible! But true, just the same; and one fine day there the post-office stood. How much nearer the old country seemed, now that you could post and get your letters close by!

A man came riding along the road on a bicycle; he got off, and had a look round. He had come from an engineering company in Chicago. Yes, they must have a branch here; the district around would be wealthy one of these days. A blue-spectacled man drove up in a buggy drawn by a pair of steaming horses. He represented a timber-merchant in the East. A branch here? Of course; the farmers would all want building materials before long, and whoever wanted to live in the center of the town would have to build.

Morten Kvidal was selling sites, and there were so many houses already that others were sure to follow. It went without saying that the chemist's shop would have to be in the center, and of course the hotel had to be situated where people forgathered. The wheel-tracks would soon converge from every part of the prairie. The baker and the blacksmith would be here; and the watchmaker, too. They would all have to build. And every time Morten sold a site he took out a map and studied it, to find a place for the next house. People couldn't pick and choose: he seemed to be following a sort of plan. Every one was talking about it; he must be making a pile of money, selling all these building sites! Or was he only acting for rich folks in the big cities?

The money from the bank was putting new life into the settlement now, and the place was changing by leaps and bounds. The summer after the bank was opened, a herd of five hundred horses arrived from a ranch far away in the prairie. Their owner was mounted on a prancing white steed and he wore leather trousers and spurs, a big hat cocked over one ear, a red scarf, and pistols in his belt. His face was tanned by sun and wind and rain. The ground rang with the sound of hoofs, and countless manes waved in the breeze, as the spirited animals plunged, neighed, and careered about, amid shouts and the cracking of whips, while his mounted assistants galloped to and fro, keeping the herd together. The new-comer camped to the west of Ola Vatne's land. What did he want? To sell horses, of course; he had heard that folks had money to spend here; and he had a thousand more animals on his ranch if these were n't enough.

The settlers assembled in crowds; it was a sight for sore eyes to see all these beautiful bay, chestnut, black, and pie-bald horses. The temptation was too great, and they began buying. They had had enough of oxen. Kal came to look on; possibly he might buy *one* more horse. In the end he bought six; but of course it was all the fault of that young cuss Anders.

That autumn there were light-footed horses to be seen all over the plain, four to each plow; and each plow had two shares. What a change! Nowadays they could plow as much land in a single day as would make a big farm in the old country.

Now that the post-office was so near, the settlers began to take newspapers. As a rule they preferred the Norwegian-American papers, with all the news from the old country; they read them aloud on Sunday evening, and every number was as good as a budget of letters from home. There was a lot about America as well, from every part of the country, and that interested the settlers too, for, after all, it was in America that they lived. It seemed that there were politics and parties and controversies even here; who would have thought it? These colonists had been so isolated up to now; their hearts had remained in the old country; they had felt that they were staying in a foreign land merely to till the soil and grow rich. But the newspapers were teaching them to think of the country which had given them the soil and the opportunity to become rich if only they had the will.

The Presidential election took place in the following summer, and politicians came and addressed open-air meetings in English and Norwegian. And of course Morten Kvidal had a hand in it. Who'd have believed that it mattered so much what people out here thought about the government of such a big country as America? Did it really depend on them who was to be the new President? Small folks had no votes in the old country, but Ola and Kal were as powerful as any millionaire, out here! They must certainly write home and tell their relatives and friends in old Norway how different things were in America. In *this* country you woke one fine day to find yourself quite a different person. And even then the new times were only just beginning. . . .

VI

Bergitta and Morten's first son was baptized Erik Foss Kvidal.

For some reason the young wife began to mope. Morten was out so much, seeing to a thousand things, that whenever he stopped at home for a day, there was a rush of work, and everything had to be done at once. For a time Bergitta thought it rather fun to see him working, and to look out at the prairie and the gray haystacks which seemed so ghostly when the dark autumn days set in, with wind and fog. But one day she came to him, very pale and with dark shadows under her eyes, and asked whether it was n't possible to sell the farm and go home.

Of course they could, he laughed, only not to-day, and perhaps not even to-morrow! He must get a few more things done, he wasn't quite free to go away, just at present. So the matter was shelved, till one day he was startled by a letter from his brother Peter, asking if he was willing to give up his claim on the farm at home in his favor. If not, Peter would emigrate too.

It took Morten a day or two to think things out. Give up his claim to Kvidal? He could, of course. What chance had he of returning there? This eternal craving for the little gray houses and the country round them, was cramping him like a strait-waistcoat, which it was high time to get rid of. And yet, in the long run, he could n't bring himself to do it. He simply could not. Who knew? Some fine day he might get ready, and go home for good. But not yet, of course; it would be several years before he could manage it.

293

So one day Peter turned up, bringing his sister Randi with him. Randi was married, and her husband came too. Morten stared at them. He had to be a sort of Providence to his younger brothers and sisters. He had helped Simen to get a quarter of homestead land farther out in the prairie; now he'd have to help these, before the unoccupied land was taken up by others who were steadily pouring into the country. As for his mother, he would have to comfort her by sending over a little more money, much as he needed it himself.

One thing puzzled him. All his neighbors borrowed from the bank. They were always wanting more horses, more machines, and new, roomier houses. But there was one who never borrowed a cent, and that was Kal. To be sure, for several years, he had had rather larger crops to sell than the others, and he didn't put the money in the bank, but in the old emigrant-chest under his bed, which actually had a lock. He could never go any distance from home without feeling afraid the place might burn down in his absence.

The children were worrying him now to build a decent house like other people. He had had to build a shed for all his horses, and when the place was full of hired laborers, in spring and autumn, they had to eat and sleep in sheds, until Kal's farm soon looked like a little town of shanties. But as for borrowing money to build a house! . . . He borrow! Kal would pull a long face, and shake his head. He remembered too well what it had felt like, in the old country, to have debts hanging round his neck!

The lad Oluf was just home from Decorah, but did that mean that he was ready to be ordained, after studying for four years? Not a bit of it! He was going to study in earnest now, in a town called St. Louis, which must be the deuce of a way off, for just to pay the fare Karen had had to sell a whole pig! Still, it was good to see him again, for he had n't come home for a holiday in all those four years; the journey was too expensive. He took a job instead, on a farm farther east, so as not to call on his mother and her chickens for money.

He arrived in his town clothes—tall, strong, and as freckled as a Turk—and Karen went round him, touching him, stroking his clothes, and thinking she'd never seen any one to beat him. Then Siri came along, and teased him by calling him Moses. Anders wanted to box with him. Paulina came in from the fields where she had been driving the self-binder, and stood gaping at him, with her big rough hands on her hips. "Well, have n't you learnt enough to preach yet?" she said. "Why, I was a parson, and married a cow and a bull, when I was a tiny thing!" Siri teased him. He revenged himself by standing up stiff and straight, and spouting Latin to the whole lot of them.

He sat all the evening telling about the college, and the teachers and all his friends, and every now and then he would look up at the old wall clock from Skaret. Nice to see that again. "And the hammer, Anders, I suppose you have n't thrown that away? Bring along the hammer!"

The next day Kal wanted to show him that they had n't been sitting with their hands in their laps, either. He took him round the new fields, and set him driving a self-binder with four horses, while he himself followed with four more. Why, they dashed along as though they were driving to a wedding; and now the lad could sit up there preaching and talking Latin to the horses, the young rip!

But who could have guessed that the boy's visit would have ended the way it did? They were sitting in the little house one Sunday evening, and the young folks were teasing one another again; Oluf was the worst. He was chaffing Paulina about Mother's Darling and his sister got furious. "If you speak of him again, I'll give you a taste of this!" she threatened him, holding out her great fist. "You 've got a hand like a leg of mutton," said Oluf. "Now I see why Anton would n't have you! You 'll never be married, with such murderous fists as those!" This was too much for the poor girl, who had suffered in secret from a wound that ached and smarted; she sprang to her feet, and banged the table till the cups rattled. "Hold on!" cried everybody. "For shame!" said Mother. "Can't you take a joke?" scolded Father.

But next day she got Kal by himself and said, "I'm going away, Father!" He stared at her. What? Had she lost her wits?

"I dare say it's true enough that I'll never get married, but I mean to provide against that while there's time. I'm turned one and twenty now, and I've a right to take up homestead land for myself. I'm going into town to secure a quarter, and shall take the one that lies west of your holding, so we shall still be neighbors. I mean to have my own place to myself, or Oluf and Anders will be having to keep me when I get old."

Mother and Father and the others argued with her, but to no purpose; she would have her own way. It was perfectly true that she had the right to claim land, being an unmarried woman over twenty-one years of age, and the day came when Kal had to set her up with oxen and plow and the necessary houses on her quarter. So she went to live there in company with a woman whom she had hired to help her. In clear weather they could be seen over to the westward, plowing with the two oxen. For the first time one of Kal's children had grown old enough to pit her will against his own. And it wasn't even one of those darned boys, but a bit of a lass! Wasn't it enough to make a man tear his hair and swear?

There was a lot of talk among the farms just now, because a big wheat firm in Chicago had started building an elevator in the little town of Nidaros. Wasn't that a sure sign that the railway was coming before long? For people would never be such fools as to build an elevator so far from the railroad; they might just as well let the farmers themselves cart their wheat to Northville as before.

No, indeed; the Chicago firm knew well enough what they were doing; they meant to be on the spot in good time, to collect and store wheat from the hundreds of neighboring farms, which were growing larger and larger every year. But the railway—when was it coming? No use asking Morten. Bergitta pretended to know nothing, and the parson only shook his head. But soon it was rumored that the railroad was already pushing its way out across the prairie, by the efforts of a little army of workmen. Then a gang of workmen started building a station in the center of the little town, and leading up to it they marked out a road, the "main street," on both sides of which there were building-sites for sale with space for large and small houses.

The homestead land hereabouts had all been taken up now, and new settlers were obliged to go far, far out into the wilds, if they wanted to get a quarter gratis. For the railway company had obtained a government grant of so many sections on each side of the line; and along its main artery, farther north, it already owned a broad tract stetching right through this vast country to the Pacific. You could buy land from the railway, though. And Morten need not keep his secret any longer. You could buy it from him, for he was the local agent for the railway. It was on the railway's behalf that he had bought those two quarters from the Dutchman, and subsequently the other farms in the neighborhood. The railway owned all the sites in the town of Nidaros.

Those people who had cultivated their two quarters, found that they could at last get more. The price was reasonable, a few dollars per acre, to be paid off within twenty years. It sounded very tempting! And as for the money which had to be paid down on the spot, they could get that from the bank; the bank would willingly advance money on land.

There was great perturbation in Ola's mind the day a saloon was opened in the little town. When he walked past it, he felt as though he was on fire inside; it seemed as though somebody had placed it there as a pitfall for him specially. "Come along, Ola, you're going to hell now, Ola!" Perhaps that was true; he felt he must either go inside and get beastly drunk, or wreck the place and thrash the saloon-keeper. That fearful urge within him—it was still there at times, though he was no longer forced to struggle against it for months on end. He was not so terribly cut off from everybody nowadays, and could find distraction in all that had been happening lately: the newspaper, meetings and lectures, the railway, the town, the romance of the bank and the money, and all the horses and machinery. All this relieved the tension, and the depression was not so bad as it used to be.

And during all these years, Else, his wonderful wife, had fostered other things in him, had tuned his ear to more delicate sounds; he couldn't say how, exactly, but it was true, all the same. And now, here was the saloon forcing itself into his life! Everything he had fought for lost! Since the very first day out here, there had been a silent rivalry among the old settlers, and until now he had kept up with them. But now he was sure to fall. There was the saloon, a trap set to catch him. "Come along, Ola! You're an official, and on the way to be a rich farmer, but it's all up with you now; come along in, make a beast of yourself, ruin everything!"

His blood boiled. He was one of the supervisors of the township of Nidaros, and the winter before, he had bought a coat with a fur collar, and fur-lined gloves, so that he might cut a better figure when he went out with his wife. And then, hadn't he planned to build houses here on his farms like those at Dyrendal, with a piano in the sitting-room,

where she might sit and strum just as she had done when
she was a young lady?

But look, Ola—the saloon! To hell with everything, Ola!
In the old days you got beastly drunk twice a year, when
you made a trip to town. Now it will be every day, till you
have drunk yourself and the farm and your wife and children
all to hell. Yes, there is the saloon. In you go, Ola!
You 're done for anyway, Ola, you and your family too!

He said one day at table, "I hear they 're opening a saloon
here."

"Yes," replied Else, looking at him quite calmly. The
children were there, too. The eldest daughter was just like
her mother; even she looked at him calmly, though she must
have seen him driven home from town, too drunk to stand.

"Had you heard of it?" he asked Else.

"Yes," she answered again. And the children looked at
him, and kept wonderfully quiet.

How this woman had aged! Her hair was turning gray,
her cheeks were hollow, and she had lost a couple of teeth—
she who was once the pretty young lady at Dyrendal. Her
hands were rough, and her back bent from the hard life of
an emigrant woman, and yet there was one thing she never
lost, something which had often made Ola feel ashamed and
which he had never been able to learn from her. Was it so
impossible? Had n't he picked up a little of it, after all?

One day he said, "I 'm going for a stroll round the town."

"Yes, do," she answered.

The elder children walked part of the way with him. When
they turned back, he stood looking after them. Ah, how
like her mother that eldest girl was! And with all she had
to see to, Else had found time to teach them. They certainly
knew more than if they had gone to old Jo.

When he came home that evening, the children were in
bed, and Else was sewing in the lamplight. She raised her
head and looked at him, but did not seem in the least sur-

prised to see him come back perfectly sober. Nobody could beat Else at keeping her thoughts to herself.

He walked about the room for a bit, then stopped in front of her and said, "Else, will you tell me something?"

"What do you want to know?"

"Well—now don't laugh at me!"

"You needn't be afraid!" and she smiled a little.

"I—I thrashed the saloon-keeper this evening!"

"I know that!" she replied, and went on with her sewing.

"You? How do you know it?"

"The schoolmaster was there and saw it. And he dropped in on his way home. He felt he must come and tell me." She threaded her needle again, and went on with her work.

Presently Ola said, "But I've been thinking that it doesn't look very well for a supervisor to mix himself up in such things."

"No, perhaps it doesn't."

"Besides, I can't very well thrash all the saloon-keepers in North Dakota!"

"No indeed, that would be too big a job, even for you!"

"But you see, Else, I might be able to thrash them in another way. Something more in keeping with my position. Look here, Else, will you teach me how to *lecture?*"

She looked at him for a minute or two; his whole face was crimson with embarrassment: there was something quite pathetic about him! "Do you mean you want to thrash the saloon-keepers by lecturing against them?" she asked, longing to throw her arms round his neck.

"Yes. Do you think I could learn to make speeches in such a way that they would be turned out of the place?"

"Yes, I don't see why you shouldn't." And she might have said a good deal more, Ola thought, but that wouldn't have been a bit like her.

After that day, he again went about the place singing. And he would stop in the middle of a job, and clench his

fists, and hit out as though he was clearing out a whole
saloon! He felt something rising up within him, as it had
so often done before, but this time he would be able to give
vent to it, by going out and thrashing all the saloon-keepers
in North Dakota; only, mind you, this time it would n't be
with his fists, but with his speeches. How should he do
that? Ah, that was where his wife came in! His Else was
going to teach him, and in that way the thing could be done.
Yes, that would do the trick. Ola strolled about singing
from morning till night.

VII

The time soon came when several trains a day whistled through Nidaros Settlement, and it was a sight, especially in the evening, to see the rows of carriages with their lighted windows speeding across the plain till they finally melted away into the horizon. At last the hermits were linked up with the great wide world, and their lives began to move to a quicker and easier rhythm.

About Christmas-time something else happened, namely the inauguration of a club in the town, set on foot by the schoolmaster and the parson's wife. During the weeks that preceded the opening, the schoolmaster had not been idle, for he had got the young people together to practise Norwegian songs; while as for the pastor's wife, she had some grand surprise up her sleeve; indeed, rumor said that she was planning nothing less than theatricals!

Once the railway was started, a gas-works was erected in next to no time, and there was no lack of light now in the little prairie town; on dark nights a couple of big incandescent lamps lighted up the road across the plain for a long distance. And now the people came driving up in their sleighs with bells jingling—men and women in fur coats. Fresh and rosy from the cold, they hurried indoors; there were lights outside and inside—with a perfect blaze of gaslights in the big hall, which still smelled of freshly planed wood. And sure enough, there was a stage at one end with a curtain in front of it, and the walls were decorated with American and Norwegian flags into the bargain!

This was the first time that the farmers had had any building, except the church, for their social gatherings, and

302

it was the first time they had ever hung up the American flag. They gazed at the blue ground with all its stars, and it told them that they had become a part of one of the great world powers. They were Norwegians, of course, but they were Americans too; they had obtained land from the Government, they had voted for the President, and it was only right that they should hoist the American flag on great occasions.

The curtain went up, and the play began. The young people had been coached by the pastor's wife. Anders Skaret was the lover, Siri a lovelorn maiden, Jo an old dominie; any one could see that at a glance. The play was "At the Sæter," and there were national costumes, yodeling, songs about love, and Norwegian scenery.

The audience sat squeezed together on the rows of benches; they could see the mountains with their forests and glaciers, and there was the sæter hut, with lasses and lads and lovemaking. Ah, that was the sort of thing they could understand! And perhaps it awakened memories in old and young alike. The lights in the hall had been lowered, but one could feel the placid enjoyment on every face; it was such an age since these prairie folks had had any sort of amusement.

Down went the curtain, but as soon as the lights were turned up, it rose again, and the pastor came forward. Hush! There 'd be a sermon now, perhaps, and reading from the Bible? No, he was going to speak about worldly things. He said that an evening like this ought to bring back their country to their minds and thoughts; and not only during the entertainment, but in their every-day lives as well. The thought.of that grand scenery should be a source of refreshment in their daily labor, a support in their struggles, an inspiration for their lives, so that other nations might think and say, "These people must have come of a good stock; they must have come from a beautiful country."

But he had something else to tell them. The best way

to preserve one's national character was through good books. They were going to inaugurate a reading-room this evening. They wanted a library here. Through the world of books they could keep in touch with the soul of their own race, whether they were at home or abroad.

At last people could begin to move about. A smell of coffee stole into the room, and most of the benches were carried out. Then a side door opened, and in came Anne and Bergitta, each carrying a big, shining, steaming kettle; and they were followed by the Irishwoman and several other women with huge trays of cakes and Vienna bread. Why, it was a regular wedding-feast!

Whenever coffee was provided, Karen always considered that she must lend a hand, so she bustled to and fro, and found plenty of empty cups to fill. Else started pouring out at one of the tables, and the others watched her. She had altered lately; her pale face had become quite fresh and plump again, and she laughed at the least thing; she seemed to have attained to a second blooming, under the influence of some secret joy or other. Her daughter stood by her, slim and dark-haired, in a red frock, with her plaits down her back; she was the very image of her mother, and made folks think of the young Miss Else of Dyrendal.

Bergitta and Anne and most of the other women still wore their kerchiefs over their heads, even in this warm room; it was all right for the parson's wife and Else and the Irishwoman to sit there with their heads uncovered, but the others followed the fashion of the old country; they did n't intend to start aping the gentry.

Morten was one of the few men who wore a tweed suit and a "town" tie; but, then, people looked up to him as representing the railway, the land, and the bank, and he had recently been elected to the county council, and had to attend important meetings in Northville. He went round shaking hands with all his friends, and looked at all the new faces of the young people who had come out lately. They were a fine-looking lot, strong, with tanned faces. His mind flew back to his own young days, and his native place seemed to rise up before him.

Why did these youngsters cut themselves adrift? Was there no work for them in the old country? Of course they had been to school, and learned to sing their national songs. And what followed? Did they buckle to and throw in their lot with their own country? Not a bit of it; they must needs cross the great ocean, and scatter themselves over the prairie. They were quite contented with a sod hut and a couple of oxen, as long as they were in a new country, and the terrible winters did not daunt them; they conquered the desert, cultivated America, and by their efforts the country was becoming richer and richer.

Yes indeed! He himself was one of them, and so were his brothers. Knut and Mette were wanting to come out now, and Mother would be left alone. It did n't bear thinking of! He looked kindly at these boys and girls, as he welcomed them to the place. "You're from Hallingdal, you say? And you—from Sparbu? Why, I used to drill with a Sparbu lad; perhaps you know him—Per Nyvold? And where are you from, my lass? Hedemarken? That's fine."

The pastor kept bringing some lad to him and asking, "Do you think you can find a job for him, Morten Kvidal?" Perhaps he could, and if not, there were Kal and the other men. They'd find the boy something! "Hey, Kal! come here!" But Morten could n't help wondering why nobody ever came to him direct; they always got the pastor or somebody else to speak for them. Did he really look so severe, when he was doing his best to be as sweet as honey?

He went over and shook hands with an old white-haired man on the other side of the hall. "Hallo, are you the new tailor? Glad to see you." The old man's shoulders were bent, and he had red-rimmed eyes and a pale, clean-shaven face. "Are you from Wisconsin?"

"Yes, but I came from Norway last year."

"Are you a new-comer here?"

"Oh, no; not at all! I first came over from Norway forty years ago."

"You don't say so! And you took a trip home last year?"

"I have been back to Norway seven times."

"That's something to boast of!"

"And each time I thought I was going back for good. 'Now I'll settle down,' I thought. But happiness is a funny thing! When you're here, you feel you can't be happy out of the old country, and when you've been there a little while, you begin to look out across the ocean, and you find that you're happier over here, after all!" The old man smiled mournfully; there was a far-away look in his eyes, as though they were always gazing across an ocean.

Then the singing began. The schoolmaster stood up, gray-haired and gray-bearded, and beat time, while the boys and girls around him sang their national anthem. Morten had never heard it so well sung, the voices thrilled through the hall as vigorously as though they meant the sound to carry right over to the old country. He felt he must join in, too, and raised his hand; the pastor followed his example, others joined in by degrees, till at last they were all singing together.

These prairie folks had been cut off for many years from home and friends, they had endured frosts and poverty and hard labor in this new country, but now they were singing. They had come to-night from their sod huts and little frame houses across the level plain, and here they stood in their best clothes, in the bright room, singing about that land which, somehow or other, they could never, never forget.

Many songs were sung, and each one carried them a little nearer to the old home. Anders Skaret, a fair, sturdy, heavy-jowled fellow, had a powerful bass voice. Siri, very smart

and slim in her blue dress, looked across at her parents as
she sang; the singing seemed to draw all these emigrants
more closely together, till they felt inclined to hold one
another's hands.

Presently a young fellow sprang up on a chair. Why, it
was Anders! That lad had worked in the town for so many
winters that he had been able to attend night-school, and
had nerve enough for anything! His parents looked down
abashed; what the deuce was the boy up to now? He was
actually making a speech, addressing them as folks who,
though no doubt good Americans by this time, still remembered their homes in the old country, however insignificant
they might have been. He spoke well, and Morten scratched
his head; he liked the boy, and yet he did n't like him.
Something seemed to warn him: "Look out for that chap!
He 'll get the better of you some day!"

After the speech was over, somebody clapped his hands and
shouted, "Is n't it about time we had a dance?" He was a
dark-haired young fellow in spectacles, a new doctor who had
just come to the place,—there were two of them in the town
now,—and he had such a pretty wife with him that every
one was looking at her.

Some one else raised his hand. It was—yes, of course
it was Peter Skaarness, and he said coldly and sourly, "I
did n't know we had come here to be led into sin and wickedness!" There was a pause, and they all looked at one another.
The doctor sneered. The young people glanced from Morten
to the parson. Could n't *they* do anything in the matter?
At last the clergyman clapped his hands, and got up on a
bench that stood against the wall, where he stood in his long
coat and white tie, still young-looking, with his fair hair
and bright blue eyes as merry as a boy's. He said: "I don't
know of any place in the Bible where dancing is forbidden.
Only evil-minded persons can call innocent fun, 'sin and
wickedness.'"

"Hurrah!" the doctor exclaimed, and "Hurrah!" echoed all the youngsters. Peter Skaarness's beard quivered. "Come along!" he said, taking his wife by the arm. As he brushed past Morten Kvidal, he hissed out: "You took the best railway land for yourself and the old settlers. And now you've let loose the devil among us!" This was the cause of many dissensions in the church later on, and, as might have been expected, Peter Skaarness finally started a sect of his own.

But at this moment Ola Vatne came in with his fiddle. He didn't play much nowadays, for he no longer roamed the country, playing at dances. The entertainment committee had been obliged to approach him in a body, and coax and press him, till at last: "Oh, well, as long as it's for charity . . ." So down he sat on the stage, a fine-looking man, though a little worn by hard work on the prairie and at the plow; not a gray streak to be seen in his thick golden hair and full reddish beard. He tuned up, with a hand that was small though rough and hairy, and began to play.

The first to start off was the doctor with his princess of a wife, such a contrast to all the rest, for to-night she had made up her mind to have a good time, and had dressed herself for dancing. The train of her pale yellow dress swept the floor, a diamond twinkled in the comb in her hair, and she wore a pearl necklace. Her face was so fresh, so dainty, so full of enjoyment! And even her long dark eyebrows quivered with happiness. Let people stare if they liked. But had any one the courage to start dancing along with those two?

Well, no young people could long resist such a waltz, and one couple after another took the floor. Men from Valdres and Hallingdal in their national costume; men from Sætersdal, with leather patches on their knee-breeches; girls in red bodices with white sleeves, and filagree brooches at the neck,

looking bashfully down as their partners dragged them along.
Who could resist such a fiddle? The floor was thronged;
long legs in homespun trousers mingled with the white stockings of the men in knee-breeches; the girls' head-kerchiefs
were slipping down on their necks, revealing their hair and
heads at last.

The hall was a sea of color. Sogn and Hardanger seemed
to have sent out their prettiest girls, and there were lads
from Telemark and Gudbrandsdal, with silver buttons on their
jackets. The dance was in full swing now. The lads lifted
their partners off the floor and whirled them round, their
long repressed gaiety finding vent at last and rebelling against
this everlastingly flat country. What memories of white
mountain peaks at sunrise, forests, waterfalls, the magic and
mystery of the light nights, or the sea in calm and in storm!
The dance expressed it all. "Gosh! Can't that fellow
play!"

There sat Ola, fiddling away with his eyes shut, and no
one could guess what he was really thinking about, as he
held the dancers with his magic all that evening. Some one
offered him a drink, but he was proof against the temptation.
Yet the old longing was surging up in him to-night; he felt
it literally boiling over, as if he had taken the lid off something deep down within himself. If they only knew, he was
re-living some of those sunny days and light nights, hunted
over hill and dale, shot at, shouted after by the soldiers and
the sheriff. He'd enticed them into one entrance of a cave,
and it was a long time before they discovered that he'd
slipped out by another. On and on he ran, and the hunt
continued for days and nights, and even weeks, and more
weeks.

These memories had been working in him for many, many
years. They were bound to find vent at last; and yet—would
he lose them for a million kroner? Didn't he tremble even
now when he poured them out in his music to make folks

dance and caper more and more madly? His boy Lorents, a lad of twelve, the apple of his mother's eye, with his father's slight figure and thick golden hair, stood with his eyes fixed on his father. "Ah, you may stare, laddie! Folks were very different in those days!"

Every one seemed bewitched that evening. Even the old people were joining in. Bergitta had been sitting there, her face pale but her eyes sparkling; the strange youths were afraid to ask her to dance, but was she going to sit there the whole night? No, for Morten came along at last, it having evidently dawned upon him that his wife was n't quite a hundred yet! Perhaps she'd been a bit homesick yesterday, and had cried last night, but now she was going to dance. "Come along," and Morten took the floor with his wife and showed that there was still some life left in him.

The schoolmaster could not dance—not very well, anyhow. Besides, he'd have to put his arm round a woman's waist, and he did n't like that. He went up to the clergyman and said, "Why the devil can't I write poetry!"

"Hush! We can't have the schoolmaster swearing!"

"All right. But now I see why it required mountain folk and sailors to conquer the prairie! Their knapsacks and their hearts were full of the wild scenery of the old country, and they lived on it, summers and winters alike! The mountains and the sea rescued the plain. What a poem it would make!"

"Well, write it then, man!"

"Can't be done! I never *can* do what I want!"

Ola struck up the Rhinelander, and the floor was thronged in an instant. Anton Noreng was prancing about with his red-haired wife—as ill-matched in dancing as they were in religion and language; no, she could n't do it, and she shrugged her shoulders, declaring that she was n't going to jump about like a rabbit! They had to stop, and she pulled herself away from him, hot and cross, and went over to sit with the old women.

"Do come, Anne!" She was sitting at the coffee-table, and Morten wanted a turn with her. She was still good-looking, with her oval olive face and black hair. Was she thinking of old times? Or perhaps of Per? She shook her head. No, no, she could n't dance.

"Oh, come along, Annie! All of us youngsters are dancing this evening!"

It really was too bad—but in the long run he persuaded her. Why, it was fifteen years since she had last danced! And now all that happened during that time faded from her mind: she even forgot where she was, and only saw the old country, the sæters, the farms, and the lakes; and thought of an evening at Whitsuntide, with bonfires on the hills, and boys and girls sporting on the greensward. She was dancing to the tune of her own memories. Once she had been the prettiest girl in the church. Ah yes, *once!*

You need n't think they left Karen Skaret alone; her Kal was suddenly possessed by the devil, and came up to her, a lean, bony figure of a man, with his chin-tuft nearly white by now, and nothing would please him but that they must come out on the floor and make fools of themselves!

"I 'll do nothing of the kind! Let me go, you old idiot!"

But the old fellow had gone stark, staring mad! He would n't let go. "Come along now, old woman. Come, we have n't had a dance for many a long day."

"You be quiet! There 's Anders looking at us."

"Come along, drat you! If you don't, I 'll go and ask Anne."

Karen glanced nervously across at Anne. No, she was n't going to let him get into her clutches; she would rather . . . And before she could speak another word, he had seized her round the waist and dragged into the whirlpool. She had a black kerchief on her head, and her old spotted shawl crossed over her chest and knotted behind; she was old and bent, and had n't danced since her wedding, thirty years ago; but here she was, Heaven forgive her, jumping about with Kal, who must have had a skinful this evening; it would be a mercy if she came out of it alive!

How they danced! The head-kerchief slipped down on her shoulders, leaving her grizzled hair uncovered; how lucky that she had washed her hair yesterday! Well, well! Many things had happened since they danced last, but she could still remember their young days, and those first happy years in the croft under the hill. She would certainly cook him a good dinner to-morrow, and they would have to go to communion together as soon as possible.

The music stopped and the musician called out: "If there's any one here who knows how to fiddle, I 'd like to have a dance myself!" A Sætersdal peasant came up and took the fiddle, tucking it lovingly under his chin. He tuned it, drew the bow across it, and began to play, his eyes shining with excitement. He played a *Springdans*.

And now every one was watching Else and Ola dancing together. He must have bewitched her, for they were whirling round like a couple of youngsters. He swung her round by the hands, her faded silk dress billowing out with the quick movement; then he loosed her, clapped his hands together, and turned such a cart-wheel that his feet cut a half-circle high up in the air. Next he spun round on one heel like a top; seized his wife again, and swept her right round the hall, all the others standing back to give them room. He must have taught her this country-dance himself, when he was the herdsman at Dyrendal. And how well she remembered it! How they were whirling round, and yet now they were no chickens!

But over by the wall sat a girl who had had no partners the whole evening. It was Paulina Skaret. She was no beauty, certainly, being coarse and masculine in appearance, with hair like tow, and a broad face with prominent eyes. She had done man's work out of doors, and woman's work indoors during all the years since they came to America. It was hard enough out of doors, but worse in the house. While the men took their after-dinner nap, she had had to help her mother with the washing and the cooking; and when all the outdoor work was finished in the evening, she had had to turn to again with the milking and more cooking.

Was she tired? No! she was soured, especially when she looked at Anton. But at any rate she had her own quarter out on the prairie; she would n't have to be beholden to any-body, even if she had to be an old maid for the rest of her days. Young? She 'd never had time to be young; the boys were young, and Siri, the apple of her father's eye.

People began to leave and the cold air blew in at the door like white mist; the sleigh-bells began to die away along the roads. The entertainment was over. "We must have some more evenings like this!" said the pastor, as he wished them all good-night.

VIII

It was springtime, and Anders Skaret was driving a coffin from the station to the church. Per Föll had returned at last from the asylum, for his widow wished him to be buried at home.

The clergyman stood by the grave, with all the old settlers around him, and, raising his voice, he spoke a few words. They were standing, he said, by the grave of a soldier who had fallen in battle—not only in the struggle to win his daily bread, but also in the never-ending struggle of humanity to make themselves masters of the earth. Then the grave was filled in, and Per Föll lay by the side of Erik Foss.

Afterward folks went to see Anne, and told her she ought to sell the farm, now that land had gone up so much in value; but she only shook her head. Kal was going to manage her two quarters for a time on the profit-sharing system, and in the long run one of her sons would inherit his father's land. Not the elder boy, Isak,—the brown-haired, dark-eyed lad,— for he cared for nothing but books; but the second boy, Per, who was almost a man, tall and sturdy, with fair, curly hair. When he had a spade in his hands, he was his father over again.

On many a snowy winter evening Anne sat in the little house with the children, telling them tales of her own young days. She had such vivid recollections of her old home that she made her listeners feel as though they knew it too. Nowadays they went to school, where they talked and read English, and their whole education was rooted in the soil of America; so it was a far cry for them to the old days of their mother's stories. She took them out skiing on steep hillsides, or skating on the glittering ice of the frozen fiord;

314

they went with her up to the sæter, where she had been
dairymaid for so many summers; they encountered bears in
the forests; they listened to fairy-tales about wood-nymphs
with blue kirtles and golden hair, who haunted the hillsides
and enticed handsome young men away into the mountains.

A mountain, with snow-topped peaks rising right up into
the sky! What ever was that like? Like a giant, who had
sat down to rest and think for a bit! The children drew
nearer, their eyes big with wonder; they had never seen woods
or mountains. "Go on, Mother! Tell us more, tell us
more!"

She had come out into the wilds, and would probably
never see the old country again, for her children were Americans, and she must stay here with them; still, they all enjoyed going home with her on one of these dream journeys.
It seemed strange to her that she had to bow her head and
admit that her youth was past, though memories of the
bonny lads, the dances, and all the fun still haunted her.
That was all over now! And yet folks used once to say she
was the prettiest girl in the church at home. But that was
long, long ago!

Sometimes Bergitta would drop in. She would shake off
the snow in the porch, the door would open, and in she would
walk.

"You're never out walking in such weather!"

"No, the stable-boy drove me."

She had a child nearly every year, and any amount to see
after, now that the farm had grown so large. But Anne
knew well enough that there was another reason for her looking so pale and shrunken.

"How are you now?" she asked her sister.

Oh, middling! The worst of it was, she couldn't sleep
properly. The dark autumn days in this desert had been
bad enough, but winter was worse still. If only one could
go home to-morrow, or see plenty of company, dance, and be

gay. No chance of that now; she was getting old; there was nothing for it but to sit down and cry.

"For shame!—with a man like Morten for your husband!"

Morten indeed! Why, it was his fault, from beginning to end. He was always promising to sell the farm, and return home, but not a bit of it! He went buzzing about like a bee in a bottle; there were those quarters he had got from the railway, which had all to be cultivated at once; there were new houses to be run up; a telephone company for the whole district; elections, and all sorts of responsibilities. How high he wanted to climb, no one knew, not even himself.

But he'd had a shock just lately.

His youngest brother wrote out and asked whether he would give up his claim to the old farm. Yes, Morten was willing—or, rather, he wasn't. He couldn't do it even now. It would be like severing a navel-string, and he couldn't make up his mind to do it. They must wait a bit; of course he was going home one of these days, only there were one or two things he must see to first. Well, of course, he might have known what would happen. His younger brothers and sisters weren't going on running that farm at their own risk; they must look after their own interests, and so they came out here. They turned up one fine day, and expected Morten to look after them in the same way as the others.

But when they told him that their mother had been obliged to sell the farm to strangers, to provide board and lodging for her old age—ah, didn't he turn pale when he heard that! And now he'd more irons in the fire than ever. He was always saying he'd go home soon, and buy back the farm, but there were one or two things he must see to first. He talked English and Norwegian in his sleep; one minute he'd be singing the praises of this great, free America, the next he'd be talking to his mother, and thinking he was at home again in Kvidal. Go home? Not he! He was getting more and more deeply rooted here, and every year made it worse.

And Bergitta went on complaining. But Anne knew the best remedy. She cheered her up by asking all manner of questions about what had occurred in the parish at home, after she herself had left Norway. She drew her on to tell one thing after another, and Bergitta recalled people and episodes, coming out into the middle of the room to show just how things had happened, till at last she could not help smiling, and laughing too. "Don't you remember him? And her? And the people at such and such a farm? Do you remember that wedding at Langmo, when we drove to church in sixteen carriages, with a man riding in front of us, playing the clarinet?"

Of course Anne remembered! And now she must put on the kettle, and they would have a little feast. It was snowy and desolate out of doors, but they had forgotten all about that; they were both young madcaps again, larking about with their friends among the fiords and hills in the old country. Those memories were food and drink to them. Suddenly Bergitta leaned back and gazed ahead of her through half-shut eyes. Then she asked her sister to forgive her.

"Whatever do you want me to forgive you for?" Oh well, it had been rather horrid of her to come there and abuse Morten. But of course Anne knew she did n't really mean it. Morten was a splendid fellow, and so good-natured, whenever he could spare time to stay at home for a bit. She herself felt so heartened up by all their reminiscences that she was n't going to fret at having to stop a little longer in America. . . . What a future the children would have, in a great country like this!

"So you may be sure we shall stay here," she wound up; "we shall never leave our fine new home here, and we 've nothing left now in the old country."

Finally she would go home quite another creature, and her sister would put on her things and accompany her part of the way.

One day Else drove up to Morten's door. What a fine carriage and pair of horses she had! "That's what happens in this country," said she. "You're rich swells almost before you know it!" Bergitta was at home, and rather down in the dumps again, but there was always such an atmosphere of calm about Else that it made one ashamed of mentioning sad or disturbing subjects before her. She sat down, but would not take off her hat, and only unfastened the top button of her coat; she had only looked in for a minute! She just wanted to tell Bergitta that Ola had given his first lecture in the town, and it had gone off wonderfully well, though of course he would do even better, with a little more practice.

"And what *do* you think, Bergitta? The other day he actually brought home a piano!"

He had told Else that it was a reward, because she had never scolded him when he used to come home drunk. But of course Else kept that to herself, and only told Bergitta that unfortunately her own fingers were past playing the piano nowadays; they were too stiff after digging in the prairie for so many years. However, she could teach her daughters—at least, as much as she knew herself.

"And now I have something important to talk to you about, Bergitta. Will you be on a committee with the parson's wife and me? We want to collect funds for a Norwegian hospital." Bergitta burst out laughing. "How can we women build a hospital?" Her friend replied: "In America, it's always the women who take the initiative in such things. You *must* join us, Bergitta!"

Bergitta allowed herself to be persuaded, and in the long run she became tremendously keen. Her elder children were already at school; how quickly time flew! They spoke English among themselves, they were Americans now; how could their mother help becoming attached to the new country, in spite of everything? A farmer's wife hadn't much spare time, but Morten would get the railway company to give them a building-site gratis. Of course they must have a hospital in Nidaros!

During the next few years Bergitta often sat at home moping for days together; then she would pull herself together again all of a sudden, and go about full steam up, both at home and out of doors. But fretting like this, day after day and year after year, while her children's schooling seemed only to estrange them from her, wore a person out by degrees, almost without her noticing it. And she was just as uncontrolled in her happiness. When she laughed, people would turn round and stare at her.

There had been no trees near her house, and she had planted a little grove, as Karen and Else and Anne had done; they grew very slowly, the winter storms were so severe; yet every spring the leaves came out on those little trees, and it was as good as a fairy-tale to go and look at them! By and by the grove would be large enough for one or two birds to settle there and begin to sing.

One day, everybody was startled by the news that the schoolmaster was going around and wishing people good-by. Good-by? Was he going away, then?

Exactly. He was going for a journey. To the old country? He laughed scornfully. Well, what would he do about his farm? Oh, he had sold it to Mother's Darling; the rascal had borrowed the money from the bank. And where on earth was Jo going? "Oh, to several places. Good-by, and good luck, all of you."

The only person to whom he confided the facts of the case was Morten Kvidal. The schoolmaster found that busy individual in his large new stable, behind a wagon with a pair of horses. Morten was carting manure, and stood in his blue overalls, loading up the cart; two long rows of cart-horses were fidgeting in the stalls on each hand.

"Hullo! Does the future governor of North Dakota stoop

to such menial tasks as this?" Yes, Morten was taking a turn at work on the farm; this was the kind of thing he really understood! The schoolmaster had come to wish him good-by. Morten stared. It was so unexpected—almost disconcerting.

Jo sat down on a box, and began to tell the whole story. He felt that his life had come to the parting of the ways. He had gone the round of the old settlers one stormy evening, and he felt that he was somehow superfluous in the world. To tell the truth, he had peeped in through the windows here and there. What did he see? A family sitting round the lamp in every house. Happiness and prosperity everywhere. Whereas he lived in a lonely hovel, and never seemed to get on. No chance of a wife and family, and as for the school, that had all come to nothing, like his plans and every-thing else. But, on the other hand, suppose he still had one little trump card up his sleeve? Supposing, when all was said and done, he had a special mission of his own? If so, now was the time to test it, for he wasn't getting any younger.

"Listen to me, Morten Kvidal. Erik Foss dreamed of many strange things: a high school in the town of Nidaros, a cathedral, a university. Are we ever going to get them? You may be quite sure we shall, some day. But what are the youngsters going to learn? Chewing the cud—the same old stuff, over and over again! Take history, now! We founded kingdoms in Ireland, Scotland, and Normandy by piratical raids, and of course the learning we established there taught about these raids. 'Splendid men, our ancestors!' says the professor, and his mouth waters for more piracy. Splendid! But what about ourselves? This new Normandy, which we shall be so proud of some day, was not conquered by blood and fire, but by pickax and spade. We have fought against the wilderness, against prairie fires, loneliness, hard winters, drought, fatigue, locusts. Were there no heroes among us?

Is there nothing worth handing down to those who come
after us?

"Now, you listen to me, Morten Kvidal. I am a poor, unlucky fellow, but I 'm starting out to do a useful bit of work.
I 'm going to travel through the States from east to west,
and collect every scrap of our history, from Leif Ericson's
time until now. I shall chat with old pioneers, and write
down all their adventures since they came out here. Did you
ever hear of Kleng Person? He traveled on foot through
the States, eighty years ago, and founded six and thirty
settlements. One day he was sitting under a tree where
Chicago stands now, and a half-breed came up, and offered
to sell him a hundred acres of land on that very spot, if only
he would change clothes with him, and give him his pipe.
But Kleng hesitated; he was a cleanly chap, and he was
afraid there might be lodgers in the other man's clothes.
That property to-day is worth more than the whole of the
national revenue of Norway!

"That is only one example from our Saga out here. Don't
laugh, but Schoolmaster Jo is going to evolve a new faculty
for the university which there will certainly be some day at
Nidaros. There shall be a new Edda, telling not of murder
and vengeance but of patience and toil. That 's my idea.
And now I 'll say good-by, Morten. We came out here together, we 've gone through a great deal, but our fortunes
have turned out very differently. Anyway, we 've been good
pals, and I wish you good luck." And the schoolmaster got
up to go.

Morten hardly knew what to say; he wiped his hand on
his overalls, and shook the other's warmly. So Jo Berg took
his departure, and his old comrades stood in the station, and
waved till he was out of sight. He leaned his gray head out
at the car window, and waved back. The old settlers were
being thinned out; and the new ones who kept on coming did
not make up for the loss.

One Sunday morning, the church bell was chiming out long and cheerily across the prairie. Per Föll, junior, was acting as bell-ringer. The roads seemed unusually crowded: were people expecting a visit from the bishop? No, the visitor was Oluf Skaret, who was to preach to his old friends that day; not only had he been educated at St. Louis, but for more than a year he had had both a church and a congregation somewhere east in Iowa.

It was no ordinary occasion in Kal's and Karen's eyes; it was all very well to count up what it had cost his mother in hens and pigs to pay for his schooling all those years, but they forgot all that when he came home, and they saw him going about the house a real clergyman, with a beard on his face and spectacles on his nose! How time had flown! He had been a bit astonished yesterday, when he arrived at the farm, and saw all the gray sheds. All the neighbors had built themselves fine new houses of late years. But he and Siri and Anders talked it over among themselves. They could do nothing with the old man; no one knew how much he had put away in the emigrant chest under his bed, and he would take nothing out of it. Why, they did not even know where he had hidden the big rusty key!

Oluf thought it was jolly to be back with his parents and brothers and sisters. The clock from Skaret ticked away, reminding him of old days. Karen dared not confess that when it struck it made her start and think of Ebbe; perhaps he might yet come back, some day! How the young folks reminisced! There was that time when they buried the cat up on the hillside, the day they left home, and they remembered the bilberries and crowberries they used to pick there, and the grouse which they raised one snowy day in winter. Perhaps Oluf had thought about all this more than the rest, for he had been away so much by himself.

"You've gotten quite gray, Father! And Mother, you really ought to take things more quietly now."

Siri had grown quite a young lady, and went to have music-lessons at the parsonage. Of course Kal had n't wanted her to do it; it was all Karen's idea!

Paulina came across from her little farm, and this time her clergyman brother was very nice to her; he shook her by both hands, and said she was something like a girl!

So it had come round to Sunday morning, and the people were flocking in, wondering a little what sort of views Oluf held. Even here, thanks to Peter Skaarness, there had been dissensions in the church. Which synod did Oluf belong to; and which side did he take in the dispute about election by grace? Well, they would probably discover that to-day.

He was coming along the road with Anders, who called himself Andrew now and was taller and stouter than his brother—a great big fellow, with a fair mustache and curly hair under his flat cap. He had just confided to his brother that he was trying to persuade all the farmers round to join together and build an elevator of their own for their wheat, so that they might be independent of speculators, and be able to sell to the best advantage. The clergyman looked at him and thought that he might have kept such conversation for another occasion.

The two sisters walked behind them; Paulina, big and clumsy, in head-kerchief and thick shoes; Siri with a hat and a sunshade. Siri was wondering whether she would dare to remind her brother to-night of the time when they had married a cow and a bull; no, it would n't be quite the thing, now! Last of all came the parents, two elderly prairie folks in their best clothes. Although Oluf was carrying his gown and ruff in a suit-case, they could not be prevailed upon to walk with him: no, a clergyman was a clergyman, and, son of theirs though he might be, it would not be proper for them to walk side by side with him.

When they got inside the church, Kal let all the others go up to the front pew, where Oluf had asked them to sit,

but he himself sneaked down to a seat at the very back of
the church; if the worst came to the worst, and that fool of
a boy made a mess of it, his father preferred being conveniently near the door!

All the same, it pleased him to see so many people, although it was only Oluf preaching that day. Even the boss
was coming,—Morten's hair and beard were getting gray
now!—and Anne and Bergitta were with him. Those two
always came to church together, and dressed more or less
alike; perhaps they liked to fancy that they were in their
parents' home at Ramsöy, wearing dresses and cloaks made
from the same piece of homespun. They sat on the women's
side. Bergitta, who was several years younger than her
sister, looked older. Strange how the prairie had aged some
of them!

Anton was now the parish clerk, but he was bald, and his
little mustache was gray.

The hymn began. Kal dared not sing. He fixed his eyes
on his boots, and on the roughened hands clasped between
his knees. Funny how things had turned out! He remembered one time at Skaret when Oluf could n't go to school,
because he had no trousers. Now and then he could not help
glancing at Karen, who was already sniffing into her handkerchief, while her daughters looked at her as if wondering
whether they ought to take her out.

Then in came Oluf in gown and ruff, the first time his
father had seen him wearing them. The only person who
did not see him was Karen; her eyes had become so dim at
that moment. Kal looked down at his hands again, and
thought of Paulina, who had worked as hard as a man after
Oluf went away, and of Karen, who had slaved away with
her hens and her pigs, to pay for the lad's keep. The clergyman went up into the pulpit, folded his hands, and began to
pray. Could it really be Oluf? Kal felt sorry he was not

sitting by Karen, who had quite broken down; she was trembling and crying the whole time.

What was the clergyman preaching about? Kal and Karen couldn't quite make it out. But God's Word was God's Word. What puzzled Karen was, that she had always thought that God was an old man, and now it seemed that that was false doctrine. He was quite young, like their Oluf! Kal soon saw that he need not have been afraid. The boy was getting on swimmingly. In after days, the two old folks often said that they had gone through a great deal both here and in the old country, but that this was the greatest day they could remember.

That evening, when they were all sitting again in the little room, the clergyman said he would like a keepsake from Skaret. What about the old hammer? He looked from his father to his brother. The old man sniggered and shook his head. He, he! Yes, if he thought it worth having! At that moment, Andrew came in, flourishing it in the air.

"Let's make a bargain!" he exclaimed.

"A bargain?"

"Yes—that the hammer shall belong to whichever of us two is first nominated chairman in the Senate of North Dakota. Who knows?—he might need it to keep order in the assembly!"

They all stared at him. Siri got up, held out her skirt, and made him a deep courtesy, as she had learned to do at the dancing-class. "Well, I'm darned!" ejaculated Kal.

IX

Kal had always declared that things were bound to go wrong some day, and, sure enough, a crisis came.

Two bad years in succession made the bank uneasy; the farmers had large houses, machinery, and horses, but there was no money to pay interest on their loans. "I'll lay there's something at the back of it all," thought Kal. The bank had been very keen on advancing money on land, and now perhaps they would get hold of the property for themselves at half-price; business was business, when all was said and done! They all knew that Morten was working for dear life to save what he could for them; he made many journeys to the head office in Minneapolis, and worked like a nigger. In the end he managed to save all the old settlers except Anton Noreng. His wife had not known how deeply he was running into debt, and folks said that when she found out she hit him over the head with a frying-pan.

Kal, however, was not affected in any way. He had never borrowed from the bank. He had been contented to put up large and small sheds on his farm, until he should be able to afford something better, but he did n't owe a cent, either to the bank or any one else.

One day Ola came along and said he must join with them in helping Anton. They could n't let one of the old settlers come to grief. Kal must stand security for him, together with himself and Morten Kvidal. "Stand security?" The old man scratched his beard. No, he would n't do that! Put his name to a bill? No, thank you!

"The devil!" said Ola, standing there in a stylish overcoat with a gray-fur collar. "Is that the sort you are nowadays, Kal!"

326

"How much money is wanted?"

"Four thousand dollars."

H'm. Kal would n't sign his name to any paper. But he would see what Karen thought. Perhaps he could lend them half of the four thousand; he was n't sure that he had so much by him, but he would ask Karen. Ola grinned, and gave him a slap on the shoulder. "That'll do the trick!" he said, and went off.

Not long after that, a disaster happened which it took Kal many a long day to get over. Paulina had bought some horses, and being strong and self-willed herself, she liked to drive something with a bit of spirit. She was driving the binder one day, when the horses took fright and bolted; she fell forward and came down on the blades, and when they found her she was only just breathing.

As the nearest of kin, Kal inherited his daughter's property, but it was a sorry inheritance. Whenever he drove over there, he always remembered that it had been bought at the price of Paulina's life, and when the time came round for him to plow it, he was half afraid of finding blood when he turned up the roots of the grass. He was always thinking of this daughter of his, who had been so headstrong but had worked so hard for him, both indoors and out, during those first years. And there she lay now in the churchyard, beside his two friends, Erik and Per. Ah well! Such is life!

But one thing kept him going—the old greed for more land, which went back to the days when he had starved in the old country. The railway company owned a great deal of prairie land out beyond Paulina's section, and Kal went on buying and buying, and plowing and plowing—he and Andrew and the hired men. Nowadays they drove teams of six horses, harnessed to plows with three shares; and that made a difference, if you like. Instead of fields, there were *landscapes* of dark plowed soil; but still Kal wanted more; he had an insatiable craving to go on breaking up new land.

But the earth revenged itself one day by overwhelming him
with such a harvest that he was at his wits' end to know what
to do with it. It was bad enough in spring, when all the
men, horses, and plows started off at daybreak for their
various destinations amid a babel of whinnying, stamping,
shouting, and clanking iron. Kal could no longer follow
them round; he had enough to do to see that everything was
in good working order, and the outlying portions of his property lay too far off for him to be able to reach them on foot:
he was obliged to drive in a pony-cart. It was very exciting,
as the summer advanced, to see all these acres of wheat tossing
in the breeze; there seemed no end to them; when he was on
one side of his property, he could see no trace of men or
horses on the other.

When the wheat had turned yellow, billowing away toward
the distant blue horizon like an ocean of food, he would wade
quietly far in among the corn, sit down in the middle, take
a handful in his fist, and rub it against his face. Ha, ha!
He remembered the time when he used to carry earth on his
back up the hills behind Skaret. Long ago, that was!
Plenty of food here. A good sackful or two this year, and
no mistake! But he was not content yet. He must have
a little bit more land, a few more acres of corn, so that he
might feel absolutely secure from starvation.

It was worse still at harvest-time, which the women had
been dreading all summer. They did not mind much so long
as all the self-binders were devastating the plain, mowing
down thousands of golden sheaves; no, the trouble began
when the steam threshing-machine arrived, together with a
lot of day-laborers. From that moment the commotion on
the farm was as bad as an earthquake. The heavy loads of
wheat came up at a gallop, and the men, with shirts open,
and sleeves rolled up, pitched the sheaves into the machine,
which droned and buzzed away, making as much noise as
half a dozen mills.

The air was so thick with dust and chaff that one could hardly see the numerous farm huts; the mechanic was as black as a demon with oil and dust, indeed, they were *all* black, as they sneezed, coughed, sweated, swore, and slaved away, while Kal walked about bareheaded among them, his hair full of straw and chaff, crying: "Now then, lads, put your backs into it!" He was n't paying these chaps several dollars a day to do nothing—and they expecting to be feasted into the bargain. All the roasting and boiling that went on day and night was enough to ruin a man!

Farm-hands expected very different fare, in this country, from what Kal had had when he worked at Lindegaard. The women went about with their skirts tucked up, and worked fifteen hours a day, for these men's appetites were not exactly small, and if their meals were n't ready on the minute . . . ! Sometimes Karen thought of the days when they threshed with oxen, or with a machine which was worked by hand, or a horse-whim. All that was over now. How quickly things changed in this country! They had left so much behind now.

When the threshing was at last finished, it seemed like a breathing-space after a season of war and pestilence: there was peace once more, and time to eat and sleep. But now-adays the men no longer drove away the wheat in ox-carts, nor were they obliged to travel a hundred miles to North-ville, for the elevator was only half an hour's journey away; the carts made several journeys in a day, and each heavy load was drawn by four spirited horses. Several hundred such loads made a difference in the emigrant chest; Kal could n't deny that!

When there had been three bumper years in succession, together with a shortage of wheat in Europe and South Amer-ica, which sent prices higher and higher, Siri and Andrew began to whisper to each other that the old man could hardly shut the emigrant chest properly; in fact, he had to sit on the lid, to make the lock catch! Kal hardly dared to leave the house now, he was always afraid of fire; his happiest moments were when he was sitting on his bed, and knew that there was not even a fire in the kitchen stove.

At last, at last, he began to build, and of course he began with the outhouses. And when they were finished, and stood there, painted red, with white window-frames, everybody noticed that they were just like those at Lindegaard in the old country, only many times larger. The big house had two projecting wings inclosing a farm-yard; in one of them Karen kept all her pigs, hens, and turkeys, and in the other Kal had his machinery and wagons. In the middle were the long red-brick stables for the cows and horses. The horses' stable was far too big, and Kal swore that that darned boy Anders was responsible for it; why, there were any number of stalls—perhaps forty, perhaps more; he dared not count them! But when the horses were in them, stamping and neighing, he had to admit that there was a fair number of *them,* too; yes, he was n't hard up for something to drive; but folks lied when they said he had thirty-eight horses; there were at least two short of that.

When he went into the light, airy stable, and saw all these beautiful creatures, and they turned their heads and looked at him, he could hardly believe it was true; Kal Skaret must be dreaming! Again they all seemed to be saying, "You worked so hard in the old days, Kal, carrying and pulling all those heavy loads; but we 'll carry and pull them for you now; you can sit on the wagon and take a rest." He thought of his little holding on the hill, and the cow which Ebbe took away.

There was a good-sized heap of planks left over, and what was he to do with them? He carted them all over, one day, to Anne's house; she had pigs and hens and a couple of cows, but her outhouses were in a very tumble-down condition. "So if you 'd like this waste stuff, you 're welcome,

Anne!" The "waste stuff" was enough to patch up her out-buildings, till they looked as good as new, but when she came to thank him, he assured her that those planks had only been lying about in his way. Besides, it had been Karen's idea.

But his own farm-buildings were not quite as he had intended them to be. At Lindegaard you could drive up a bridge which entered the barn high up at one end, traversed the whole length of the building, and passed out again at the opposite end; as you drove across this you threw out the hay on each side into the hay-lofts down below. What could be more convenient? But it would n't do here: the hay-carts, drawn by two or four horses, were too big, and you could n't possibly have a door large enough for them to go through; there was nothing for it but to do as others did out here, first dumping the hay near the wall outside, then hoisting it in with what they called a hay-sling, and finally dropping it down into the lofts inside.

Without saying a word to any one Kal had had a room made inside the machine-house—a pretty big one, too—of which he kept the key. Here he stowed away every year a few dozen sacks of wheat. They would be all right there; they did n't need board or clothing, they could just stay there. Kal remembered only too well what it had felt like, in the old country, when there was n't a scrap of food in the house. And of course, bad times did come again, and lean years, when the new settlers were thankful to have him to go to, having no credit as yet with the tradespeople. He always declared that he preferred cash down, but he would have a word with Karen; there might be some way of arranging it, all the same.

At last the young people got their way about the new house too, but Kal would n't have any advice or chatter about it; no, he 'd had it all planned out in his head years ago. The house was long, and painted white, with dormer-windows on the high sloping roof—Lindegaard over again; just such a manor-farm as that on which he had worked in times past. Kal knew well enough what he wanted, now that he had entered Paradise. The furnishing was left to the youngsters: there were polished floors, and swell furniture, and pictures on the walls, of course. But Kal and Karen never moved in there, for it was n't their idea of comfort; Kal preferred a room where he might cut up the tobacco for his pipe on any chair he liked.

He and Karen would often walk to a little distance from the farm, and stop to gaze at the new buildings. The two old people would stand and review the result of their labors during all those long years. Yes, they looked very well, those houses did! And Karen's grove had grown so large, it was quite a little wood now, where birds sat and piped in the spring. There stood the splendid, big new house, with wire-gauze screens over the doors and windows to keep out the flies. How it shone against the green foliage of the grove! And in the middle of the courtyard, which had at last been tidied up, was the windmill, towering up above the roofs, and drawing up water from a well, into a butt from which pipes carried water for both men and beasts. Close by the farm-buildings was the tower-shaped corn silo, in which the corn fermented from one year to another. Everything was in its place. Now, perhaps, they might take their rest, and hand over everything to the young people.

No, not *quite* yet. It was really extraordinary how the Skaret folk had risen in public estimation, once the new houses were built. It was "Miss" Siri, with every one nowadays. She always wore a hat, and smart town clothes, and she had attended classes in Minneapolis. And before any one guessed what was up, a man came to propose to her —no less than the new lawyer from the town. That was something to be proud of! But Kal scratched his head, and did n't know what was to be done. Lose Siri? She 'd always been such a one to talk to her old dad.

Just then Andrew turned up, and announced that he was soon getting married, too. The old people stared at him. Really! Had he actually been engaged for more than a year? Well, she was the daughter of a doctor in Minnesota, and he had n't liked to bring her over here before the new house was built. Fancy that! Was she so particular?

Kal invited one guest to the wedding whom the young folks had to make much of whether they wanted to or not. He smartened himself up one day as though he were going to church. Then his best horses must be put in the buggy, and it was ages before they were groomed to his liking; he must have the new nickel-mounted harness, and the smartest whip, and finally he drove off to the station.

The train stopped, and a good many people came trooping out of the carriages. Kal stood still, watching them. Presently there came along an old, white-bearded, doddering man in a homespun suit, his hat rammed down on his head, leaden rings in his ears, and a knapsack on his back. This could be none other than his brother Siver, who had taken on Skaret after Kal left. He had been left a widower several years before, in the little homestead on the gray hillside. Then Kal sent him a good round sum to pay his fare out, so he started off as soon as he could find a congenial traveling companion. And by way of smartening himself up, he had bought a stiff black hat; but it was far too large for him, and there was a dent in the crown. Good old Siver!

"How de do, lad?" Kal shouted, seizing him by the hand. They stood gazing at each other for a minute, for it was twenty years since they last met, and each was thinking, "So that 's what you look like now!"

How old Siver eyed the fine carriage and spirited horses as Kal took the reins and told him to get in! "What's all this? You don't mean to say this belongs to *you*, Kal?" They chatted all the way home, both talking at once and smacking each other on the back: "No! You don't say so!

How time flies!"   But they had not quite forgotten all their
pranks when they were boys together.

"That 's where I live!" said Kal, pointing toward the house
with his whip.   Siver stared in amazement.   "You—you 're
crazy, man!   You never live there!"   Kal had never been
one to show off, but he could not resist the temptation to
boast a little to this brother of his from Skaret; he wanted
to strike him dumb with astonishment.   Siver could no
longer doubt, for they were driving right into the place; it
must really be Kal's home.   Well, well!   The old man pulled
himself together and asked a question.   "I say, Kal, I suppose you 've given a very grand name to such a swell farm
as this?"

"A name?   We call the farm Skaret."

"Skaret?   Go on!   You 're joking!"

"Why the devil should n't it be Skaret?   Don't you think
that 's a good enough name?"   The other shook his head
and looked ready to cry.   It seemed impossible that such a
splendid place could have the same name as the tiny home
from which he himself had come.   Why, Kal . . . Kal!

Such an important guest as Kal's own brother must of
course sleep in the main building.   He was given the best
bedroom, next to the one which the doctor was to have when
he came for the wedding.   There was a four-poster, and a fine
china toilet set; as soon as Siver came into the room, he
slipped on the polished floor and tumbled down.   Kal slapped
himself on both thighs; he had never had such fun in all his
life.

"Well, you 're a boss, and no mistake, Kal," said his
brother, looking round him as though he were in Paradise.
And as soon as they came down to the fine sitting-room, Kal
must needs light the long, silver-mounted meerschaum pipe
which his children had given him at Christmas.   He preferred his brier, but he wanted to show what sort of man he
really was.

His brother went from one bewilderment to another. All the splendid horses in the stable, all the machinery, the carts, the massive cows and oxen, the countless numbers of pigs and poultry—it was all like a dream or a fairy-tale. But when Kal took him round his property, and showed him what enormous tracts he owned, it seemed as though he ruled over the whole world. This was too much, and the old man burst out: "No, no, Kal! Dang me if you are n't lying now!"

Then came the wedding. All sorts of grand people arrived; several of the guests wore evening dress, and there were healths and speeches. Morten Kvidal was in his element, and proposed the health of the old folks, in a speech which made Karen cry. Kal and Siver exchanged glances. When cigars and coffee were brought in, they slunk away together to the old house, and enjoyed a smoke of good honest twist instead.

One day something happened which Kal had been looking forward to for years. He invited his brother to stop on with him. He could have a quarter, with a house on it, and horses and farm implements. Kal needed him. The children were getting married, and he and Karen would be left alone. Or if he liked to cast in his lot with them, and live in the same little house, he should never want for anything. At first his brother could say nothing; he only shook his head; it was really too much; he did not know how to express his thanks. Oh, Kal . . . Kal!

He decided to stay. All went well till autumn descended on the plains, with gales and sleet and gray mists. Then Siver began to complain of rheumatism and sleeplessness. He had such an ache in his back, such shooting pains in all his limbs; they could n't think how bad he felt! When the first snow fell, he came one day and poured out his troubles to his brother. He was n't happy. Kal must help him to go back to the old country, to Skaret.

All right. Kal gave him another fat bunch of notes, and

drove him to the station. But there was no joking this time. It's a sad thing to feel you are seeing your only brother for the last time. "Remember me to the old country! And to Skaret!" So the train carried his brother away, and left Kal behind in the flat country.

That winter, the laborers on the farm began to say that it was haunted. They could hear something walking about in the hay-loft, and sometimes they could even see something moving in the dusky corners. The same thing happened in other rooms in the outhouse, wherever it was dark: there was something walking about with muffled footsteps. Karen heard it, and would not admit that she knew what it was. But she felt she must go and see whether the brownie really had moved into the new houses.

And soon her son's young wife would come upon her even in the new house—down in the cellars, up in the dark attics, in any place where there were unlighted corners. There the old woman would stand, but she never liked being discovered. She wanted to find out whether the silver spoon, which she had secretly buried under the foundations, had enticed the wee folk here in good earnest.

It was mid-harvest, the year after this, when Kal drove up to the door one day, and his wife came out to meet him, in her Sunday clothes. He had had considerable difficulty in persuading her to come, for there were no end of things for her to see to just then, as mistress of a large farm. "Where are we going?" But Kal would not say. "How long shall we be gone?" "Oh, not so very long." "What a man it is!—and always has been!" murmured the old woman, getting into the carriage.

So off they drove. But Kal was still mysterious. He had a hamper behind the seat, which Siri, the lawyer's wife, had packed for him yesterday. Where ever could they be going to-day? The horses tossed their heads and trotted along, first through the town, where there were now two churches, then on past all the farms, farther and farther. Karen began to feel anxious; where in Heaven's name were they bound for? Did he imagine that she had time to spare for this sort of thing?

It tickled Kal hugely to see his wife sitting there on tenterhooks. For nearly forty years she had never taken a day off. She was the first up in the morning, and the last to go to bed at night, working, working away, even while the men had their midday rest. That had been her life during all those many years. She had never been anywhere, not even as far as Northville, since they came out, and had not had a new dress until they insisted on arraying her in a black silk gown for the young people's wedding. To-day, however, she was out on a spree—and high time, too!

They were passing through districts which she had never seen, and the farms were becoming poorer; just a few haystacks and a gray frame cottage, with a small piece of cultivated land. These were newly emigrated settlers, who had not got on much as yet. Ah, they themselves knew what that meant! At last there were only sod huts to be seen, and Karen sighed, for she had not forgotten what a winter on the prairie was like when one lived in a house of that sort. And then they were out on the prairie itself, stretching far away under the hot sunshine, brown and green, and violet in the dim distance where it merged, like the ocean, into the dazzling sky.

Finally Kal turned off from the road, and she looked at him; what was he up to? She was really getting quite cross; whatever could he be thinking of? As if she had time for this sort of thing! Why, he was actually unharnessing the horses, and turning them loose! Was he quite off his head? Next he brought out the hamper. "Let's sit down in the shade of the carriage and take things quietly, old woman!" he said. "You sit down there, and I'll give you something nice."

She shook her head, grumbled and scolded, and declared she would do nothing of the kind. He must drive back straight away; think of all she had to do at home! Now what, in Heaven's name, was the man doing? He pulled out a white cloth from the hamper—not one of hers, she could tell at a glance—and spread it rather awkwardly on the ground. Ah, one could see he wasn't accustomed to that sort of thing! Then out came a bottle, glasses, plates, and knives, a silver-covered dish; she knew that; it belonged to Siri. Well . . . !

"Come to dinner, old woman!" She sighed, but she had to give in. There was a regular feast spread out on the grass, and Kal was pouring something out of the bottle. "Here's luck, Karen." She didn't care much for claret, but as long as they had to make fools of themselves . . . !

"Can't we go back soon?" she suggested, fidgeting. Then Kal lifted his glass, as he had seen the great folks do, and said: "You're to have a holiday to-day, old woman. And it's a holiday for me too, to-day, and every day in future. This morning Anders took over the farm, so we can take a rest now, both of us."

This was so bewildering that she could not take it in for some time, although it was not altogether unexpected. At last he succeeded in calming her down. Yes, she quite understood now; but why on earth should they sit here? "Good luck, to you, Karen. And thank you."

"What in the world are you thanking me for?"

"Oh, I don't know. But we've been married six and thirty years, and we've done a deal of hard work both in the old country and out here." Karen sighed, and gazed into space. There never was a truer word, once one started thinking of things. "You've been a champion worker, Karen."

"Don't you talk such nonsense, when you know there's such a lot I haven't been able to get done."

"Rubbish! We'll both be moving on to the churchyard

soon." That was true, too, and Karen still sat staring into space.

Presently they began to chat, and to feel that they were really resting now. They talked about the children. Oluf had written and said that he wanted them to leave him either the clock or the hammer from Skaret. And Siri would like the emigrant chest. Kal scratched his beard, and said he must think about it.

After that, he spread out a horse-blanket, and they lay down on it for a little after-dinner nap. Peace had at length descended upon Karen also. They stretched themselves out, blinking up at the infinite depths of the vast prairie sky . . . till at last their eyelids closed. They were asleep, and there would be no need for them to turn out at dawn to-morrow morning. When they woke up, the long holiday would have begun.

X

Years went by, and the greater number of the old settlers were lying in the churchyard.

It was a day in spring, with a clear blue sky. A white-haired woman wearing gold spectacles was driving a motor-car toward the manor-farm of Kvidal. The white house, built in the style of a country villa, was surrounded by green lawns with concrete paths. She did not stop there, but drove on to the back of the farm, where all the red outhouses stood; the principal farmers had their own corn-elevators nowadays, towering skyward. She made for a small, white, one-storied house close to the grove, where she stopped, got out, and went indoors.

An elderly man in blue spectacles and dark overalls was doing some carpentry there. He had a square-cut white beard and his mop of white hair was still thick, standing up in a tuft above his forehead. He turned his head on hearing the door open.

"Good morning, Morten."

"Good morning. It's you, isn't it, Else?"

"How are you, my friend?"

"Not getting on very fast."

She looked at the helpless man, pottering over some little job to pass the time. Fate is a strange thing. He to whom America had given scope for all his plans—who had set so many things going, and had become more and more prosperous, rising steadily from one position of trust to another— he had been stricken down by misfortune just as he was on the verge of attaining his dearest wish, to be elected a member of Congress. As he was fixing a carbide lamp, it exploded, leaving him—blind! Done for! And now he was

a widower, and had been pottering about like this for the
last ten years. Books in Braille-type were limited in number,
and, worst of all, he could not read the newspapers; however, things were rather better now that little Morten, his
grandson, was getting to be a big boy, and read aloud both
American and Norwegian papers to him, whenever he could
spare time from school.

"Have you come from the hospital?" he asked.

"Yes, we 've been having a committee meeting. You can't
think what a splendid place it has become, since the latest
extension. What a pity—*what* a pity Bergitta could not
have lived to see it finished!"

"H'm." He moved his head as though his sightless eyes
could see something through the glasses. "We Norwegians
have to pay for settling in a flat country. It never suited
Bergitta from the first."

"The second generation have a better time of it than we
had, Morten."

"Yes, as far as money goes. And with all these blessed
machines and motor-cars. But would you care to change
places with them? They lack one important thing."

"And what may that be, Morten?"

"Vision, Else. Or homesickness, if you like! They are
Americans, who know a certain amount of Norwegian—
that 's all."

"Are you still homesick, Morten?"

"Ha, ha! Can you ask? Do you suppose there has been
a single day, in all these long years, when I did n't say to myself, 'I 'm going home, soon, to buy back Kvidal'?"

"And yet you have always been such a stanch American?"

"Well, you see, we who came out here have two souls, and
two countries. Of course I 'm a stanch American now.
When my two sons went to the war, I said: 'That 's quite
right. They are fighting for America.' But think of all
I 've meant to do in Norway!"

"That's something like Ola felt."

Morten did not smile. Now that this woman was a widow, she worshiped the memory of her husband. She would not admit that he had had any faults. Whenever she heard anything that pleased her, it always turned out that Ola had had those ideas, too.

Morten remarked, "It's a pity he didn't live to see prohibition in North Dakota."

She sighed. "Yes, after the way he had worked for it."

"And how are they getting on with the Norwegian university in Nidaros?"

"We're collecting money; and the response has exceeded our expectations. That's all I can say at present." She stood up, and took his hand. "Good-by, my dear friend. And take care of yourself."

"Thank you for coming. You mustn't forget me." And he listened as she drove away.

Then he went on with his attempts at carpentering. He managed pretty well, too, now, for as the years went on his hands had learned to take the place of his eyes, and he had made a few things which he knew could be used. People were kind to him. If any celebrated Norwegian visited Nidaros in the course of a lecturing-tour, Morten would be sitting in the front row, a sort of Moses in the community. "There he is!" they would say.

When any of their more important countrymen was to be buried, the other members of Morten's household would dress the old man in his best suit and top-hat, so that he could attend, and at the graveside he would step forward, hat in hand, a blind and venerable figure, and make a short speech.

He had learned by degrees to find his way about the farm, with a curious gliding step, and if he approached a wall or any other obstacle, some sixth sense would warn him to put out his hand and feel in front of him. Most of his rambles, indoors or out, were taken in company with his little favorite,

Morten, who would hold his hand on their longer expeditions, and read aloud to him; they suited each other in every way: the boy was never tired of hearing stories of the old country, or of Grandfather's old home.

He came back from school in the afternoon, and made straight for his grandfather's workshop. He had been talking English all day, and had heard nothing but English spoken by his teachers and companions; yet now he dropped quite naturally into his grandfather's dialect, the language of a district where he had never been.

"I say—what do you think? Andrew Skaret has been elected a senator!"

"You don't say so!" the old man passed his hand through the boy's hair. "Well, he deserves it. He 's worked hard enough for it, all these years." And Morten called to mind the lad from Skaret, with that big mouth of his, which seemed made for calling the cattle on the hills. And one fine day it had come in useful on the platforms of the United States. "Well, my dear, you run along now, and get something to eat; and I 'll come too."

He found the nights very long. Memories came and went, of the days when he could see and the world seemed made just for him and his plans. A short time before his accident, he had been driving back in his car from a meeting at Northville. It was a cool day in autumn, and he had a clear view across the prairie which had been a wilderness when he and the others had come there in their ox-carts, and which was now one of the granaries of the world; large and small farmers were settled all over it, cultivating thousands of square miles; church spires pointed upward, and in the graves around them slept many a countryman after his toilsome day. It was a new Normandy. How much they could accomplish, he thought, once they were far enough away from home! Did any one remember now all that it had cost? Those groups of trees close to most of the farm-houses, the sacred

grove—almost worthy to be called a wood in some cases—
which the women had planted, bore witness of their unquench-
able yearning for the land of forests.

As twilight was falling on that same day, the farmers began, by common agreement, to burn the superfluous straw-
stacks on their spacious corn-lands. He had always loved
this sight: flames seemed to be rising skyward from every
corner of the boundless plain, and the darker it grew, the
more weirdly did all those shifting fires shine up into the
clear autumn sky, till at last it looked as if the very earth
were trying to adorn itself with suns—a romance of autumn
which was renewed every year. That was all past. He
could never see it again.

Then his thoughts would stray to the old country, and
one recollection after another would engross him. A very
foolhardy plan began to possess him: he would lie and smile
to himself, as he realized how ridiculous it was. And
yet . . . !

One day he suggested that the boy should accompany him
on a short visit to Oluf, who had a parish in Iowa. The
others tried to dissuade him, but little Morten was wild to
go. Did they imagine he was n't capable of looking after
Grandfather on a journey? They got off in the end. It
was extraordinary what a lot of clothes and money Morten
thought it necessary to take, but old folks were often a bit
fanciful!

They went farther than Iowa. They went right on to
New York. And one morning the boy came into his grandfather's room and found the old man chuckling by the
telephone.

"What would you say to a trip to the old country, Morten?" The boy was struck dumb, and could only shuffle his
feet and stare. "I have just booked two berths on the ship.
But you 'd better write home; go and get some paper, and
I 'll dictate to you."

XI

The gangway from the fiord steamer was nothing but a plank, and most people would probably find landing a dangerous job when the sea was rough. The old man was obliged, very reluctantly, to accept the help of another passenger, who went gingerly ahead, leading him by one hand, while the boy came along behind, holding the other. At last he stood on the beach, white-haired and white-bearded, well dressed, and wearing spectacles. When he moved on a few paces, it was with his usual gliding step. He drank in the scent of the brine and sea-weed and damp sand, as if it were something well known and longed for. Everybody was looking at him, but no one recognized him.

The boy was in knickerbockers and a reefer; he had a fair, rosy face, with well-cut features, and his eyes were big with all the experiences of the journey and of the actual moment. Grandfather's stories had come true! All that he had heard about blue fiords and mountains, forest-clad heights, boats, sails, swarms of sea-birds—he was seeing it all! It was not a dream. It was quite real. This was Grandfather's old home.

"Morten! Are you there?"

"Yes, they've landed our trunk, and here's the carriage from the boarding-house."

"They call it a *pension* in Norwegian."

It was not until they were sitting in the carriage that it occurred to the old man that there was no one here for him to go and see, now. He was a stranger. He knew nothing of Kvidal; were the old houses still standing, or had they been pulled down? And for the first time he wondered what was the use of his coming over here, now that he could not

345

even see anything. After all, though, he *could* still see after a fashion, with the help of his own memory and of little Morten, who could see things for him. He bent down to the boy and said, in too low a voice for the driver to hear: "Do you see a white house with red out-buildings at the back, on a hill where there are pine-trees growing?"

"Yes, Grandfather; we're just going to drive past it. And the farm's exactly like Skaret, out on the prairie."

"That's Lindegaard, Morten; Kal Skaret worked there many a day as a laborer." The boy opened his eyes wider than ever. The old man pointed to the right. "Now, can you see two gray houses right away on the hillside, to the left of the main road? There ought to be a little wood behind the byre."

The boy looked intently. "Yes, Grandfather. But the houses are painted now. They're red. I can't see any gray ones."

"Ah, well, I dare say they've patched them up. That was Kal's home, where the children went hungry and cold many a time."

At the pension, the two Mortens shared a bedroom. The old man insisted on having the window open all night. It was midsummer, and he knew that the nights were as light as day; he was never tired of lying and listening to the waves splashing and dashing on the beach. The sun would rise again shortly after midnight, and he could feel the room growing red in the sunlight, while a soft breeze fanned the curtains, bringing in a smell of the sea, and the tar on the boats. Then a tumult of bird voices would rise up into the sky, and he could recognize the different cries, as the birds perched on the rocks in the harbor, and greeted the dawn; there were red-legged oyster-catchers, crested peewits, white and black-backed gulls, eider-ducks—Mother in brown and Father in black and white. Who could sleep with this ecstatic chorus pealing in honor of the sunrise?

It took some time for the other guests at table to realize what was amiss with his sight, for he quickly learned his way about the house, and helped himself from the dishes as though he had eyes at his fingers' ends. He would tuck his table napkin under his chin, but in spite of that he sometimes asked the boy whether he had dropped anything on his clothes, and now and then he would touch his collar and tie to make sure that they were all in order.

He listened to the old and young voices around him. Most of them were townsfolk, and several said that they had read about him in the newspaper. "A well-known American over on a visit." He returned brief answers to their inquiries as to things in America. Were there many Norwegian parishes there? Oh yes; about four thousand altogether. And how many clergy? A fair number: about three thousand Norwegian Lutherans. Did they preach in Norwegian? Oh no, not always. And what about high schools? They had a fair number of them. Why had America become such a rich country? He smiled, and hesitated a little before replying, "Because we who went out there were so poor that we had to fend for ourselves."

He preferred asking endless questions, himself. They were astonished to find how he had kept in touch with political matters at home. One might have thought he'd done nothing but watch the old country all the time he lived out there! And how were things going in the parish? Had they made that new road on the opposite side of the fiord, which there had been so much talk about in his time? Oh, a committee was settling all that, was it? He smiled again.

Well, well; things went faster on the other side than they did here in the Old World. He told them that he had seen whole towns spring up in a few weeks. That the gas-works in Nidaros had been finished before people realized that it was being built. That in one short generation the farmers in Dakota had passed through the whole period of evolution, from the stone age to the century of the motor—an evolution which in Europe had taken several thousand years. But he must n't boast. . . . And he went on asking questions about the parish.

Really—were people still leaving? The young folks were emigrating, and the old folks dying off. Mountain farms were being turned into sæters, and the sæters themselves were going to rack and ruin. H'm. He bowed his head and sighed. He knew well enough that the tide of emigration was flowing farther and farther westward. Now that the prairie had been cultivated, it was rolling on to the Pacific, even to Alaska. Well, it was n't for him to judge.

The neighbors came to inquire about their various acquaintances. Did he remember Anne Ramsöy, and Per Föll? How had their children turned out? Oh, they had n't done badly. Isak, the elder boy, was professor of jurisprudence in the university at Madison. The second one carried on the farm, in succession to his father. And what about the children of the colonel's daughter who had eloped with a farm laborer? He thought a moment. Well, some of them were farmers. The eldest son was a lumber-merchant in Chicago. He answered question after question; but the sad thing was that none of his own friends came to see him, because they were all dead.

He could not bring himself to ask about Kvidal. Perhaps he was afraid of what he might hear. One day the proprietor asked whether he was not going over there. Yes, he had thought of doing so. Well, perhaps he had heard that the farm also had been turned into a sæter now? The two last owners declared that they could n't keep body and soul together there. So the little property had been bought by one of the large farms, to pasture cows on during the summer. The old man's head fell forward, as though some one had struck him.

Little Morten and he were strolling along the beach one

day, in the warm sunshine. The grandfather stood still. "I say, do you see any women about?" No, there was nobody at all. "It's all soft sand here, is n't it? Not many stones?"

"No, Grandfather. It's just fine light-gray sand, as far as I can see."

Then, to the boy's consternation, the old man began to undress. He stood up naked in the sunshine, feeling before him tentatively with his toes, and set off in the direction of the sea. He waded out, farther and farther, took a header into the waves, and disappeared.

"Grandfather! Grandfather!" screamed the child. The white head reappeared, gasping and laughing: "Be quiet, lad! I must feel the touch of salt water once more."

Another evening a man rowed them out to sea to fish for coalfish. It was a grand treat for the boy; gulls swarming and shrieking about the boat, while Grandfather wielded his rods and hauled in the fish as though he were still a sailor in the prime of life. Little Morten would indeed have something to talk about when he got back to the prairie.

At last a day came which saw them driving up the hills toward Kvidal. There was nobody there awaiting him, and yet he felt that he was going home. The well-known rush of Kvidal waterfall greeted his ears. And it seemed to him that the mountains, the woods, the hills, and the slopes were beginning to call him too: "You belong to us. We are you, and you are we." He was on the point of asking the boy in a whisper whether the houses were gray or painted, but he stopped himself. Perhaps it was as well not to know of any more changes.

As they approached the farm, he recognized the scent of the big old mountain-ash that grew in the yard, and from that moment he required no further help. He walked steadily toward the porch, his hand grasped the familiar latch, he opened the door and walked in, and found himself in the well-known atmosphere of Mother and home.

"Good day." A girl stood there churning butter, and she asked him to come in and sit down. (But why did n't Mother come out of the bedroom?) He sat for a while in a reverie, with eyes closed, breathing that curious, homelike air which the new-comers had not succeeded in driving away.

His mother used to sit by yonder window, during the last years of her life—so Mette had told him when she came over—and pick out stars in the evening sky, one for each of the children who had gone so far, far away from her. And perhaps she gazed so long at the stars that at last she became reconciled to the course things had taken.

He must go outside again. "Run along, Morten; you need n't think I can't find my way about *here!*" He went with a firm step in the direction of the outhouses, walked round behind the barn, and began to grope for something. "Now where's the grindstone? What, have *you* gone the way of all flesh, too?"

Then the boy had to follow him along a path, up which the old man went with the same gliding step, just as if his feet could see where they were going. He stood still presently, and pointed: "Do you see the hill on the other side of the river?"

"Yes, Grandfather."

"Are there any corn-fields or meadows there?"

"No, there's nothing but trees."

"H'm."

By and by he sat down on a rock just beyond the farm. He knew that the sea lay deep down at the foot of the hills, and he fancied he could see the snow-capped mountains beyond the great fiord to the west, and Blaaheia to the north. He pulled a handful of leaves from a bush, and sniffed at it. He could remember a blue spring evening, with bonfires on the hills around, and a boat on the lake, with two girls on board. Bergitta and Anne. How long ago! The boy was standing a little lower down, looking up at his grandfather, whose

white head and beard were clearly outlined against the sky.
He dared not speak to him. He would just have to go on
waiting till the old man was ready.

At night big Morten lay by the open window, meditating
on destiny. The waves were breaking and murmuring outside, receding and advancing, rising, falling, always in motion. He thought of the old tailor who had come home
seven times, and had always gone back, because happiness
invariably seemed to be on the other side of the ocean. And
there were others who had done the same. A young fellow
would shout, "Hurrah!" for his country one day—and leave
it the day after. He might become rich in this world's goods
in the new country, but he would always feel homesick for
the old one.

If you came back, you wanted to leave again; if you went
away, you longed to come back. Wherever you were, you
could hear the call of the home-land, like the note of a herdsman's horn far away in the hills. You had one home out
there, and one over here, and yet you were an alien in both
places. Your true abiding-place was the vision of something
very far off, and your soul was like the waves, always restless,
forever in motion. Was he not longing already to get back
to his big farm, Kvidal, with his children and relations
close by? Wasn't Bergitta waiting for him in the churchyard over there? Well, he would soon be back now. He and
little Morten would pack up to-morrow.

He slept and dreamed. What, was he making a poem at
last? He saw a woman, with the glory of morning about her
brow, wandering out into the world, and sowing, as she went,
the corn that she needed for her own land. But was it corn?
No—it was a host of young men and women. And now he
understood who the sower was.

GLOSSARY

P. 3   Dyrendal. Like Lindegaard (p. 9), a large farm in the parish, whose owner provides housing for tenant farmers and usually a plot of ground for their own use in exchange for labor on the farm.

P. 5   military service. Every able-bodied male was required to undergo a brief period of military training.

P. 9   sæters. Pastures high in the hills and mountains where herds are taken for summer pasturage. A rough building provides shelter for the girls who tend the cattle and goats, and make cheese and butter.

P. 12   the sheriff as one of "the quality." In such a parish the pastor would head the social order, followed by large landowners, military officers, and government officials.

P. 14   Whitsuntide. Pentecost season, the week beginning the seventh Sunday after Easter, especially the first three days.

P. 14   spinneys. British: a small wood with undergrowth. (The Norwegian word *lövaasene* actually means "fresh foliage of the hills.")

353

P. 22   on tick. British: "on the cuff," on credit.

P. 22   Whitsuntide bonfire. It is traditional in Norway to build a bonfire on Whitsunday evening.

P. 35   Blaaheia. Literally, "the blue heights," a heath-covered upland.

P. 41   brownie. The "hus-nisse" in Norway is a household spirit, both helpful and mischievous, who is cherished in house and barn.

P. 86   Ragna Adilsdatter's kingdom. Ragna was daughter to the rich and powerful King Adil in one of the sagas.

P. 114 *Synnöve Solbakken.* A beloved Norwegian novel by Björnstjerne Björnson.

P. 114 *Asbjörnsen's Fairy-Tales.* The most famous Norwegian collection of fairy tales, by Asbjörnsen and Moe, published in 1841.

P. 114 Snorre. The Icelandic storyteller, Snorri Sturluson, famous for his *Prose Edda* and sagas about kings and heroes.

P. 151 *The Emigrant.* A weekly newspaper published in Norwegian as *Emigranten* in Madison, Wisconsin, 1852–68.

P. 151 bannocks. British: flat rounds of bread baked on a griddle. The Norwegian word is "flatbröd," a thin sheet of crisp, unleavened bread.

P. 161 "Terje Viken." A poem in the epic style by Henrik Ibsen about a rugged Norwegian mariner.

P. 161 "Dyre Vaa." A poem by Johan S. Welhaven about a bold, irrepressible Norwegian who rows a troll across the fjord on Christmas Eve.

P. 164 Nidaros. The ancient name of the Norwegian cathedral city now called Trondheim, an indication of the place of origin of these particular emigrants.

P. 186   Sverdrup. The reference is to Johan Sverdrup, who became prime minister on July 2, 1884. The event would interest these Norwegian-Americans because it marks a shift of power to the left and establishes parliamentary government, putting an end to the control of an entrenched bureaucracy.

P. 224   horse-whim. The Norwegian word "hestvandring" means a "horse walk," referring to a drum and pulley arrangement for moving heavy loads powered by the circular motion of a horse.

P. 275   Neckan. The Norwegian word is "nökk," a supernatural creature dwelling in lakes, rivers, and waterfalls who tries to lure its victim to drowning. It can change its shape at will although usually it resembles a tangle of half-submerged roots and weeds.